GROUP THEORY

GROUP THEORY

EUGENE SCHENKMAN

Professor of Mathematics
Purdue University
Lafayette, Indiana

D. VAN NOSTRAND COMPANY, INC.
Princeton, New Jersey

Toronto   New York   London

D. VAN NOSTRAND COMPANY, INC.
120 Alexander St., Princeton, New Jersey (*Principal*)*office*
24 West 40 Street, New York 18, New York

D. VAN NOSTRAND COMPANY, LTD.
358, Kensington High Street, London, W.14, England

D. VAN NOSTRAND COMPANY (Canada), LTD.
25 Hollinger Road, Toronto 16, Canada

COPYRIGHT © 1965, BY
D. VAN NOSTRAND COMPANY, INC.

Published simultaneously in Canada by
D. VAN NOSTRAND COMPANY (Canada), LTD.

PRINTED IN THE UNITED STATES OF AMERICA

TO
AGNES

PREFACE

The object of this book is to introduce the reader to some basic concepts of group theory and to present some of the theory of three important classes of groups — abelian groups, nilpotent groups, and solvable groups. The notion of free group and the method of presenting a group by means of generators and relations is introduced early and a little elementary theory of free groups is given. Special emphasis is placed on the role of the cyclic groups, quasicyclic groups, and subgroups of the additive rationals in the development of the theory of abelian groups.

An important place is given to the study of endomorphisms and automorphisms of groups, and to the construction of the semi-direct product as a way of studying non-abelian groups. Enough character theory is developed to prove the Burnside theorem on which is based the recent characterization of a finite solvable group as a product of pairwise commuting nilpotent subgroups. Also presented are some of the recent developments in the theory of nilpotent and locally nilpotent groups, and of finite groups with normal p-complements.

The treatment of the subject is based on the assumption that the reader is familiar with the elementary facts of set theory; otherwise the discussion is self-contained. Examples are introduced to illustrate and illuminate the theory.

Many exercises are given as a means of presenting routine parts of the theory and expanding the text while presenting the reader an opportunity to work with the concepts. The short bibliography of books and recent articles will serve as a reference source for essentially all the material discussed.

The author is grateful to a number of friends for help during the course of the writing. J. Wiegold and R. Gilmer read an earlier version of the manuscript and gave many good suggestions. Thanks are also due to K. Gruenberg, B. H. and H. Neumann, M. F. Newman, L. Kovacs, H. Flanders, M. Drazin, O. F. G. Schilling, and D. Hertzig for constructive criticism and ideas. Finally, appreciation is due Miss Elizabeth Young for typing the manuscript so beautifully and to Mr. Richard Lane for help with the proofreading and index.

Lafayette, Indiana   EUGENE SCHENKMAN
July, 1965

CONTENTS

INDEX OF NOTATION

Chapter I

FUNDAMENTAL CONCEPTS

This chapter introduces some fundamental notions and methods of group theory. In studying groups, much information can be gained by examining subgroups, homomorphic images, direct decompositions, maximal subgroups, and generating sets. These concepts are defined here, and a complete study of cyclic groups is made from this point of view.

In studying arbitrary groups, the notions of free group, reduced free group, and groups given in terms of generators and defining relations arise in a natural manner; and in studying classes of groups, the notion of variety seems to be a unifying concept. These ideas are all introduced, even though briefly and perhaps sketchily, in the hope that the reader will see their underlying importance for the general theory and that he will consult more comprehensive works for further details.

Some examples are given to indicate connections with other branches of mathematics.

1. Semigroups and groups

The study of groups is based on the notion of associativity, the fundamental structure being the semigroup as defined below.

I.1.a. Definition. A **semigroup** S is a set with an associative binary operation. That is, with each ordered pair (a, b) of elements

1

of S is associated a unique third element of S called the product of a and b and written ab or $a \cdot b$. This product satisfies the associative law

$$(ab)c = a(bc)$$

for each triple (a, b, c) of elements of S.

In view of the associative law, the element $a_1 a_2 a_3$ is uniquely defined without parentheses; one may prove that $a_1 a_2 \cdots a_n$ is also uniquely defined without parentheses (cf. [J] or [Z]). In particular, the product of an element b by itself n times is unique; it is written b^n and is called the nth power of b. The element $a_1 \cdots a_n$ is sometimes written $\prod_{i=1}^{n} a_i$.

It should be observed that, with each element a of S, there is associated a map from the set S into itself, namely, the map ρ_a (**right multiplication** by a), defined by the equation $x\rho_a = xa$ for each $x \in S$. The set of right multiplications ρ_S is a semigroup with $\rho_a \rho_b$ defined to be the composition of the maps ρ_a and ρ_b. That is, for each x in S, $x(\rho_a \rho_b) = (x\rho_a)\rho_b$. Since S is associative, $\rho_a \rho_b = \rho_{ab}$.

I.1.b. Definition. A **group** G is a semigroup in which there is also a unary operation, which associates with each element a of G an element denoted by a^{-1}, such that $aa^{-1}b = b = baa^{-1}$ for each a and b in G. This element a^{-1} is the **inverse** of a.

It follows that for each a and b of G, $aa^{-1} = aa^{-1}bb^{-1} = bb^{-1}$; this unique element aa^{-1} is the **identity** of G and is denoted by 1. It is easy to see that 1 is the only element of G such that $1b = b = b1$ for each b in G; for if an element f were such that $fb = b = bf$, then the two sets of equations would imply that $1 = 1f = f$.

Groups have the following elementary properties:

(i) *Right cancellation: if* $xb = yb$, *then* $x = y$.
(ii) $b^{-1}b = 1$.
(iii) *Left cancellation: if* $bx = by$, *then* $x = y$.
(iv) $(b^{-1})^{-1} = b$.
(v) $(ab)^{-1} = b^{-1}a^{-1}$.

To prove the above assertions we note first that if $xb = yb$, then $xbb^{-1} = ybb^{-1}$ and hence $x = y$. Then from the fact that $bb^{-1} = 1$, it follows that $b^{-1}bb^{-1}=b^{-1}$ and hence by canceling b^{-1} on the right that $b^{-1}b=1$. From this it follows that $bx=by$ implies that $b^{-1}bx=b^{-1}by$ or $x=y$. Then if $bx=1=bb^{-1}$ or if $yb=1=b^{-1}b$, it follows that $x=b^{-1}=y$ and hence that $(b^{-1})^{-1}=b$. Finally $1=(ab)^{-1}(ab)=(b^{-1}a^{-1})(ab)$ and hence $(ab)^{-1}=b^{-1}a^{-1}$.

I.1.c. Examples. The set of non-zero complex numbers is a group under the usual multiplication, the inverse of a number is its reciprocal, and the identity is the number 1. The set of non-zero real numbers and the set of non-zero rational numbers are also groups under multiplication. The set of integers and the set of positive integers are semigroups under multiplication but are not groups.

I.1.d. Examples. The set of complex numbers is a group under addition; the inverse of a is $-a$ and the number 0 is the identity. The set of real numbers, the set of rational numbers, the set of integers, and the set of even integers are also groups under addition. If m is a non-negative real number, then the sets of integers, rational numbers, and real numbers greater than m (or greater than or equal to m) are semigroups under addition but are not groups.

I.1.e. Exercise. *Show that (cf. [Z], p. 1) a semigroup S is a group if and only if*

(i) *S has a left identity e so that $ea=a$ for all $a \in S$.*
(ii) *To each $a \in S$ there is a left inverse a^{-1} so that $a^{-1}a=e$.*

I.1.f. Example. The reader should check that the set of all maps of an arbitrary set M into itself is a semigroup with the product $\theta\phi$ of two maps θ and ϕ defined by composition: $m(\theta\phi)=(m\theta)\phi$ for each $m \in M$. The reader should also check that the set of all one-one maps of a set M onto itself is a group with the product defined as before and the inverse defined in the obvious way as the usual inverse of a one-one map. A one-one map of M onto M is a **permutation** of M. The group of all permutations of M is the **symmetric group** on M.

It is instructive to consider two particular symmetric groups in further detail.

I.1.g. Examples.   If M is the set of two elements, the symmetric group on M also consists of two elements.   These are the identity permutation and the permutation which interchanges the elements of M.   If M is the set of three elements $\{1, 2, 3\}$, a permutation of M may be described by writing the image of each element underneath it; thus if $1\theta = 3$, $2\theta = 1$, $3\theta = 2$, then θ is written $\begin{pmatrix} 1 & 2 & 3 \\ 3 & 1 & 2 \end{pmatrix}$.   A more compact notation for the above element θ is (1 3 2) or (3 2 1), the general rule being to write in ( ) the image of a symbol to its right starting with any symbol and closing ( ) with the symbol which maps onto the first symbol of ( ); then continuing with new ( ) as long as necessary.   Thus $\begin{pmatrix} 1 & 2 & 3 \\ 2 & 1 & 3 \end{pmatrix} = (12)(3)$ or merely (12), it being understood that if a symbol is not written it is mapped onto itself by the permutation.   The six elements of the permutation group on M are 1, (12), (13), (23), (123), (132).   With this notation it is possible to compute products by inspection, thus $(123)(23) = (13)$ since 1 maps onto 2 by the first permutation and 2 onto 3 by the second, then 3 maps onto 1 by the first permutation and 1 onto 1 by the second and the ( ) is closed; it is clear then that 2 maps onto 2 and hence 2 is not written in the product.   Similarly $(13)(12) = (132)$.

A group is **commutative** or **abelian** (after Niels Abel, 1802–1829) provided $ab = ba$ for each a and b of the group.   In dealing with an abelian group one often uses additive notation with $+$ between two elements instead of juxtaposition and one writes $\sum_{i=1}^{n} a_i$ instead of $\prod_{i=1}^{n} a_i$.   The identity is then denoted by 0 and the inverse of b by $-b$ instead of b^{-1}.   The symmetric group on $\{1, 2, 3\}$ of Example I.1.g is not an abelian group.

I.1.h. Exercise.   *Show that the semigroup ρ_G of right multiplications of a group G is a group and that $\rho_a^{-1} = \rho_{a^{-1}}$.*

2. Subgroups and cosets

I.2.a. Definitions.   A non-empty subset of a group G is a **subgroup** of G if it is a group under the operations of G.   The notation $H \leq G$

will signify that H is a subgroup of G.   A subgroup of a group G is
proper if it is not G.   The notation $H < G$ will signify that H is a
proper subgroup of G.   The subgroup consisting of the identity
alone is the **trivial** subgroup; it will also be denoted by 1.   A subgroup other than 1 is **non-trivial.**   A subgroup is **maximal** if it is
proper and not a proper subgroup of a proper subgroup.

I.2.b. Examples.   The set of non-zero rational numbers and the
set of non-zero real numbers are subgroups of the group of non-zero
complex numbers under multiplication (cf. I.1.c).   The set of non-
zero rational numbers is also a subgroup of the group of non-zero real
numbers under multiplication.   Similar statements may be made for
the various pairs of groups of I.1.d.   In particular, the set of even
integers is a maximal subgroup of the group of integers under addition.

The proof of the following important criterion is left to the reader.

I.2.c. Criterion.   *A non-empty subset H of a group G is a subgroup of
G if and only if $ab^{-1} \in H$ for each ordered pair a, b of elements of H;
or equivalently if and only if $a^{-1} \in H$ for each $a \in H$ and $ab \in H$ for each
pair a, $b \in H$.*

In view of the above criterion the following proposition is immediate.

I.2.d. Proposition.   *The intersection of a collection of subgroups of a
group is a subgroup.   If a collection of subgroups of a group has the
property that of each pair of subgroups in the collection, one of them
contains the other, then the union of the collection is a subgroup.*

I.2.e. Definition.   If S and T are non-null subsets of a group, their
product consists of all elements st, $s \in S$, $t \in T$, and is denoted by ST
(in additive notation, the **sum** of the non-null subsets S and T consists
of all elements $s + t$, $s \in S$, $t \in T$, and is denoted by $S + T$).

It is clear that the associative law holds for this multiplication of
subsets; that is, $S(TU) = (ST)U$.   If S^2 denotes SS, then $S^2 \subseteq S$

when S is a semigroup, and $S^2 = S$ when S is a subgroup.   If S is a non-null subset of a group, the set of all elements s^{-1} with $s \in S$ will be denoted by S^{-1}.   If S is a subgroup, $S = S^{-1}$.   For arbitrary non-empty subsets S and T, $(ST)^{-1} = T^{-1}S^{-1}$.

The proof of the following proposition is left to the reader.

I.2.f. Proposition.   *If H and K are subgroups of a group, HK is a subgroup if and only if $HK = KH$.*

I.2.g. Definition.   If H is a subgroup and x an element of a group G, then the product Hx ($H + x$ in additive notation) of the set H with the set consisting of the single element x is the **right coset** of H in G containing x; similarly, xH is the **left coset** of H in G containing x. If K is also a subgroup of G, then HxK is the **double coset** of H with K containing x.

If H is a subgroup of G, call two elements x, y of G right equivalent modulo H if $xy^{-1} \in H$.   We leave the verification to the reader that this right equivalence is an equivalence relation on G (cf. [J] for the definition of equivalence relation), and that two elements are in the same right coset if and only if they are right equivalent modulo H. Since each element x of G is in a right coset of H, namely Hx, we have the following proposition.

I.2.h. Proposition.   *If H is a subgroup of a group G, then G is the union of the right cosets of H in G and any two distinct right cosets are disjoint.*

A similar proposition holds for left cosets and double cosets.

I.2.i. Definitions.   The cardinality of a set S will be denoted by $|S|$. The cardinality of a group G is its **order** $|G|$.   The cardinality of the set of right cosets of a subgroup H of a group G is the **index** of H in G; it will be denoted by $|G:H|$.

A "left index" could be defined similarly in terms of left cosets but it is equal to the index as defined above; for the map θ from the set of right cosets of H in G, defined by the equation $(Hg)\theta = g^{-1}H$, is a one-one map onto the set of all left cosets.

The elements of any right (or left) coset of the subgroup H are in one-one correspondence with the elements of H, and hence with the elements of any other coset of H. In particular, two cosets of a subgroup of a finite group have the same number of elements and thus the number of cosets of a subgroup of a finite group is a divisor of the group order.

In view of the above remarks we have the following basic theorem.

I.2.j. Theorem (*Lagrange*).   *The order times the index of a subgroup of a finite group is equal to the group order. In symbols,* $|H| \circ |G:H| = |G|$.

If H and K are subgroups of a group G and $x \in G$, then $(H \cap K)x \subseteq Hx \cap Kx$. On the other hand, if $y \in Hx \cap Kx$, then $y \in Hx$ and $yx^{-1} \in H$. Similarly, $yx^{-1} \in K$, and hence $yx^{-1} \in H \cap K$. Thus $y \in (H \cap K)x$ and hence $(H \cap K)x = Hx \cap Kx$. We conclude that a right coset of $H \cap K$ is the intersection of a right coset of H with a right coset of K. As an immediate consequence of the above argument we have the special case for two subgroups of the following proposition. An obvious induction gives the general case.

I.2.k. Proposition (*Poincaré*).   *The intersection of a finite number of subgroups of finite index is a subgroup of finite index.*

We leave to the reader the direct proof of the following proposition which will be needed later.

I.2.l. Proposition.   *Let G be a group with subgroups A and B and suppose that $G = AB$. Then for each $b \in B$, $B \cap Ab = (A \cap B)b$; if θ is the map defined on the set of cosets of A in G by the equation $(Ab)\theta = (A \cap B)b$; then θ is a one-one map onto the set of cosets of $A \cap B$ in B.*

3. Homomorphisms and normal subgroups

Of great importance in the study of groups are the maps which preserve the group operations; these are the homomorphisms as defined below.

I.3.a. Definition. A **homomorphism** of a group G into a group $\bar{G}$ is a map θ from G into $\bar{G}$ such that for arbitrary elements a and b of G, $(ab)\theta = (a\theta)(b\theta)$; in this case $G\theta$ is a **homomorphic image** of G. If, in addition, θ is one-one, then θ is an **isomorphism**.

We mention immediately two important properties of homomorphisms. Let θ be a homomorphism of a group G onto a group $\bar{G}$, then we have the following.

(i) 1θ *is the identity of* $\bar{G}$.

For $(1\theta)(g\theta) = (1g)\theta = g\theta = (g\theta)(1\theta)$.

(ii) *For* $g \in G$, $(g\theta)^{-1} = g^{-1}\theta$.

This is because $(g\theta)(g^{-1}\theta) = 1\theta$.

I.3.b. Example. Under the usual multiplication the set of positive real numbers is a group which will be denoted here by P. If b is any positive number except 1, let the map β be defined on P by the equation $x\beta = \log_b x$ for x in P. Then β is an isomorphism from P onto the additive group of real numbers; for β is one-one and onto, and $\log_b(xy) = \log_b x + \log_b y$.

We now list three easily verified but important facts about homomorphisms and isomorphisms.

(iii) *The identity map is an isomorphism.*
(iv) *If a homomorphism (as a map) has an inverse, this inverse is a homomorphism.*
(v) *The composition (as maps) of two homomorphisms is a homomorphism.*

We shall say that G is **isomorphic** to $\bar{G}$, denoted $G \cong \bar{G}$, if there is an isomorphism from G onto $\bar{G}$. In view of (iii), (iv), and (v), it follows that this notion is an equivalence relation on the class of all groups.

The following theorem shows how a group may be considered as a group of permutations.

I.3.c. Theorem (*Cayley*). *Each group is isomorphic to its group of right multiplications.*

Proof. Let G be an arbitrary group and consider its group ρ_G of right multiplications acting in G. If ρ is the map from G to ρ_G defined by the equation $g\rho = \rho_g$, then ρ is a one-one map onto ρ_G; for $\rho_g = \rho_h$ implies that $1g = 1h$, that is, $g = h$. Furthermore $(gh)\rho = (g\rho)(h\rho)$, since $\rho_{gh} = \rho_g \rho_h$. Hence ρ is an isomorphism from G onto ρ_G. This proves the theorem.

I.3.d. Example. The usual one-one map θ from the set of real numbers to the set of points on a straight line may be used to give the line the structure of an abelian group. The sum of two points a and b is defined to be $(a\theta^{-1} + b\theta^{-1})\theta$. A **translation** of the line is a right multiplication; translation by the point b is the map sending a into $a + b$ for each point a of the line. By the above theorem the group on the line is isomorphic to the group of translations of the line.

The verification of the following important fact is left to the reader.

I.3.e. Proposition. *Let G be a group and $\bar{G}$ a set in which a binary operation is defined. If there is a map θ from G onto $\bar{G}$, such that for all a and b of G, $(ab)\theta = (a\theta)(b\theta)$, then $\bar{G}$ is a group under the operation defined in it and θ is a homomorphism from G onto $\bar{G}$.*

I.3.f. Example. Let n be a fixed integer and let J_n denote the set of integers $0, 1, 2, \cdots, n-1$. Any integer r can be written in only one way in the form $mn + r'$ with m and r' integers and $r' \in J_n$. For $x, y \in J_n$ we define the "sum" of x and y to be $x + y$ if $x + y < n$ and to be $x+y-n$ otherwise.   Let θ be the map defined on the set of all integers by the equation $r\theta=r'$.   Then $(r+s)\theta=r\theta+s\theta$ and hence, by I.3.e, J_n is a group.   It is the **group of integers modulo** n and is a homomorphic image of the group of integers under addition.

I.3.g. Example.   Let R be the set of non-negative real numbers less than 1.   For $x, y \in R$ define the sum of x and y to be $x+y$ if $x+y<1$ and to be $x+y-1$ otherwise.   Any real number r can be written in only one way in the form $n+r'$ with n an integer and $r' \in R$.   Let θ be the map defined on the real numbers by the equation $r\theta=r'$.   Then if r and s are real numbers, $(r+s)\theta=r\theta+s\theta$, and hence, by I.3.e, R is a group.   It is the group of **real numbers modulo 1.** This group is isomorphic to the group (under multiplication) of complex numbers of absolute value 1; the isomorphism θ is defined by the equation $r\theta=e^{2\pi i r}$ with $r \in R$.   In view of the usual one-one map of the set of complex numbers onto the plane, the unit circle may be given a group structure which is thus also isomorphic to the group of real numbers modulo 1.   The right multiplications of this group on the circle are in one-one correspondence with the rotations of the plane about the origin.   Hence, by I.3.c, the group of rotations of the plane about the origin is also isomorphic to the group of real numbers modulo 1.

I.3.h. Definition.   If θ is a homomorphism of a group G, the set of elements k of G such that $k\theta=1$ is the **kernel** of the homomorphism.

I.3.i. Examples.   The set of multiples of n is the kernel of the homomorphism of I.3.f.   The set of integers is the kernel of the homomorphism of I.3.g.

I.3.j. Definitions.   A subgroup or subset H of a group G is **normal** or **invariant** in G if $gH=Hg$ for each $g \in G$.   The notation $H \lhd G$ will signify that H is a normal subgroup of G.   When G and 1 are the only normal subgroups of G, then G is said to be **simple**.

I.3.k. Examples.   Any subgroup of an abelian group is normal.   A group, whose order is a prime number, is a simple group (cf. I.2.j).

If H is a subgroup of index two in a group G, then H is normal in G; for if g is an element of G not in H, then Hg is the set complement of H in G and hence $Hg = gH$.

The reader should verify the following important fact.

I.3.1. Proposition.   *The kernel K of a homomorphism θ of a group G is a normal subgroup.   Two elements of G have the same image under θ if and only if they are in the same coset of K.*

We shall now show how a normal subgroup determines a homomorphism.   Let $H \lhd G$ and let $x, y \in G$.   Then $xHyH = xyH$ and hence the set of cosets of H is closed under the multiplication introduced in I.2.e.   In view of I.3.e, the map θ defined by the equation $g\theta = gH$, for each $g \in G$ is a homomorphism from G onto the set of cosets, and the set of cosets is a group.

I.3.m. Definitions.   If H is a normal subgroup of a group G, the homomorphism defined by the map $g\theta = gH$ for $g \in G$ is the **canonical homomorphism** of G determined by H.   The group of cosets is the **factor group** of G by H; it is denoted by G/H and is called **G modulo H**.   If X is a subset of G/H the **complete inverse image** of X is the set of all $g \in G$ with $gH \in X$.

The connection between normal subgroups and homomorphisms is given in the following fundamental theorem.

I.3.n. Theorem.   *If H is the kernel of a homomorphism θ of a group G onto $\bar{G}$, then $G/H \cong \bar{G}$.*

Proof.   For $g \in G$ let the map ϕ be defined by the equation $(gH)\phi = g\theta$.   By 1.3.1, ϕ is a one-one map from G/H onto $\bar{G}$.   Since H is normal in G, for $f, g \in G$, $gfH = gHfH$; and since θ is a homomorphism, $(gf)\theta = (g\theta)(f\theta)$.   It follows that $(gfH)\phi = (gH)\phi \cdot (fH)\phi$ and hence that ϕ is an isomorphism.

We conclude this section with some elementary facts about normal subgroups, two more basic isomorphism theorems, and the notion of full invariance.

I.3.o. Criterion.   *A subgroup H is normal in the group G if and only if $g^{-1}Hg = H$ for all $g \in G$, or equivalently, if and only if $g^{-1}hg \in H$ for all $h \in H$, $g \in G$.*

The verification of the above is immediate and is left to the reader. We deduce immediately the following proposition.

I.3.p. Proposition.   *The intersection of a non-empty set of normal subgroups is a normal subgroup.*

We now introduce the notion of normal closure which is of importance in view of Proposition I.3.p.

I.3.q. Definition.   The **normal closure** of a subset S of a group G is the intersection of all normal subgroups containing the subset; it will be denoted by $\mathscr{K}(S)$.

I.3.r. Proposition.   *If A is a normal subgroup of a group G and B is any subgroup of G, then $A \cap B$ is normal in B, and AB is a subgroup of G.   If B is also normal in G, then so also is AB.*

Proof.   The first statement follows from I.3.o; for if $h \in A \cap B$ and $b \in B$, then $b^{-1}hb \in B$ since B is a subgroup and $b^{-1}hb \in A$ since A is normal.   The second assertion follows immediately from 1.2.f; for $AB = BA$ when A is normal.   The last assertion follows immediately from the definition of normality; for if $g \in G$, $gAB = AgB = ABg$.

We can now give the second basic isomorphism theorem.

I.3.s. Theorem.   *If A and B are subgroups of a group G and if A is normal in G, then $AB/A \cong B/A \cap B$.*

In view of I.3.r, AB is a subgroup and $A \cap B$ is normal in B. We leave it to the reader to verify that the map θ of I.2.1 is in fact an isomorphism.

Our last isomorphism theorem is as follows:

I.3.t. Theorem. *Let θ' be a homomorphism from a group G with kernel K onto a group $\bar{G}$. Let $\mathscr{S}$ denote the set of subgroups of G containing K and let θ be the map defined on $\mathscr{S}$ by the equation $A\theta = A\theta'$ for $A \in \mathscr{S}$. Then the following statements hold:*

(1) *θ is a one-one map from $\mathscr{S}$ onto the set of all subgroups of $\bar{G}$.*
(2) *θ preserves inclusion; that is, if $A, B \in \mathscr{S}$, then $A < B$ if and only if $A\theta < B\theta$ and in particular A is maximal in B if and only if $A\theta$ is maximal in $B\theta$.*
(3) *θ preserves normality, that is, $A \lhd B$ if and only if $A\theta \lhd B\theta$, and in this case $B/A \cong B\theta/A\theta$; in particular, $A/K \cong A\theta$.*
(4) *$(A \cap B)\theta = A\theta \cap B\theta$.*

The proof of the above theorem is direct and is left to the reader.

I.3.u. Definitions. A subgroup H of a group G is **fully invariant** in G if $H\theta \leq H$ for each homomorphism θ of G into G. If H is an arbitrary subset of a group G, then the subgroup generated (see Definition I.4.a below) by all subsets $H\theta$, with θ ranging over the set of homomorphisms of G into G, is the **fully invariant closure** of H in G; it will be denoted by $\mathscr{F}_G(H)$ or merely by $\mathscr{F}(H)$.

4. Cyclic groups

I.4.a. Definitions. Let M be a non-empty subset of a group G. The set of products of elements of $M \cup M^{-1}$ is a subgroup of G; it is the **subgroup generated by** M and is denoted by $\mathfrak{S}(M)$, or by $\mathfrak{S}(m, m \in M)$, or if $M = H \cup K \cup \cdots$, by $\mathfrak{S}(H, K, \cdots)$. The set M is a **generating set** of $\mathfrak{S}(M)$ and its elements are generators of $\mathfrak{S}(M)$. If M is the empty set we adopt the convention that $\mathfrak{S}(M) = 1$.

We note some immediate facts.

    (i) *$\mathfrak{S}(M)$ is the intersection of all subgroups of G which contain M.*
    (ii) *If $ab = ba$ for each pair of elements a, b, of a generating set of a group, then the group is commutative.*
    (iii) *If H is a subgroup of a group G and if $Hm = mH$ for each m in a generating set of G, then H is normal in G.*

I.4.b. Definitions. If $\mathfrak{S}(M) = G$ for some finite subset M of a group G, then G is **finitely generated.** If M consists of a single element b, then $\mathfrak{S}(M)$ is **cyclic** and will also be denoted by (b). The element b is a **generator** of (b). If b is any element of a group G, the **order** of b is the order of the subgroup (b); it will be denoted by $|b|$. If G is any group, the least common multiple of the orders of its elements is the **exponent** of G.

We can give two immediate consequences of the theorem of Lagrange.

I.4.c. Corollary of I.2.j. *The order of an element of a finite group divides the group order. Moreover the exponent of a finite group divides the group order.*

I.4.d. Corollary of I.4.c. *A group of prime order is cyclic.*

I.4.e. Example. The group of integers modulo n of I.3.f is a cyclic group; the number 1 is a generator. This group is isomorphic to the subgroup generated by the number $1/n$ of the group of real numbers modulo 1, and is also isomorphic to the subgroup of rotations of the plane whose elements are rotations through angles $2\pi m/n$ with m and n integers and $0 \leq m < n$. A regular n-sided polygon centered at the origin is mapped onto itself by the elements of the above subgroup of rotations.

I.4.f. Example. The additive group of integers is a cyclic group; the number 1 (or -1) is a generator. This group is isomorphic to the subgroup generated by any irrational positive number less than 1 in the group of real numbers modulo 1.   It is also isomorphic to the subgroup generated by a rotation of the plane through an angle which is an irrational multiple of π.

If n is a negative integer and b a group element, we define b^{-n} to be $(b^{-1})^n$ and b^0 to be 1.   Then it is easy to prove by induction that for all integers m, n,

(iv) $b^m b^n = b^{m+n}$
(v) $(b^m)^n = b^{mn}$.

We leave it to the reader to verify the following elementary but basic facts.

I.4.g. Proposition.   *Let b be a group element of finite order m.   Then the following statements hold:*

(1) $b^t = 1$ *if and only if m divides t.*
(2) $(b^r) = (b)$ *(or b^r is a generator of b) if and only if r is prime to m.*
(3) *If $m = rs$, then (b^s) is a subgroup of order r of (b), in fact (b^s) is the only subgroup of (b) of order r.*
(4) *If $m = rs$, $(b)/(b^s)$ is a factor group of order s.*
(5) *(b) is isomorphic to the integers modulo m.*

I.4.h. Proposition.   *Let b be a group element of infinite order.   Then the following statements hold:*

(1) *$b^t \neq 1$ for each integer $t \neq 0$.*
(2) *$(b^r) = (b)$ or b^r is a generator of (b) if and only if $r = \pm 1$.*
(3) *For each integer r, not ± 1 (b^r) is a proper subgroup isomorphic to (b).*
(4) *For each integer r, the factor group $(b)/(b^r)$ is a cyclic group of order r.*
(5) *(b) is isomorphic to the additive group of integers.*

We shall use the notations C_m for the cyclic group of order m and C_∞ for the infinite cyclic group.   In view of (5) of 1.4.g, (5) of I.4.h, and I.3.f, C_m is always a homomorphic image of C_∞.

I.4.i. Exercise.   *Let n be a prime power and let A and B be distinct subgroups of C_n; show that either $A < B$ or $B < A$.   Conversely, suppose* *that for each pair A, B of distinct subgroups of C_n, either $A < B$ or $B < A$; show that n is a prime power.*

I.4.j. Exercise. *Let G be a cyclic group and (g) a subgroup of index m in G. Show that G has a generator b such that $b^m = g$.*

5. Generators and defining relations; free groups

In the last section we saw that if G is a cyclic group there is a homomorphism from C_∞ onto G. In this section we shall give a general construction of a group F_γ that may be mapped homomorphically onto any group that can be generated by a set of cardinality γ.

We begin with the construction of the free semigroup on a given set of symbols. Let M be a set of symbols. For each $n > 0$ let M^n denote the set of sequences of symbols $\alpha_1 \alpha_2 \cdots \alpha_n$ with $\alpha_1, \alpha_2, \cdots, \alpha_n \in M$, and let $S = \bigcup_{n=1}^{\infty} M^n$. If $\alpha_1 \cdots \alpha_m$ and $\beta_1 \cdots \beta_n$ are any two elements of S, we define their product to be $\alpha_1 \cdots \alpha_m \beta_1 \cdots \beta_n$. It is clear that this multiplication is associative and hence that S is a semigroup.

I.5.a. Definitions. If M is a set of symbols and S is the semigroup constructed as above, then S is the **free semigroup on M**. The elements of S are **words**. The **length** $L(w)$ of a word w is the unique integer n such that $w \in M^n$.

We now wish to construct a group on a given set M, "free" or satisfying certain relations. To do so we begin with a set $N = M \cup \overline{M}$ which is the union of M with a set $\overline{M}$ of symbols $\bar{\alpha}$ disjoint from M and in one-one correspondence with the symbols α of M. Let S be the free semigroup on N and let R be a subset of S which contains all words in N of the form $\alpha\bar{\alpha}$ and $\bar{\alpha}\alpha$ with $\alpha \in M$, $\bar{\alpha}$ the element of $\overline{M}$ corresponding to α, and possibly other words. Thus

$$\{\alpha\bar{\alpha}, \bar{\alpha}\alpha \mid \alpha \in M\} \subseteq R \subseteq S.$$

The word s will be said to be related to the word s' if s' is obtainable from s by the insertion or deletion of a finite number of words of R; for example, $\beta_1 \beta_2 \bar{\beta}_2 \beta_3$ is related to $\bar{\beta}_1 \beta_1 \beta_1 \beta_3$ and $\beta_1 \beta_3$.

At this point it is convenient to define the **empty word,** i.e., the word with no symbols which is obtained for instance by deleting $\beta\bar\beta$ from itself; the set consisting of the empty word will be denoted by M^0 and the length of the empty word is zero.   The relation defined above is an equivalence relation and partitions S into equivalence classes.   The set of these classes will be denoted by $S \mid R$ and will be turned into a group by defining the product of two classes $R(s)$ and $R(t)$ of $S \mid R$ to be the class of $R(st)$, where s is a word of $R(s)$, t a word of $R(t)$, and st is the product of s and t in S.   This product is well defined; for if s is equivalent to s', and t to t', then st is equivalent to $s't'$.   The inverse $R(s)$ of $R(s)$ is the class of the element obtained by writing down s in reverse order, and then replacing each α in the resulting expression by $\bar\alpha$, and each $\bar\alpha$ by α.   Multiplication in $S \mid R$ is associative since S is a semigroup, and $R(s) \cdot R(s)^{-1} \cdot R(t) = R(t)$ $= R(t) \cdot R(s) \cdot R(s)^{-1}$; it follows that $S \mid R$ is a group.   The identity element is the class containing R.

The words of S represent the elements of $S \mid R$, many words of S corresponding to one and the same element of $S \mid R$.   In particular, the words of R are among the words which represent 1 in $S \mid R$. Furthermore, $S \mid R$ is generated by all $R(\alpha)$ with $\alpha \in M$ since $R(\bar\alpha)$ $= R(\alpha)^{-1}$.   We therefore identify the symbols α of M with these generators of $S \mid R$ and say that $S \mid R$ is generated by M.   The symbols $\bar\alpha$ of $\overline{M}$ will then be identified with the elements α^{-1} of $S \mid R$, and the words of S are now products of the generators α and their inverses.

I.5.b. Definition.   The group $S \mid R$ is the **group on the generators** α **in** M **with defining relations** $r = 1$, $r \in R$.   It is denoted by $\mathfrak{G}(M \mid R)$, $\mathfrak{G}(a_j \mid r_j)$, or $\mathfrak{G}(a_j \mid s_j = t_j)$, with a_j an enumeration of the elements of M and r_j or $s_j \, t_j^{-1}$ an enumeration of the elements of R.

Since R always contains $\alpha\bar\alpha$ and $\bar\alpha\alpha$, this will usually not be mentioned explicitly again.

I.5.c. Example.   The cyclic group of order m, C_m is isomorphic to $\mathfrak{G}(a \mid a^m)$.   It is clear that $a^{mk} = 1$ in $\mathfrak{G}(a \mid a^m)$ for each integer k.

I.5.d. Definitions.   If in the construction above R contains only the words $\alpha\bar\alpha$, $\bar\alpha\alpha$ for $\alpha \in M$, then the group $S \mid R$ is the **free group on** M

and will be denoted simply by $\mathfrak{G}(M)$, and the set M is a free set of generators of the free group $\mathfrak{G}(M)$. If M is the empty set we adopt the convention that $\mathfrak{G}(M)$ is the trivial group. The cardinality of M will be called the **rank** of $\mathfrak{G}(M)$. The words of S will now be called **words of** $\mathfrak{G}(M)$.

I.5.e. Example. The infinite cyclic group C_∞ is isomorphic to the free group on one generator $\mathfrak{G}(a)$. We emphasize again that there is a homomorphism from the free group on one generator onto each one-generator (i.e., cyclic) group.

Any group G may be presented in the form $\mathfrak{G}(M \mid R)$ by choosing for M a set of symbols in one-one correspondence with a generating set of G, and for R the set or an appropriate subset of all words corresponding (in the obvious way) to the set of all products of elements from the generating set with each product equal to 1.

I.5.f. Example. If $G = \mathfrak{G}(a, b \mid a^3, b^2, b^{-1}aba^{-2})$, then $a^3 = 1$, $b^2 = 1$, and $ab = ba^2$ in G. Thus G consists of the six elements $a^i b^j$ with $i = 0, 1, 2$, and $j = 0, 1$. The reader should check that in S_3, the symmetric group on three symbols of I.1.g, the element (123) has order 3, the element (12) has order 2, and that $(123)(12) = (12)(123)^2$. Hence S_3 has two generators satisfying the defining relations of G; and in fact the map ϕ defined by the equations $(a^i b^j)\phi = (123)^i(12)^j$ is an isomorphism of G onto S_3.

Let M, $\bar{M}$, and $N = M \cup \bar{M}$ be as before, and let S be the free semigroup on N. We are interested in the relation between $\mathfrak{G}(M \mid R)$ and $\mathfrak{G}(M \mid \bar{R})$ when $R \subset \bar{R} \subset S$. In this case we have the following fundamental theorem.

I.5.g. Theorem (*Dyck*). *Let M, N, and S be as indicated above and suppose that $R_1 \subseteq R_2 \subseteq S$; let $G_1 = \mathfrak{G}(M \mid R_1)$ and $G_2 = \mathfrak{G}(M \mid R_2)$ Then there is a homomorphism from G_1 onto G_2.*

Proof. For $i = 1, 2$, the elements of G_i are the classes $R_i(s)$ of $S \mid R_i$. Since $R_1 \subseteq R_2$, for $s \in S$ we have $R_1(s) \subseteq R_2(s)$. It follows that if ϕ is defined by the equations $R_1(s)\phi = R_2(s)$ for all $R_1(s) \in S \mid R_1$, then ϕ is a well-defined map from G_1 onto G_2. It is clear that ϕ is a homomorphism as the theorem asserts.

I.5.h. Corollary. *Any group is the homomorphic image of some free group, and any map from a set M into a group G is the restriction of a homorphism from $\mathfrak{G}(M)$ into G.*

Proof. If the given group is presented in the form $\mathfrak{G}(M \mid R)$ as in the remark following I.5.e, then by the theorem it is a homomorphic image of $\mathfrak{G}(M)$.

It is clear that the kernel of the above homomorphism from $\mathfrak{G}(M)$ onto $\mathfrak{G}(M \mid R)$ is the normal closure of the set of elements of $G(M)$ corresponding to R.

The reader will profit from verifying the statements in the following examples.

I.5.i. Example. The group $\mathfrak{G}(a_n, n = 1, 2, \cdots \mid a_{n+1}^{n+1} = a_n)$ is isomorphic to the group of additive rationals with a_n and $1/n!$ corresponding elements for each n. It is also (cf. I.7.a below) an ascending union $\bigcup_{n=1}^{\infty} (a_n)$, where each (a_n) is an infinite cyclic subgroup of index $n+1$ in (a_{n+1}).

I.5.j. Example. If p is a fixed prime, the group

$$\mathfrak{G}(a_n, n = 1, 2, \cdots \mid a_{n+1}^{p} = a_n)$$

is isomorphic to the subgroup of the additive rationals whose denominators are powers of p, with a_n and $1/p^n$ corresponding elements for each n. This group is an ascending union of its subgroups (a_n) but is not isomorphic to the group of the additive rationals.

I.5.k. Example. If p is a fixed prime, the group

$$\mathfrak{G}(a_n, n = 1, 2, \cdots \mid a_{n+1}^{p} = a_n, a_1^{p})$$

is isomorphic to the subgroup of the additive rationals modulo 1, consisting of those elements whose denominators are powers of p; a_n and $1/p^n$ are corresponding elements for each n. This group is isomorphic to the multiplicative group of roots of unity which have p-power order. It is an ascending union $\bigcup_{n=1}^{\infty} A_n$ of its subgroups A_n with $A_n < A_{n+1}$ and $A_n \cong C_{p^n}$; any proper subgroup of it is one of the A_n.

I.5.l. Definition. The group of I.5.k is the **p-quasicyclic group** for the prime p; it is denoted by C_{p^∞}.

I.5.m. Examples. The subgroup of symmetries of the plane generated by a rotation of the plane about a fixed origin together with a reflection in a fixed line through the origin is isomorphic to $\mathfrak{G}(a, b \mid abab, b^2)$ if the rotation has infinite order. It is the infinite **dihedral group** and is denoted by D_∞. If the rotation has finite order n, the subgroup is isomorphic to $\mathfrak{G}(a, b \mid abab, b^2, a^n)$. This is the **dihedral group of order** $2n$ and is denoted by D_{2n}. For each n, D_{2n} is a homomorphic image of D_∞ by I.5.g. The symmetric group on three symbols, S_3, is isomorphic to D_6 as can easily be seen from I.5.f.

One motivation for the study of groups given by generators and defining relations comes from topology as follows. The elements of the fundamental group of a topological space are equivalence classes $C(s)$ of closed directed paths s starting and ending at a fixed point of the space; two paths are equivalent if one can be deformed continuously into the other within the space, keeping the end points fixed throughout the deformation. The product of two classes, s and t, is the class of the path st, obtained by following path s by path t. The inverse of $C(s)$ is $C(s^{-1})$, where s^{-1} is the path s with direction reversed. The reader is referred to the book on knot theory by Crowell and Fox [C-F] for the material treated below.

I.5.n. Examples. The fundamental group of the Euclidean plane consists of the identity alone. The plane with a point omitted has the infinite cyclic group for fundamental group; a path circling the point once may be taken as generator.   The space consisting merely of the circumference of a circle also has the infinite cyclic group for fundamental group.   The plane with n points omitted has a free group on n generators for fundamental group.

I.5.o. Example.   Suppose K is Euclidean 3-space minus the trefoil knot shown in Figure 1.   The three points of the knot hidden from

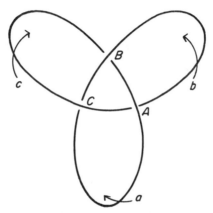

Fig. 1 The Trefoil Knot

the observer are labeled A, B, and C, and the arc between A and B not containing C will be denoted by AB.   The equivalence class of closed paths starting and ending at the observer's eye, and looping around AB in the direction of the arrow, is called c.   Classes a and b are defined similarly.   It can be shown that the fundamental group of K is $\mathfrak{G}(a, b, c \mid a^{-1}b^{-1}cb, b^{-1}c^{-1}ac, c^{-1}a^{-1}ba)$.

I.5.p. Exercise.   *Show that $\mathfrak{G}(a, b, c \mid a^{-1}b^{-1}cb, b^{-1}c^{-1}ac, c^{-1}a^{-1}ba)$ can be expressed in terms of two generators and one relation by eliminating c to get $\mathfrak{G}(a, b \mid aba = bab)$.*

We conclude this section by showing that there is precisely one word of minimum length in the class of words representing an element of the free group $\mathfrak{G}(M)$.

I.5.q. Definition. Let M, N, and S be as before and consider the elements of the free group $\mathfrak{G}(M)$ again as classes of words of S. The word $\alpha_1\alpha_2 \cdots \alpha_m$ is a **reduced word** of $\mathfrak{G}(M)$ if for no

$$i = 1, 2, \cdots, m-1,$$

is $\alpha_i = \alpha_{i+1}^{-1}$; in particular, α_i, α_i^{-1}, and the empty word are reduced words.

I.5.r. Theorem. *There is exactly one reduced word in each class of words representing an element of a free group $\mathfrak{G}(M)$.*

Proof. It is clear that each class of words representing an element of $\mathfrak{G}(M)$ contains at least one reduced word—namely the word obtained by deleting all inverse pairs $\alpha\alpha^{-1}$, or $\alpha^{-1}\alpha$ where possible for $\alpha \in M$.

We shall now prove that if s is a reduced word in such a class, and w an arbitrary word of the same class, then w may be obtained from s by insertion of inverse pairs only; consequently, in fact s is the only reduced word of its class. To prove this we suppose that w is obtained from s by some insertions and deletions of inverse pairs, and consider the first deletion which occurs in this sequence of operations. If this deletion does not involve the symbols of the insertion immediately preceding it, these two operations may be interchanged; that is, the deletion may be performed before the insertion.

It follows that the sequence of operations taking s to w may be changed so that the first deletion to occur is either the first operation of the sequence or else follows immediately an insertion involving one of its symbols. But as s is a reduced word, a deletion cannot be the first operation performed on s. On the other hand, it is easy to check that the combined effect of an insertion, followed by a deletion involving one of the symbols of the insertion, is to leave the word unchanged as a product of the generators. Thus the sequence of operations taking s to w may be changed so that the first deletion may be omitted. In this way all the deletions may be dispensed with, and there is a sequence of operations taking s to w, involving only insertions, as was to be shown. This proves the theorem.

In view of the above theorem, the elements of a free group may be thought of as the reduced words in the generators.   Then multiplication amounts to mere juxtaposition of reduced words, followed, if necessary, by the cancellation of inverse pairs of generators, if the product word is not reduced.   The **length** of an element is the length of the reduced word expressing it.

6. Cartesian and direct products

In this section we construct the cartesian product of a given set of groups and study one of its important subgroups, the direct product.

For each α in an index set A, let G_α be a group and consider the set of all functions f on A such that $f(\alpha) \in G_\alpha$.   This set of functions is the cartesian product of the sets G_α.   It can be turned into a group by defining the product ff' of two functions f, f' by the rule $ff'(\alpha) = f(\alpha) \cdot f'(\alpha)$ for each α; the identity element is the function i such that $i(\alpha)$ is the identity element of G_α for each α, and the inverse of f is the function f^{-1} such that $f^{-1}(\alpha) = f(\alpha)^{-1}$ for each α.

I.6.a. Definitions.   If for each α in an index set A, G_α is a group, the **cartesian product** of the groups G_α is the group of functions described above.   It is denoted by $\mathsf{P}_{\alpha \in A}\, G_\alpha$.   If for each $\alpha \in A$, G_α is isomorphic to a group G, the cartesian product of the G_α is the **cartesian power** of G indexed by A and is denoted by G^A as well as $\mathsf{P}_{\alpha \in A}\, G_\alpha$.

Each element of the cartesian product may be pictured intuitively as a collection of group elements, one from each of the G_α, and will be denoted by $(\cdots, g_\alpha, \cdots, g_\beta, \cdots)$ with $g_\alpha \in G_\alpha$, $g_\beta \in G_\beta$, $\alpha, \beta \in A$, or alternatively will be denoted by $\mathsf{P}_{\alpha \in A}\, g_\alpha$.   The product of two such elements is then given by "group wise" or "componentwise" multiplication; thus $\mathsf{P}_{\alpha \in A}\, g_\alpha \cdot \mathsf{P}_{\alpha \in A}\, h_\alpha = \mathsf{P}_{\alpha \in A}\, g_\alpha h_\alpha$.

I.6.b. Examples.   The additive group of Euclidean n-space E_n is the cartesian product of n copies of the additive group of real numbers. The elements of E_n are n-tuples $(a_1, \cdots, a_n)$ of real numbers.   Similarly if J_m is the group of integers modulo m (cf. I.3.f), the cartesian product of n copies of J_m is the set of n-tuples $(a_1, \cdots, a_n)$ of integers modulo m. In both cases the group operation is addition, thus $(a_1, \cdots, a_n) + (b_1, \cdots, b_n) = (a_1 + b_1, \cdots, a_n + b_n)$; $(0, \cdots, 0)$ is the identity element, and $(-a_1, \cdots, -a_n)$ is the negative of $(a_1, \cdots, a_n)$. The cartesian product of 2 copies of J_2 is known as the **Klein four-group**; it is a non-cyclic group of order 4.

Consider a cartesian product $\mathsf{P}_{\alpha \in A}\, G_\alpha$ again. If for a fixed γ in A, K_γ denotes the set of those functions f_γ such that for $\alpha \neq \gamma$, $f_\gamma(a) = 1$ in G_α, then K_γ is a subgroup of $\mathsf{P}_{\alpha \in A}\, G_\alpha$ which is isomorphic to G_γ and will be identified with G_γ. Thus each G_α is a subgroup of $\mathsf{P}_{\alpha \in A}\, G_\alpha$.

I.6.c. Definitions. The subgroup $\mathfrak{S}(G_\alpha, a \in A)$ of $\mathsf{P}_{\alpha \in A}\, G_\alpha$ is the **direct product** (**direct sum** in additive notation) of the groups G_α. It is denoted by $\prod_{\alpha \in A} G_\alpha$ (in additive notation, $\sum_{\alpha \in A} G_\alpha$). The subgroups G_α are the **direct factors** (in additive notation **direct summands**). If A is finite and contains n members, then the direct product is also written $G_1 \times \cdots \times G_n$ (or in additive notation $G_1 \oplus \cdots \oplus G_n$).

The circled plus sign is used here to distinguish the direct sum from the sum of subsets as defined in I.2.e.

The direct product $\prod_{\alpha \in A} G_\alpha$ consists of those functions f of $\mathsf{P}_{\alpha \in A}\, G_\alpha$ such that $f(\alpha) = 1$ except for a finite number of α. It follows that $\prod_{\alpha \in A} G_\alpha = \mathsf{P}_{\alpha \in A}\, G_\alpha$ if and only if A is finite or almost all the G_α are trivial. If B is a finite subset of A and if $A = B \cup C$, then $\mathsf{P}_{\alpha \in A}\, G_\alpha = \prod_{\alpha \in B} G_\alpha \times \mathsf{P}_{\alpha \in C}\, G_\alpha$ when B and C are disjoint.

I.6.d. Examples. The groups of I.6.b are direct sums. The additive group of formal power series in one variable with integer coefficients is isomorphic to $\mathsf{P}_{n=1}^{\infty} G_n$ with G_n the infinite cyclic group. The subgroup of polynomials of $\mathsf{P}_{n=1}^{\infty} G_n$ is isomorphic to $\sum_{n=1}^{\infty} G_n$.

I.6.e. Definitions. The subgroups A and B of the group G are **complementary** subgroups (or A is a **complement** of B) if $G = AB$ and $A \cap B = 1$.

Consider now the direct product $D = \prod_{\alpha \in A} G_\alpha$, and for each $\alpha \in A$ let G_α^* denote $\mathfrak{S}(G_\beta, \beta \in A, \beta \neq \alpha)$. It is easy to check that the following three important assertions are true of D.

(i) *For each $\alpha \in A$, G_α and G_α^* are complementary.*

(ii) *For $\beta \neq \alpha$, $b \in G_\beta$, $a \in G_\alpha$, $ab = ba$.*

(iii) *Each element g of D can be expressed as a product $\prod_{\alpha \in A} g_\alpha$, $g_\alpha \in G_\alpha$ (it being understood that almost all g_α are 1), of uniquely determined elements, no two from the same G_α.*

It is easy to see immediately that when condition (ii) above holds then (i) is equivalent to (iii). It is also immediate that when (i) holds, then (ii) is equivalent to the condition that each G_α is normal in D. For clearly (ii) implies that each G_α is normal in D. Conversely, if each G_α is normal in D, then $a^{-1}b^{-1}ab = a^{-1}(b^{-1}ab) = (a^{-1}b^{-1}a)b \in G_\alpha \cap G_\beta$; but $G_\alpha \cap G_\beta \subseteq G_\alpha \cap G_\alpha^* = 1$ so that $ab = ba$ and (ii) holds.

In view of the unique expression of (iii) for each $g \in D$, there is a map π_α for each α from D onto G_α defined by the equation $g\pi_\alpha = g_\alpha$. The map π_α is a homomorphism; it is called the **projection** from D onto G_α.

We now wish to determine whether a given group is isomorphic to a direct product of some of its subgroups. Let D be a given group and suppose that D has a set of normal subgroups G_α which generate D, where α ranges over some index set A. For each $\alpha \in A$ let G_α^* denote $\mathfrak{S}(G_\beta, \beta \in A, \beta \neq \alpha)$ and suppose that $G_\alpha \cap G_\alpha^* = 1$ for each α. Thus the equations (i), (ii), and (iii) above hold for D, G_α, and G_α^* for all $\alpha \in A$.

We leave it to the reader to show that if for each α there is an isomorphism θ_α so that $G_\alpha \theta_\alpha = H_\alpha$, then the given group D is in fact isomorphic to $\prod_{\alpha \in A} H_\alpha$ under an isomorphism θ whose restriction to G_α is θ_α. Thus we may say that D is the direct product of its subgroups G_α for $\alpha \in A$. This is the "internal" direct product in contrast to the "external" direct product of I.6.c. We use the same notation again for this internal direct product; thus $D = \prod_{\alpha \in A} G_\alpha$ now.

The situation may be summarized as follows.

I.6.f. Theorem.   *Let D be a group with a set of subgroups G_α indexed by α in an index set A, and let G_α^* denote $\mathfrak{S}(G_\beta, \beta \in A, \beta \neq \alpha)$ for each α. Then D is the direct product of its subgroups G_α if and only if for each $\alpha \in A$, G_α is normal in D and G_α is a complement of G_α^*.*

We conclude this section with a description of the possible decompositions of cyclic groups, and the construction of ascending unions of groups.

I.6.g. Definitions.   A group is **decomposable** if it can be written as the direct product of some of its proper non-trivial subgroups. Otherwise it is **indecomposable**.

If a group is decomposable, it is the direct product of any factor in the decomposition by the subgroup generated by all the remaining factors.

I.6.h. Theorem.   *The groups C_∞ and C_{p^m}, p a prime, are indecomposable.   If $n = \prod_{i=1}^{k} p_i^{m_i}$ where the p_i are different primes, then* $C_n \cong \prod_{i=1}^{k} C_{p_i^{m_i}}$.

Proof.   If C_∞ were the direct product of two of its proper non-trivial subgroups A and B, then each would have finite index in C_∞ and therefore so also would $A \cap B = 1$, which is impossible. Accordingly we conclude that C_∞ is indecomposable.

The group C_{p^m} cannot be the direct product of two of its non-trivial proper subgroups A and B since $A \cap B$ is either B or A in view of I.4.i.

To prove the last assertion of the theorem, suppose that $C_n = (b)$, and let $b_i = b^{s_i}$ where $s_i = n p_i^{-m_i}$ so that $|b_i| = p_i^{m_i}$.   It follows from I.6.f that $(b) = (b_1) \times \cdots \times (b_k)$.   Thus $C_n \cong \prod_{i=1}^{n} C_{p_i^{m_i}}$ as the theorem asserts.

I.6.i. Exercise.   *Show that each subgroup of the additive rationals and each p-quasicyclic group is indecomposable.*

I.6.j. Exercise.   *Show that any non-cyclic group of order 4 is isomorphic to the Klein four-group of I.6.b.*

I.6.k. Exercise.   *If p and q are primes, show that the number of proper non-trivial subgroups of $C_p \times C_q$ is greater than or equal to two and that equality holds if and only if $p \neq q$.*

I.6.l. Exercise. *If G and H are simple groups, show that G and H are the only proper non-trivial normal subgroups of $G \times H$ unless $|G| = |H|$ and $|G|$ is a prime number.*

I.6.m. Exercise. *For $i = 1, 2, \cdots, n$, let G_i be a group of exponent $m_i < \infty$. Show that the exponent of $\prod_{i=1}^{n} G_i$ is the least common multiple of the m_i.*

I.6.n. Exercise. *For each α in an index set A, let G_α be a group with no elements of infinite order. Show that $\prod_{\alpha \in A} G_\alpha$ has no elements of infinite order in view of I.6.m. On the other hand, $\mathsf{P}_{\alpha \in A} G_\alpha$ has elements of infinite order if and only if there is an infinite sequence of groups G_i, $i = 1, 2, \cdots$, of the collection, and an infinite sequence of elements $g_i \in G_i$, such that $|g_i| > |g_j|$ for $i > j$.*

The cartesian product is used to form an ascending union of groups as follows. For $n = 1, 2, \cdots$, let G_n be a group and C the cartesian product $\mathsf{P}_{n=1}^{\infty} G_n$; let θ_n be an isomorphism from G_n into G_{n+1}, and let Θ be the set of all the θ_n, their inverses, and the identity maps of the G_n. This implies that for a fixed $g_n \in G_n$ and arbitrary G_m, there is at most one element of G_m which is an image of g_n under a product of elements of Θ. We shall define the **relative** of g_n in G_m to be such an image if there is such and otherwise to be 1. Now let ϕ_n be the map which assigns to the element g_n of G_n, the element of C whose component in G_m is the relative of g_n in G_m. It is easy to check that for each n, ϕ_n is an isomorphism of G_n into C, that $G_n \phi_n \leq G_{n+1} \phi_{n+1}$, and that the set of all elements $g_n \phi_n$ for all n and all $g_n \in G_n$ is a group. It is the **ascending union** of the given groups G_n and will be denoted by $\bigcup_{n=1}^{\infty} G_n$. This is the "external" ascending union in contrast to the "internal" ascending union of subgroups G_n of a given group as in Examples I.5.i, I.5.j, and I.5.k.

7. The Frattini subgroup

The main object of this section is to define the Frattini subgroup and to develop one of its important properties. In order to do this we begin with the concepts necessary for a formulation of Zorn's lemma.

I.7.a. Definitions.   A **partially ordered set** $\mathscr{S}$ is a set in which there is an order relation, $\leq$, defined for certain pairs of elements of $\mathscr{S}$.   This relation is **transitive**; that is, if S, T, and U are elements of $\mathscr{S}$ with $S \leq T$ and $T \leq U$, then $S \leq U$.   It is **reflexive**, that is, $S \leq S$; and it is **anti-symmetric**, that is, if $S \leq T$ and $T \leq S$, then $S = T$.   A **linearly ordered subset** or **chain** of $\mathscr{S}$ is a subset $\mathscr{T}$ such that, if T and U are in $\mathscr{T}$, then either $T \leq U$ or $U \leq T$.   In connection with subgroups of a group, a **chain** is a linearly ordered set of subgroups ordered by inclusion; and the union of the subgroups of such a chain is an **ascending union**.   An **upper bound** of a subset $\mathscr{W}$ of $\mathscr{S}$ is an element B of $\mathscr{S}$, such that $W \leq B$ for all W in $\mathscr{W}$. An element M of $\mathscr{S}$ is *maximal* if $M \leq S$ for S in $\mathscr{S}$, implies that $M = S$.   A partially ordered set in which every linearly ordered subset has an upper bound is an **inductive set**.

The following statement is equivalent to the Axiom of Choice and is known as Zorn's Lemma.

I.7.b. Zorn's Lemma.   *A non-empty inductive set has a maximal element.*

Let $\mathscr{S}$ be an inductive set and $S \in \mathscr{S}$; it is easy to check that the set $\mathscr{T}$ of all $T \in \mathscr{S}$ such that $T \geq S$ is also an inductive set, and hence we get the following equivalent formulation of Zorn's Lemma.

I.7.b′. Zorn's Lemma.   *Each element of a non-empty inductive set is bounded above by a maximal element.*

The following general theorem can now be proved.

I.7.c. Theorem.   *If K is a non-empty subset and V a subgroup of a group G, then there is at least one subgroup N of G, containing V, and maximal with respect to the property that its intersection with K is $V \cap K$: that is, if $\mathfrak{S}(N, x) \cap K = V \cap K$, then x is in N.*

Proof. The set of subgroups of G, each containing V and intersecting K in $V \cap K$, is a non-null partially ordered set under inclusion, which we will denote by $\mathscr{S}$. If $\mathscr{T}$ is a linearly ordered subset of $\mathscr{S}$, then the union U of all the subgroups in $\mathscr{T}$ is likewise a subgroup (cf. Proposition I.2.d) of G which contains V and intersects K in $V \cap K$, so that in fact U is an upper bound for $\mathscr{T}$. Thus $\mathscr{S}$ is an inductive set and, by Zorn's Lemma, $\mathscr{S}$ contains a maximal element N. This subgroup N contains V and intersects K in $V \cap K$; whereas if $\mathfrak{S}(N, x) \cap K = V \cap K$, then x is in N as the theorem asserts.

By a similar method of proof, which will be left to the reader, we have the following proposition.

I.7.d. Proposition (*B. H. Neumann*). *A non-trivial finitely generated group always has a maximal subgroup and also a maximal normal subgroup.* (*A **maximal normal** subgroup is a proper normal subgroup which is not a proper subgroup of a proper normal subgroup*).

The p-quasicyclic group of I.5.k is not finitely generated and has no maximal subgroup. Thus the hypothesis in Proposition I.7.d, that the group be finitely generated, is a necessary hypothesis.

The finiteness conditions of the following definitions will occasionally be of interest in the sequel.

I.7.e. Definitions. A group satisfies the **maximum condition** for subgroups if every non-empty chain of subgroups has a maximal element; that is, every ascending chain of subgroups becomes constant after a finite number of steps. The **minimum condition** is satisfied if every non-empty chain has a minimal element.

We list some elementary facts.

   (i) *If a group satisfies the maximum (or minimum) condition, then so also does each of its subgroups and each of its homomorphic images.*

   (ii) *If a group satisfies the minimum condition, each of its elements has finite order.*

For an element of infinite order generates the infinite cyclic group which contains no minimal subgroups. On the other hand, the infinite cyclic group satisfies the maximum condition.

   (iii) *Let A be a normal subgroup of a group G; then both A and G/A satisfy the maximum condition if and only if G does. More generally, if $1 = A_0 \lhd A_1 \lhd \cdots \lhd A_n = G$, then G satisfies the maximum condition if and only if for each $i = 1, \cdots, n$, A_i/A_{i-1} satisfies the maximum condition.*

The strength of the maximum condition may be seen from the following proposition.

I.7.f. Proposition.   *A group satisfies the maximum condition if and only if each of its subgroups is finitely generated.*

   Proof.   Suppose H is a subgroup of the group G which cannot be finitely generated; then there is a sequence of elements of H, $h_1, h_2, \cdots, h_n, \cdots$ such that if $H_n = \mathfrak{S}(h_1, \cdots, h_n)$, the chain of subgroups $H_1, H_2, \cdots$, has no maximal element. Thus if G satisfies the maximum condition, then each subgroup is finitely generated.

   Conversely, suppose G does not satisfy the maximum condition, and let $A_1 < A_2 < \cdots A_n < \cdots$ be a properly ascending chain of subgroups of G. Then the union A of this chain cannot be finitely generated since any finite set of elements of A is in some A_n; hence, in particular, the finite generating set would be in some A_n, and $A = A_n$ contrary to the fact that the chain is properly ascending.

I.7.g. Corollary.   *A group is not finitely generated if it is an infinite ascending union $\bigcup_{n=1}^{\infty} A_n$ with each A_n proper in A_{n+1}, or if it is an infinite direct product $\prod_{n=1}^{\infty} B_n$ with each B_n non-trivial.*

I.7.h. Definition.   The element x is said to be a **non-generator** of a group G if for every subset S of G such that $G = \mathfrak{S}(S, x)$, then $G = \mathfrak{S}(S)$ also.

   The set of non-generators of a group G is a subgroup. It is non-empty, since it contains 1 (the empty set is a generating set for the trivial group by the convention of I.4.a); whereas if $G = \mathfrak{S}(xy^{-1}, S)$ with x and y non-generators, then $G = \mathfrak{S}(x, y, S) = \mathfrak{S}(x, S) = \mathfrak{S}(S)$. Hence xy^{-1} is a non-generator when x and y are such, and therefore by I.2.c the set is a subgroup.

I.7.i. Definition.   The subgroup of non-generators of a group G is the **Frattini subgroup** (after Giovanni Frattini, 1852–1925) of G and is denoted by $\Phi(G)$.

It is clear that if θ is a homomorphism defined on a group G, then $\Phi(G\theta) \geq (\Phi(G))\theta$; for if x is a non-generator of G, then $x\theta$ is a non-generator of $G\theta$.   Hence in particular the Frattini subgroup is a normal subgroup.

The Frattini subgroup is related to the maximal subgroups in the following way.

I.7.j. Theorem.   *The Frattini subgroup of a group G is the intersection I of G with the maximal subgroups of G.*

Proof.   If M is a maximal subgroup of G which does not contain the element x of $\Phi(G)$, then we have the contradiction $\mathfrak{S}(M) = M < G = \mathfrak{S}(M, x)$.   Hence $\Phi(G)$ is contained in I.

Now suppose x is not in $\Phi(G)$.   Then there is a proper subgroup V of G, such that $G = \mathfrak{S}(x, V)$.   Thus $x \notin V$ and by I.7.c there is a subgroup M of G maximal in that $x \notin M$.   Since $G = \mathfrak{S}(x, V) = \mathfrak{S}(x, M)$, M is a maximal subgroup of G.   Hence the set of elements of G not in $\Phi(G)$ is contained in the set of elements not in I, and the theorem is proved.

In view of I.7.j and I.7.d we have the following fact.

I.7.k. Proposition.   *If G is a finitely generated simple group, then $\Phi(G) = 1$.*

It is an unsolved problem to determine whether the Frattini subgroup of a direct product of groups is the direct product of the Frattini subgroups of the factors (cf. [4]).   We first give a lemma on which we base the proof of one theorem in this direction.

I.7.1. Lemma.   *Let $G = G_1 \times G_2$ and for $i = 1, 2$, let π_i be the projection of G onto G_i.   Let M be a subgroup of G and let M_i denote $M \cap G_i$.   Then*

(1) $M_i \vartriangleleft M\pi_i$ for $i = 1, 2$.
(2)   *If $M\pi_i = G_i$ for $i = 1, 2$, then $G_1/M_1 \cong G_2/M_2$.*
(3)   *If $M\pi_i = G_i$ and M is a maximal subgroup of G, then G_i/M_i is simple.*

Proof.   If $m_1 \in M_1$ and $n_1 \in M\pi_i$, there is a $g \in M$ so that $g = n_1 n_2$ with $n_2 \in M_2$; then $n_1^{-1} m_1 n_1 = g^{-1} m_1 g$.   But the latter element is both in M and in G_1.   It follows that $M_1 \vartriangleleft M\pi_1$, and similarly $M_2 \vartriangleleft M\pi_2$. Thus (1) is proved.

By the hypothesis of (2), for each $g_1 \in G_1$ there is a $g_2 \in G_2$ so that $g_1 g_2 \in M$.   It follows that $M_1 g_1 g_2 M_2 \subseteq M$.   We shall show if, for $i = 1, 2$, H_i is a subset of G_i containing a coset of M_i such that $H_1 H_2 \subseteq M$, then in fact each H_i is a coset of M_i.   Indeed, if $h_1 \in H_1$, $h_2, h_2' \in H_2$, then $h_2' h_2^{-1} = h_2' h_1 h_1^{-1} h_2^{-1} \in M \cap G_2 = M_2$ and hence h_2 and h_2' are in the same coset of M_2.   Hence H_2 is a coset of M_2 and similarly H_1 is a coset of M_1.   It follows that there is a one-one map ϕ from the set of cosets of M_1 in G_1 onto the set of cosets of M_2 in G_2 given by $g_1 M_1 \phi = g_2 M_2$ with $M_1 g_1 g_2 M_2 \subseteq M$. It is clear that ϕ is a homomorphism; for if $g_1 g_2 \in M$, $r_1 r_2 \in M$ with $g_1, r_1 \in M_1$, $g_2, r_2 \in M_2$, then $g_1 g_2 r_1 r_2 = g_1 r_1 g_2 r_2 \in M$.   It follows that ϕ is an isomorphism and (2) is proved.

To prove (3) we suppose that N_1 is a normal subgroup of G_1 with $M_1 < N_1 \leq G_1$.   Then $M < \mathfrak{S}(M, N_1)$ so that by the maximality of M, $\mathfrak{S}(M, N_1) = G$.   Since $N_1 \vartriangleleft G_1$, $N_1 \vartriangleleft G$ and therefore $\mathfrak{S}(M, N_1)$ $= MN_1 = G$.   If $f_1 \in G_1$, then $g_1 = mn_1$ with $m \in M$, $n_1 \in N_1$.   But $m = m_1 m_2$ with $m_1 \in G_1$, $m_2 \in G_2$, and hence $g_1 = m_1 m_2 n_1$.   Since $G = G_1 \times G_2$, $m_2 = 1$ and $m = m_1$ so that $m_1 \in M_1 = M \cap G_1$.   Hence $m_1 n_1 \in N_1$ and $g_1 \in N_1$.   Thus $G_1 = N_1$, and hence G_1/M_1 and similarly G_2/M_2 are simple as is asserted in (3).   This proves the lemma.

I.7.m. Theorem   (*Dlab and Kořínek*).   *Let $G = \prod_{\alpha \in A} G_\alpha$; then $\Phi(G) \leq \prod_{\alpha \in A} \Phi(G_\alpha)$; the equality holds in the above if each G_α is finitely generated.*

Proof. For each $\alpha \in A$ let $G_\alpha{}^*$ denote $\prod_{\beta \in A, \beta \neq \alpha} G_\beta$. If for some $\alpha \in A$, M_α is a maximal subgroup of G_α, then $M_\alpha \times G_\alpha{}^*$ is a maximal subgroup of G. If follows that $\Phi(G) \leq \prod_{\alpha \in A} \Phi(G_\alpha)$ as the theorem asserts. It is also clear that, since $\Phi(G_\alpha) \leq M_\alpha$, $\prod_{\alpha \in A} \Phi(G_\alpha) \leq M_\alpha \times G_\alpha{}^*$ for each α and each maximal subgroup M_α of G_α.

Suppose now that M is a maximal subgroup of G not of the form $M_\alpha \times G_\alpha{}^*$. If for each α, π_α is the projection of G onto G_α, it follows that $M\pi_\alpha = G_\alpha$. For if for some α, $M\pi_\alpha < G_\alpha$, then $M \leq M\pi_\alpha \times G_\alpha{}^* < G$ with equality holding in view of the maximality of M; but this is contrary to the choice of the form of M. Since $M\pi_\alpha = G_\alpha$ for each α, it follows that if $\pi_\alpha{}^*$ projects G into $G_\alpha{}^*$, then $M\pi_\alpha{}^* = G_\alpha{}^*$. Then if M_α denotes $M \cap G_\alpha$ and $M_\alpha{}^*$ denotes $M \cap G_\alpha{}^*$, it follows from I.7.1 that G_α/M_α is simple. Since G_α is finitely generated, so also is G_α/M_α; therefore, G_α/M_α has maximal subgroups by I.7.d. Hence by I.7.k. and I.7.j, $\Phi(G_\alpha/M_\alpha) = M_\alpha$. Therefore, $\Phi(G_\alpha) \leq M_\alpha \leq M$. It follows that $\prod_{\alpha \in G} \Phi(G_\alpha)$ is contained in every maximal subgroup of G and hence that $\prod_{\alpha \in A} \Phi(G_\alpha) \leq \Phi(G)$. Thus equality holds when each G_α is finitely generated as the theorem asserts.

It can be observed from the above proof that $\Phi(\prod_{\alpha \in A} G_\alpha) = \prod_{\alpha \in A} \Phi(G_\alpha)$ whenever for each α, each simple homomorphic image of G_α has a maximal subgroup. In fact (cf. [4]), equality will fail to hold in the theorem if and only if there exists a simple group with no maximal subgroup. It is as yet unknown if there is such a simple group.

We conclude this section with a description of the Frattini subgroups of some special groups.

I.7.n.   Proposition.   *If G is the cyclic group of order n, then $\Phi(G) = \mathfrak{S}(b^m)$ where b is a generator of G and m is the product of the distinct prime divisors of n. If $G = C_\infty$, then $\Phi(G) = 1$. If G is a p-quasicyclic group or the additive group of rationals, then $\Phi(G) = G$.*

The proof is left as an exercise for the reader.

8. Varieties

The notion of variety is of great importance in some branches of group theory. It will be introduced here with an indication of how it connects some of the basic notions already mentioned; details will often be left to the reader. Important classes of groups to be studied in the sequel are varieties; for instance, the abelian groups, the nilpotent groups of class less than a fixed integer k, and the solvable groups of derived length less than k (cf. Chapters II, VI, and VII) are varieties.

I.8.a. Definition. Let R be a subset of a free group $\mathfrak{G}(M)$, that is, R is a set of words $w = w(x_1, \cdots, x_{n(w)})$ in M. If G is a group such that for each $w(x_1, \cdots, x_{n(w)}) \in R$ and for arbitrary $g_1, \cdots, g_{n(w)}$ of G, $w(g_1, \cdots, g_{n(w)}) = 1$, then G **satisfies the relations R identically.**

The notion introduced above has an important characterization in terms of mappings as follows.

I.8.b. Proposition. *Let R be a subset of a free group $\mathfrak{G}(M)$ and let G be a group; then G satisfies the relations R identically, if and only if, for every homomorphism θ of $\mathfrak{G}(M)$ into G, the kernel of θ contains R.*

The proof is direct and is left to the reader.

I.8.c. Definitions. Let $\mathfrak{G}(M)$ be a free group. A subset R of $\mathfrak{G}(M)$ determines the class of groups, denoted by $\mathbf{V}(R)$, which satisfy the relations R identically; such a class is a **variety.** Similarly a class of groups $\mathbf{C}$ determines a subset of $\mathfrak{G}(M)$, namely, the set of elements s such that $\mathbf{C} \subseteq \mathbf{V}(\{s\})$; this subset is the **relation set** of $\mathfrak{G}(M)$ determined by $\mathbf{C}$ and is denoted by $\mathfrak{F}_M(\mathbf{C})$.

The justification for the simpler notation $\mathbf{V}(R)$ instead of the more correct notation $\mathbf{V}_M(R)$ will be given below.

I.8.d. Examples. If R consists of the single word $x^{-1}y^{-1}xy$, then $\mathbf{V}(R)$ is the variety of abelian groups; for if g and h are elements of a group of $\mathbf{V}(R)$, then $g^{-1}h^{-1}gh = 1$ or $gh = hg$ for all g, $h \in G$. If R_m consists of the two words $x^{-1}y^{-1}xy$ and x^m, then $\mathbf{V}(R_m)$ is the variety of abelian groups of exponent m.

I.8.e. Exercise.   *If R consists of the single word x^2 show that $\mathbf{V}(R)$ is the variety of abelian groups of exponent 2.   In other words, a group is abelian if each of its non-trivial elements has order 2.*

The following propositions may be verified directly; I.8.g is merely a reformulation of I.8.b.

I.8.f. Proposition.   *If G is a group belonging to a variety $\mathbf{V}$, then each subgroup and homomorphic image of G also belongs to $\mathbf{V}$.   Furthermore, if for α in some index set A, G_α is a set of groups belonging to $\mathbf{V}$, then $\mathsf{P}_{\alpha \in A}\, G_\alpha$ also belongs to $\mathbf{V}$.*

I.8.g. Proposition.   *If R is a subset of a free group $\mathfrak{G}(M)$ and G is any group, then G satisfies the relations R identically if and only if G satisfies the relations $\mathfrak{F}(R)$ identically where $\mathfrak{F}(R)$ is the fully invariant closure of R, i.e., $\mathbf{V}(R) = \mathbf{V}(\mathfrak{F}(R))$.*

Some properties of the functions $\mathbf{V}$ and $\mathfrak{F}_M$ introduced in I.8.c will be given next; the verifications are left as exercises.

I.8.h. Proposition.   *If $\mathfrak{G}(M)$ is a free group, then the functions $\mathbf{V}$ and $\mathfrak{F}_M$ introduced in I.8.c satisfy the following formulas.*

(1) *If $R \subseteq S$, then $\mathbf{V}(R) \supseteq \mathbf{V}(S)$; i.e., $\mathbf{V}$ is non-increasing.*
(1') *If $\mathbf{C} \subseteq \mathbf{D}$, then $\mathfrak{F}_M(\mathbf{C}) \supseteq \mathfrak{F}_M(\mathbf{D})$; i.e., $\mathfrak{F}_M$ is non-increasing.*
(2) $\mathbf{V}(\bigcup_{\alpha \in A} R_\alpha) = \bigcap_{\alpha \in A} \mathbf{V}(R_\alpha)$.
(2') $\mathfrak{F}_M(\bigcup_{\alpha \in A} \mathbf{C}_\alpha) = \bigcap_{\alpha \in A} \mathfrak{F}_M(\mathbf{C}_\alpha)$.
(3) $\mathfrak{F}_M(\mathbf{V}(R)) \supseteq R$.
(3') $\mathbf{V}(\mathfrak{F}_M(\mathbf{C})) \supseteq \mathbf{C}$.
(4) $\mathbf{V}(\mathfrak{F}_M(\mathbf{V}(R))) = \mathbf{V}(R)$.
(4') $\mathfrak{F}_M(\mathbf{V}(\mathfrak{F}_M(\mathbf{C}))) = \mathfrak{F}_M(\mathbf{C})$.

I.8.i. Proposition.   *If R is a subset of a free group $\mathfrak{G}(M)$ and if $\mathfrak{F}(R)$ is the fully invariant closure of R, then $\mathfrak{F}(R) = \mathfrak{F}_M(\mathbf{V}(R))$.*

Proof.   It is clear that $\mathfrak{G}(M)/\mathfrak{F}(R)$ is in $\mathbf{V}(R)$; hence $\mathfrak{F}_M(\mathbf{V}(R))$ $\subseteq \mathfrak{F}(R)$.   On the other hand, by I.8.g and by (3) of I.8.h, $\mathfrak{F}_M(\mathbf{V}(R))$ $= \mathfrak{F}_M(\mathbf{V}(\mathfrak{F}(R)) \supseteq \mathfrak{F}(R)$ and the proposition follows.

I.8.j. Proposition.   *If **C** is a class of groups and $\mathfrak{G}(M)$ a free group, then the relation set $\mathfrak{F}_M(\mathbf{C})$ determined by **C** is a fully invariant subgroup of $\mathfrak{G}(M)$.*

Proof.   Applying I.8.i to (4′) of I.8.h, it follows that $\mathfrak{F}(\mathfrak{F}_M(\mathbf{C})) = \mathfrak{F}_M(\mathbf{C})$ and hence $\mathfrak{F}_M(\mathbf{C})$ is fully invariant.

In view of I.8.j and (4) of I.8.h we have the following theorem.

I.8.k. Theorem.   *There is a one-one correspondence between the fully invariant subgroups of a free group $\mathfrak{G}(M)$ and the varieties determined by the subsets of $\mathfrak{G}(M)$.*

I.8.l. Definition.   *If H is a fully invariant subgroup of a free group $\mathfrak{G}(M)$, then $\mathfrak{G}(M \mid H)$ or $\mathfrak{G}(M)/H$ is a **reduced free group** of the variety $\mathbf{V}(H)$.*

The above terminology is justified in view of the following characterization of the reduced free groups.

I.8.m. Theorem.   *Let a subset H of a free group $\mathfrak{G}(M)$ determine the variety $\mathbf{V}(H)$. If G is any group of $\mathbf{V}(H)$ and θ any map of M into G, then θ is the restriction (if we agree to identify the elements of M in $\mathfrak{G}(M)$ with those of M in $\mathfrak{G}(M)/\mathfrak{F}(H)$) of a homomorphism of the reduced free group $\mathfrak{G}(M)/\mathfrak{F}(H)$ into G. Conversely, if F is any group on the set of generators M (i.e., $F = \mathfrak{G}(M)/K$ for some K) and if F is in $\mathbf{V}(H)$ such that each map θ of M into any group G of $\mathbf{V}(H)$ is the restriction of a homomorphism of F into G, then F is a reduced free group of $\mathbf{V}(H)$.*

Proof.   Let G be a group of $\mathbf{V}(H)$ and θ a map of M into G. Then by I.5.h, θ is the restriction of a homomorphism of $\mathfrak{G}(M)$ into G. By I.8.g and I.8.b the kernel of this homomorphism contains $\mathfrak{F}(H)$ and hence the homomorphism induces a homomorphism of $\mathfrak{G}(M)/\mathfrak{F}(H)$ into G whose restriction to M is θ as the theorem asserts.

Conversely, if $F = \mathfrak{G}(M)/K$ is in $\mathbf{V}(H)$, then $K \supseteq \mathfrak{F}(H)$ by I.8.g and I.8.b.   On the other hand, by the hypothesis on F, the map θ which maps each generator m of M in $\mathfrak{G}(M)/K$ onto m in $\mathfrak{G}(M)/\mathfrak{F}(H)$ is the restriction of a homomorphism; hence $K \subseteq \mathfrak{F}(H)$ and consequently $K = \mathfrak{F}(H)$.   Thus, F is the reduced free group $\mathfrak{G}(M \mid \mathfrak{F}(H))$ as the theorem asserts.

It may be of interest to remark here that if R is the empty set, then $\mathbf{V}(R)$ is the variety of all groups.   Since the empty set generates the trivial subgroup which is fully invariant, any reduced free group $\mathfrak{G}(M \mid 1)$ of the variety of all groups is simply a free group $\mathfrak{G}(M)$ as would be expected.

It is a simple matter to check that if A is a direct sum of infinite cyclic subgroups (x) for each x in some set M, then any map from M into any abelian group is the restriction of a homomorphism of A. Hence, in view of I.8.m we have the following.

I.8.n. Proposition.   *A direct sum of infinite cyclic groups is a reduced free group of the variety of abelian groups.*

It is clear that the invariant subgroups $\mathfrak{F}_M(\mathbf{C})$ and the reduced free groups $\mathfrak{G}(M)/\mathfrak{F}(H)$ depend on M or at least on $|M|$ in the case of the reduced free groups.   On the other hand, the set R in I.8.a is merely a collection of words.   Since each word is finite, it may be written in terms of a finite number of symbols.   Hence any variety may be defined by a subset of $\mathfrak{G}(U)$, where U is one fixed "universal" countable infinite set.   This is the justification for writing $\mathbf{V}(R)$ instead of $\mathbf{V}_M(R)$.

In view of (2) of I.8.h, we have the following proposition and definition.

I.8.o. Proposition.   *The intersection of varieties is a variety.*

I.8.p. Definition.   The variety **generated by a group** G is the intersection of all varieties containing G; it is denoted by $\mathbf{V}(G)$.   The **relation set** of G is the set of all $s \in \mathfrak{G}(U)$ (with U the "universal" countable infinite set) so that G is in $\mathbf{V}(\{s\})$; it is denoted by $\mathfrak{F}_U(G)$.

By way of contrast with I.8.o, the following example and exercise show that even a "towered union" of varieties need not be a variety.

I.8.q. Example.   Let K be an infinite set of distinct positive integers such that if m, n are in K with $m < n$, then m divides n, and for each $m \in M$ let $\mathbf{V}(R_m)$ be the corresponding variety defined as in Example I.8.d.   Then $\mathbf{V}(R_m) \subset \mathbf{V}(R_n)$, but $\bigcup_{m \in K} \mathbf{V}(R_m)$ is not a variety since the cartesian product $\mathsf{P}_{m \in K} \, C_m$ has elements of infinite order (cf. I.6.n).

I.8.r. Exercise.   *Show that a towered union of varieties is a variety if and only if it is a finite union.*

The following lemmas will be used in the proof of the last theorem of this section.   The first lemma is obvious; the second lemma gives an explicit construction of a reduced free group of the variety generated by a given group.

I.8.s. Lemma.   *If for each α in an index set A, G_α is a group and P denotes $\mathsf{P}_{\alpha \in A} \, G_\alpha$, then $\mathfrak{F}_U(P) = \bigcap_{\alpha \in A} \mathfrak{F}_U(G_\alpha)$ and $\mathbf{V}(P) \supseteq \bigcup_{\alpha \in A} \mathbf{V}(G_\alpha)$; furthermore, a group and any cartesian power of it generate the same variety.*

I.8.t. Lemma.   *Let G be a group, let S be the set of all maps of G into G, and let $D = \mathsf{P}_{\sigma \in S} \, G_\sigma$, where for each $\sigma \in S$, there is an isomorphism θ_σ so that $G\theta_\sigma = G_\sigma$.   Then D contains a subgroup isomorphic to the reduced free group of $\mathbf{V}(G)$ on a set of cardinality $|G|$.*

Proof.   For each $g \in G$ consider the set T of elements f_g of D with $f_g(\sigma) = g\sigma\theta_\sigma \in G_\sigma$, and let H denote $\mathfrak{S}(T)$.   Let M be a set such that there is a one-one map θ from M onto T.   Let $\mathfrak{G}(M \mid K)$ be the reduced free group of $\mathbf{V}(G)$ determined by M.   Then by I.8.m, θ is the restriction of a homomorphism, which will also be denoted by θ, of $\mathfrak{G}(M \mid K)$ onto H.   We shall show that θ is an isomorphism by showing that the kernel of θ is 1.   But this is immediate; for if $w = w(x_1, \cdots, x_n)$ is in the kernel of θ, then $w(g_1, \cdots, g_n) = 1$ for all

$g_1, \cdots, g_n \in G$ in view of the properties of T and S. Thus G satisfies the relation $w(x_1, \cdots, x_n)$ identically; therefore $w(x_1, \cdots, x_n)$ is in K and hence is 1 in $\mathfrak{G}(M \mid K)$.

I.8.u. Theorem (*Birkhoff*). *A class of groups is a variety if and only if it includes all subgroups, homomorphic images, and cartesian products of its members.*

Proof. If the class is a variety, then the conclusion follows from Proposition I.8.f.

Conversely, let **C** be a class of groups including all subgroups, homomorphic images and cartesian products of its members. Consider the set of all varieties $\mathbf{V}_\beta$, β in some set N, such that there is a group G_β in **C** with $\mathbf{V}_\beta = \mathbf{V}(G_\beta)$; and for each β pick one G_β in **C**. Then if $P = \mathrm{P}_{\beta \in N}\, G_\beta$, P is in **C** and by I.8.s,

$$\mathbf{C} \subseteq \bigcup_{\beta \in N} \mathbf{V}(G_\beta) \subseteq \mathbf{V}(P).$$

To prove that $\mathbf{C} \supseteq \mathbf{V}(P)$, we suppose that Q is an arbitrary group of $\mathbf{V}(P)$, and let G be a cartesian power of P indexed by the elements of Q, so that $|G| \geq |Q|$. By I.8.t, **C** contains a reduced free group H of the variety $\mathbf{V}(G)$ on a set of cardinality $|G| \geq |Q|$; hence there is a homomorphism from H onto Q, and consequently Q is in **C**. Thus $\mathbf{C} \supseteq \mathbf{V}(P)$, and hence $\mathbf{C} = \mathbf{V}(P)$. This proves the theorem.

Chapter *II*

ABELIAN GROUPS

The object of this chapter is to introduce the reader to some elementary abelian group theory. Abelian groups merit attention because they are fundamental in all of group theory as well as in many other branches of mathematics. There are several important classes of abelian groups for which there is a satisfying elementary theory. Some of these classes are studied here, namely, the locally cyclic groups, finitely generated groups, groups of bounded order, direct sums of cyclic groups, and divisible groups. The reader is referred to [K], [Ka], and [F], for more extensive and detailed accounts of the theory as well as for references to essentially all the material presented here.

1. Elementary facts about abelian groups

II.1.a. Definitions. Two elements a and b of a group **commute** if they satisfy the equation $ab = ba$. A group or subset of a group is **abelian** or **commutative** if each pair of its elements commutes.

We list some basic facts about commutative sets of elements of a group, the direct verifications of which are left to the reader.

   (i) *If a and b are elements of a group and if $ab = ba$, then for any integer m, $(ab^{\pm 1})^m = a^m b^{\pm m}$.*
   (ii) *If for $i, j = 1, 2, \cdots, n$, $a_i a_j = a_j a_i$, then $(\prod_{i=1}^n a_i)^m = \prod_{i=1}^n a_i^m$.*
   (iii) *If σ is any permutation of the numbers $1, 2, \cdots, n$ and if for $i, j = 1, 2, \cdots, n$, $a_i a_j = a_j a_i$, then $a_1 a_2 \cdots a_n = a_{1\sigma} a_{2\sigma} \cdots a_{n\sigma}$.*
   (iv) *A group is abelian if it has a generating set in which each pair of elements commute.*

In this chapter additive notation will be used for abelian groups; the equations of (i), (ii), (iii) above will then be as follows.

(i*) $m(a \pm b) = ma \pm mb$;

(ii*) $m \sum_{i=1}^{n} a_i = \sum_{i=1}^{n} ma_i$;

(iii*) $a_1 + a_2 + \cdots + a_n = a_{1\sigma} + a_{2\sigma} + \cdots + a_{n\sigma}$.

If a and b are elements of a group such that $ab = ba$ and if m and n are integers such that $ma = 0$, $nb = 0$, then $mn(a - b) = mna - mnb = 0$. Accordingly we have the following.

    (v) *In an abelian group G the set of elements of finite order is a subgroup.*

II.1.b. Definitions.   The subgroup of elements of finite order of an abelian group G is the **periodic** or **torsion subgroup**.   An element of finite order of any group (not necessarily abelian) is a **periodic** or **torsion element**.   If all the elements of a subgroup are periodic, the subgroup is **periodic (torsion)**; if no element, other than the identity element 0, is periodic, the subgroup is **aperiodic (torsion-free)**.

    (vi) *If p is a fixed prime, the set of elements of p-power order of an abelian group G is a subgroup.*

For if $p^n a = 0$ and $p^m b = 0$, a, b in G, then $p^{n+m}(a - b) = 0$ so that $a - b$ has order dividing p^{n+m}.

II.1.c. Definition.   The subgroup of elements of p-power order, p a fixed prime, of an abelian group G is the **p-component** of G.   If each element of any group G (not necessarily abelian) has p-power order, then G is a **p-group**.

In view of Theorem I.6.h, the proof of the following theorem is direct and is left to the reader.

II.1.d. Theorem.   *An abelian torsion group is the direct sum of its p-components.*

It will now be convenient to introduce for each integer m and each arbitrary (not necessarily abelian) group G, two important subsets of

G and also the subgroups they generate. The subsets are the subset of elements of G whose orders divide m and the subset of elements which are mth powers (in multiplicative terminology) in G. It is clear that each of these subsets is mapped into itself by any homomorphism of G into G. It follows that each subset generates a fully invariant subgroup of G. The subgroup generated by the elements whose order divides m will be denoted by $G(m)$ in both additive and multiplicative notation. The subgroup generated by the mth powers of elements of G will be denoted by mG in both additive and multiplicative notation.

The reader may readily verify that for the integer 2 and the infinite dihedral group of I.5.m, neither of the above mentioned subsets is a subgroup. He should also prove the following proposition for abelian groups.

II.1.e. Proposition. *Let G be an abelian group and m a fixed integer. Then the subset of elements of G whose orders divide m is a subgroup, and the subset of mth powers of elements of G is also a subgroup.*

II.1.f. Definition. An abelian group G such that $pG = 0$ for some prime p, is an **elementary** abelian p-group. Every non-zero element of such a group has order p.

II.1.g. Exercise. *Show that each non-trivial subgroup of an elementary abelian p-group G has a complement in G and hence that an elementary abelian p-group has maximal subgroups.*

II.1.h. Proposition. *If G is an abelian group and if Λ is the set of all primes, then the Frattini subgroup of G is $\bigcap_{p \in \Lambda} pG$.* Hint: *A subgroup is maximal in G if and only if it has prime index in G.*

2. Locally cyclic groups

II.2.a. Definition. A group has a property **locally** if each of its finitely generated subgroups has the property. In particular a group is **locally cyclic** if each of its finitely generated subgroups is cyclic.

An ascending union of groups $\bigcup_{n=1}^{\infty} A_n$, $A_n \subseteq A_{n+1}$, has any property locally that each of the A_n has locally; thus, in particular, each subgroup of the group of additive rationals (cf. I.5.i) is a locally cyclic group. In fact, the additive subgroup generated by a finite number of rational numbers, whose denominators have least common multiple k, is contained in the subgroup $(1/k)$. It is clear that locally cyclic groups are abelian and that subgroups and homomorphic images of locally cyclic groups are locally cyclic.

The object of this section is to describe the structures of locally cyclic groups and to show that a group is locally cyclic if and only if it is isomorphic to a subgroup, either of the additive rationals or of the additive rationals mod 1.

In order to describe the subgroups of the additive rationals we introduce for each prime number p, a map v_p on the rationals as follows. Let Λ be the set of all primes, and for each $p \in \Lambda$ let the map v_p from the non-zero rationals into the integers be defined by the equation $r = \pm \prod_{p \in \Lambda} p^{v_p(r)}$. Although the latter expression is written as an infinite product, it is in fact only a finite product, since $v_p(r) = 0$ for almost all primes. Each map v_p satisfies the following:

(1) $v_p(rs) = v_p(r) + v_p(s)$.
(2) $v_p(r+s) \geq \min (v_p(r), v_p(s))$ *if* $r \neq -s$.

Such a map is a **valuation.**

If G is a subgroup of the additive rationals, let $v_p(G)$ denote the greatest lower bound of the $v_p(g)$ as g ranges over G. It is clear that $-\infty \leq v_p(G) < \infty$ and that, if $G \neq 0$, then $v_p(G) \leq 0$ for almost all p. We shall call $v_p(G)$ the **value** of G at p.

Our first goal is to describe an arbitrary subgroup of the additive rationals in terms of its values. This is done in the following theorem.

II.2.b. Theorem. *If G is a subgroup of the additive rationals, then G consists of zero together with the set of all rationals r such that $v_p(r) \geq v_p(G)$ for each prime p.*

Proof. Let Λ_G be the set of primes p for which $v_p(G) > 0$ and let $n_G = \prod_{p \in \Lambda_G} p^{v_p(G)}$. We shall show that n_G is in G and hence is the least positive integer in G (it is clear that n_G divides every integer in

G). For each prime p_i in Λ_G, pick a quotient of integers m_i/n_i (with m_i prime to n_i) in G so that $v_{p_i}(m_i/n_i) = v_{p_i}(G)$; and for each prime p_j not in Λ_G, which divides the greatest common divisor of the m_i already chosen, pick a quotient of integers m_j/n_j (with m_j prime to n_j) in G so that m_j is prime to p_j. Then the m_i and m_j are in G and their greatest common divisor is n_G; on the other hand, this greatest common divisor is in G since it is a combination of the m_i and m_j with integer coefficients. Thus n_G is the least positive integer in G.

We shall now show that for $p \notin \Lambda_G$ and for $k \geq v_p(G)$, $n_G p^k \in G$. In view of the above it is only necessary to show this for $k < 0$. Suppose then that $k < 0$ and let u and w be integers prime to p, so that $p^k u/w$ is in G, and hence so that $p^k u$ is in G. Then there are integers a and b, so that $p^{-k}a + ub = 1$; multiplying by $p^k n_G$, we see that $a n_G + (p^k u)(n_G b) = p^k n_G$. Since n_G and $p^k u$ are in G, it follows that $p^k n_G$ is in G, as we wished to show.

Finally we observe that $\prod_{i=1}^{k} p_i^{k_i}$, with the k_i negative integers greater than or equal to $v_{p_i}(G)$ and the p_i distinct primes, has a partial fraction decomposition of the form $\sum_{i=1}^{k} a_i p_i^{k_i}$ for suitable integers a_i. It follows that $n \sum_{i=1}^{k} a_i p_i^{k_i}$ is in G if n is any integral multiple of n_G, and we have proved the theorem.

II.2.c. Definition. A **type** is a function on Λ to the set consisting of the integers and $-\infty$, such that only for a finite number of primes is the value of the function a positive integer.

Thus the set of values of a non-zero subgroup of the additive rationals defines a type. In fact, in view of the above definitions, II.2.b has the following corollary.

II.2.d. Corollary. *There is a one-one correspondence between the set of non-zero subgroups of the additive rationals and the set of types.*

Now suppose that θ is an isomorphism of a subgroup S of the group of additive rationals Q onto a subgroup T of Q; if t is a fixed element of S, let r_θ denote $(t\theta)t^{-1}$ so that $t\theta = tr_\theta$. Then if m and n are integers and $mtn^{-1} \in S$, we have $n(mtn^{-1})\theta = (mt)\theta = m(t\theta) = mtr_\theta$.

and $(mtn^{-1})\theta = (mtn^{-1})r_\theta$; thus there is a rational number r_θ such that $s\theta = sr_\theta$ for all $s \in S$.   Accordingly we have the following.

II.2.e. Proposition.   *Two subgroups S and T of the group of additive rationals are isomorphic if and only if $\sum_{p \in \Lambda} | \, v_p(S) - v_p(T) \, | \, < \infty$.*

Consider now the uncountable set of types whose values are either zero or $-\infty$.   Each such type defines a subgroup of the additive rationals.   By II.2.e, no two such subgroups are isomorphic.   Thus we have the following conclusion.

II.2.f. Proposition.   *The group of additive rationals has an uncountable set of subgroups, no two of which are isomorphic.*

The easy proofs of the following propositions are left to the reader.

II.2.g. Proposition.   *Let T be a subgroup of the group of additive rationals.   If S is a subgroup of T then S is maximal in T if and only if*
$$\sum_{p \in \Lambda} (v_p(S) - v_p(T)) = 1.$$

II.2.h. Proposition.   *Let M be the Frattini subgroup of a subgroup T of the group of additive rationals.   Then $v_p(M) = v_p(T) + 1$ for each prime p.*

II.2.i. Corollary.   *The Frattini subgroup of a subgroup T of the group of additive rationals is non-zero if and only if almost all the values of T are negative.*

We shall need the second statement of the following proposition in the proof of the main theorem of this section.   The proof of this proposition is easy and is left to the reader.

II.2.j. Proposition.   *The group R of the additive rationals mod 1 is isomorphic to a direct sum of p-quasicyclic groups, one for each prime.   A* *group is isomorphic to a subgroup of R if and only if it is a direct sum of groups G_p, one for each prime p, with G_p a subgroup of a p-quasicyclic group (i.e., either a group of order p^n or a p-quasicyclic group). Finally, a homomorphic image of R is a direct sum of p-quasicyclic groups for some set of primes p, no two of which are isomorphic.*

The reader will find it instructive to present an arbitrary locally cyclic group by means of a set of generators and defining relations.

Our characterization of locally cyclic groups is as follows.

II.2.k. Theorem. *A group is locally cyclic if and only if it is isomorphic to a subgroup of a homomorphic image of the group of additive rationals.*

Proof. In view of the remark following Definition II.2.a, a subgroup of a homomorphic image of the additive rationals is locally cyclic. Conversely, suppose G is a locally cyclic group. Then G is abelian and, moreover, either a torsion group or torsion-free; for if a is an element of non-trivial finite order, and b an element of infinite order, then $\mathfrak{S}(a, b)$ is $(a) \oplus (b)$ and therefore is not cyclic.

In the case that G is a torsion group, it will be enough in view of Theorem II.1.d, and the second statement of II.2.j, to show that for each prime p, the p-component G_p is isomorphic to a subgroup of a p-quasicyclic group. But this follows immediately from the fact that G_p has at most one subgroup (a_k) of order p^k; for if a and b are elements of order p^k, then the orders of the elements of the cyclic group $\mathfrak{S}(a, b)$ are at most p^k, so that $\mathfrak{S}(a, b) = (a) = (b)$. Since $(a_{k+1}) \supset (a_k)$, either there is a maximum (a_k) and G_p is cyclic of order p^k, or G_p is an ascending union of cyclic groups of order p^k and G_p is p-quasicyclic.

If G is torsion-free, then for any element a of G and any n in J, the set of natural numbers, there is at most one element x in G such that $nx = a$; for if $nx = ny = a$, then $n(x - y) = 0$ and $x = y$. Now let $c \neq 0$ be a fixed element of G and define c_n to be the element of G such that $nc_n = c$ if there is such an element; otherwise define c_n to be 0. Then $\mathfrak{S}(c_n, n \in J) = G$; for if x is in G, since $\mathfrak{S}(x, c)$ is cyclic, there is a generator c_n of $\mathfrak{S}(x, c)$ and a natural number n with $nc_n = c$. If now, for each integer $i \geq 1$, G_i is the cyclic group $\mathfrak{S}(c_1, \cdots, c_i) = (a_i)$, then $G_i \leq G_{i+1}$, and there are natural numbers m_i such that $a_i = m_i a_{i+1}$. It follows that there is an isomorphism between $G = \bigcup_{i=1}^{\infty} G_i$ and $\mathfrak{S}(\prod_{k=0}^{i-1} m_k^{-1}, \ i = 0, 1, 2, \cdots, m_0 = 1)$ of the additive rationals, a_i corresponding with $\prod_{k=0}^{i-1} m_k^{-1}$.   This proves the theorem.

3. Finitely generated abelian groups

In Chapter I we studied cyclic groups and direct products.   Here we prove the important theorem that a finitely generated abelian group is a direct sum of cyclic subgroups.   This theorem is known as the **basis theorem** for finitely generated abelian groups in view of the following definition.

II.3.a. Definition.   If A is a subset of non-zero elements of a group G such that $G = \sum_{g \in A} (g)$, then A is a **basis** for G.   We shall use the convention that the empty set is a basis for the subgroup it generates, namely, the trivial group.

Thus the basis theorem merely asserts that a finitely generated abelian subgroup has a basis.   Certain invariants of such a group will be discussed in the following section.

The proof of the basis theorem will depend on the following lemma.

II.3.b. Lemma.   *If $x_1, \cdots, x_n$ are generators of an abelian group G, and if $a_1, \cdots, a_n$ are integers with greatest common divisor 1, then the element $y = a_1 x_1 + \cdots + a_n x_n$ is one of a set of n generators of G.*

Proof.   For $n = 1$ the lemma is clear.   For $n = 2$, there are integers c_1, c_2, such that $a_1 c_1 + a_2 c_2 = 1$.   Then

$$x_1 = c_1(a_1 x_1 + a_2 x_2) + a_2(c_2 x_1 - c_1 x_2)$$
$$x_2 = c_2(a_1 x_1 + a_2 x_2) - a_1(c_2 x_1 - c_1 x_2)$$

and

$$G = \mathfrak{S}(x_1, x_2) = \mathfrak{S}(y, c_2 x_1 - c_1 x_2).$$

For $n > 2$, let $a_i = b_i d$, $i = 1, \cdots, n-1$, with d the greatest common divisor of $a_1, \cdots, a_{n-1}$, so that the greatest common divisor of $b_1, \cdots, b_{n-1}$ is 1. Then if $y_1 = b_1 x_1 + \cdots + b_{n-1} x_{n-1}$, by an induction argument on n we can assume that there are elements $y_2, \cdots, y_{n-1}$, so that $\mathfrak{S}(x_1, \cdots, x_{n-1}) = \mathfrak{S}(y_1, \cdots, y_{n-1})$; and hence

$$G = \mathfrak{S}(y_1, \cdots, y_{n-1}, x_n).$$

But $y = dy_1 + a_n x_n$, and the greatest common divisor of d and a_n is 1; hence there is an element z such that $\mathfrak{S}(y, z) = \mathfrak{S}(y_1, x_n)$. Then $G = \mathfrak{S}(y_1, \cdots, y_{n-1}, x_n) = \mathfrak{S}(y, y_2 \cdots y_{n-1}, z)$ as was to be shown. This proves the lemma.

II.3.c. Basis Theorem. *Let G be a finitely generated abelian group. If n is the least integer so that G is generated by n elements, then G is the direct sum of n cyclic subgroups.*

Proof. Let $x_1, \cdots, x_n$ be generators of G so chosen that x_n has order k, with k minimal in that no other set of n generators has an element of smaller order. If $H = \mathfrak{S}(x_1, \cdots, x_{n-1})$, $H < G$. By an induction argument on n, H is a direct sum of $n-1$ cyclic subgroups. We shall show that $H \cap (x_n) = 0$. If this were not so, then for some positive integer $a_n < k$, and integers $a_1, \cdots, a_{n-1}$, we would have

$$a_1 x_1 + \cdots + a_{n-1} x_{n-1} - a_n x_n = 0.$$

If d is the greatest common divisor of $a_1, \cdots, a_n$, then according to Lemma II.3.b, the element $a_1 d^{-1} x_1 + \cdots + a_{n-1} d^{-1} x_{n-1} - a_n d^{-1} x_n$ is a member of a set of n generators of G. Its order is at most d, and $d \leq a_n < k$. This is contrary to the minimality of k in the choice of x_n. We conclude that $H \cap (x_n) = 0$, and hence G is a direct sum of cyclic subgroups, as the theorem asserts.

Since $C_6 \cong C_2 \oplus C_3$, the number of elements of a basis of an abelian group is not an invariant of the group. On the other hand, if in a finitely generated abelian group, each basis element of finite order is required to have prime power order (this is always possible by Theorem I.6.h, since any element of composite order is a sum of elements, each of which has prime power order), then the number of such basis elements and their orders are invariants of the group.   This will be seen in connection with the discussion on rank in the next section. Here we give a special case of this fact which will be needed directly.

II.3.d. Proposition.   *The number of elements of a basis of a finitely generated torsion-free abelian group G is an invariant of the group.*

Proof.   If $G = \sum_{i=1}^{n} (x_i)$ with each x_i an element of infinite order, then it is easy to check that $G/2G$ has order 2^n; hence n is an invariant as was asserted.

II.3.e. Proposition.   *A commutative subset A of a group G is a basis for the subgroup it generates, if and only if, when n and a_i are integers and g_i elements of A, $\sum_{i=1}^{n} a_i g_i = 0$ implies that $a_i g_i = 0$ for each i.*

The proof is direct and is left to the reader.

II.3.f. Proposition.   *Let the group G be the direct sum of n infinite cyclic subgroups.   If $y_1, \cdots, y_n$ are n elements which generate G, then $G = \sum_{i=1}^{n} (y_i)$.*

Proof.   If G is not the direct sum of the (y_i), there are non-zero integers a_i by II.3.e so that $\sum_{i=1}^{n} a_i y_i = 0$.   Let d be the greatest common divisor of the a_i and let $a_i = b_i d$.   Then $\sum_{i=1}^{n} b_i y_i$ is one of a set of n generators of G by II.3.b.   Since G is torsion-free, $\sum_{i=1}^{n} b_i y_i$ is 0 as it has finite order.   It follows that G is generated by $n-1$ elements, and hence by II.3.c is the direct sum of $n-1$ or fewer cyclic subgroups contrary to II.3.d.

In view of II.3.b we have the following corollary.

II.3.g. Corollary.   *If $G = \sum_{i=1}^{n} (x_i)$ with each x_i an element of infinite order, and if $a_1, \cdots, a_n$ are integers with greatest common divisor 1, then $a_1 x_1 + \cdots + a_n x_n$ is one element of a basis of G.*

II.3.h. Proposition.   *Let the group G be the direct sum of n infinite cyclic subgroups and let H be a non-trivial subgroup of G.   Then a basis $\{z_i,\ i = 1, \cdots, n\}$ may be chosen for G, so that for appropriate integers c_i, the set of non-zero elements of $\{c_i z_i,\ i = 1, \cdots, n\}$ is a basis for H.*

Proof.   If $n = 1$, G is cyclic and the theorem is clear.   We proceed by induction on n.   Let $\{x_i,\ i = 1, \cdots, n\}$ be a basis for G and let $y = a_1 x_1 + \cdots + a_n x_n$ be a non-trivial element of H.   If d is the greatest common divisor of the a_i, let b_i be chosen so that $a_i = b_i d$. Then by II.3.g, $y_1 = \sum_{i=1}^{n} b_i x_i$ is one element of a basis $\{y_i, i = 1, \cdots, n\}$ of G; and furthermore a multiple of y_1, $y = d y_1$ (with d a divisor of a_1) is an element of H.   Among all such possible bases of G, let us assume the basis $\{y_i\}$ so chosen that d is minimal with d times one of the basis elements ($d y_1$ without loss of generality) an element of H.   In view of this choice we shall show directly that if $y' = a_1' y_1 + \cdots + a_n' y_n$ is in H, then d divides a_1'; for otherwise a_1' when divided by d leaves a remainder $q < d$ (i.e., $a_1' = md + q$ for some integer m), and by the argument above applied to the element $h = y' - m d y_1$, there will be a basis $\{y_i'\}$ such that $h = d' y_1'$ with $d' \leq q < d$ contrary to the minimality of d in the choice of the basis $\{y_i\}$.

It now follows that $H = \mathfrak{S}(y, K)$, where $K = H \cap \mathfrak{S}(y_2, \cdots, y_n)$. By the induction assumption, a basis $\{z_i,\ i = 2, \cdots, n\}$ may be chosen for $\mathfrak{S}(y_2, \cdots, y_n)$, so that for appropriate integers $c_2, \cdots, c_n$, the set of non-zero elements of $\{c_i z_i,\ i = 2, \cdots, n\}$ is a basis for K.   Let $c_1 = d$; then the set of non-zero elements of $\{c_i z_i,\ i = 1, 2, \cdots, n\}$ is a basis for H as the proposition asserts.

Let $G = (a) \oplus (b)$ with a of order p^3 and b of order p, and let H be the subgroup of G generated by $pa + b$.   It is easy to see, since $pa + b$ is not a pth power, that the conclusion of Proposition II.3.h does not hold for this group G and its subgroup H.   Thus it is an essential hypothesis in II.3.h that the cyclic subgroups be infinite.   On the other hand, the following propositions are valid; the proofs are left to the reader.

II.3.i. Proposition.   *If H is a subgroup of a finite p-group, the elements of any basis of H are in one-one correspondence with the elements of a* *subset of a basis of G, each element of H corresponding with an element of G of the same or higher order.*

II.3.j. Proposition.   *If G is an abelian group with n generators, any subgroup H of G can be expressed as the direct sum of k cyclic groups for suitable k not exceeding n.   If exactly r of the original generators of G are of infinite order, and H is torsion-free, then $k \leq r$.*

II.3.k. Corollary.   *A subgroup of a finitely generated abelian group is finitely generated and is a direct sum of cyclic subgroups.*

It will be seen in Section 6 that a subgroup of any direct sum of cyclic groups is also a direct sum of cyclic groups.

In view of Corollary II.3.k, each finitely generated abelian group satisfies the maximum condition.   Then in view of I.7.f, we have the following theorem.

II.3.l. Theorem.   *An abelian group is finitely generated if and only if it satisfies the maximum condition.*

II.3.m. Exercise.   *Give a proof of II.3.k based on Proposition I.7.f.*

II.3.n. Exercise.   *Let G be a finite abelian group and k a natural number dividing $|G|$.   Prove that G has a subgroup of order k and in particular that G has an element of order p for each prime p dividing $|G|$.*

II.3.o. Exercise.   *Let B be a basis of an abelian group G consisting of elements of infinite or prime power order; thus $G = \sum_{b \in B} (b)$.   Then the Frattini subgroup of G is the direct sum of the unique maximal subgroups of those (b) which are finite (cf. I.4.i).*

4. Rank and linear independence

The object of this section is to introduce a certain set of invariants for abelian groups which, in the case of a direct sum of cyclic groups, determines the group up to isomorphism.

II.4.a. Definitions. A subset A of an abelian group G is an **independent set** if it is a basis for the subgroup that it generates; the elements of A are then said to be **linearly independent.**

The empty set is an independent set since it is a basis for the subgroup that it generates. The zero element is never a member of an independent set. In view of II.3.e, the following facts are immediate.

(i) *A subset of an independent set is an independent set.*
(ii) *The union of a chain of independent subsets is an independent set.*
(iii) *Each independent set is contained in a maximal independent set.*
(iv) *Each independent set of elements of infinite order (of order n) is contained in a maximal independent set of elements of infinite order (of order n).*

Our first goal is to show that in any abelian group two maximal independent sets of elements of infinite order have the same cardinality. This will be a consequence of the following three lemmas.

II.4.b. Lemma. *Let A and B be independent sets of elements of a torsion-free abelian group. If A is a maximal independent set of elements and if $|A|$ is finite, then $|B| \le |A|$.*

Proof. If C is a finite subset of B, then by II.3.c, C and A generate a group which is a direct sum of a finite number n of cyclic subgroups. In view of II.3.h and the maximality of A, we have $|A| = n \ge |C|$. It follows that $|B| \le |A|$, as the lemma asserts.

II.4.c. Lemma. *If A is a maximal independent set of elements of a torsion-free abelian group G and if $|A|$ is infinite, then $|A| = |G|$.*

Proof. The cardinality of the set W of words on the symbols of A is equal to $|A|$ and hence $|\mathfrak{S}(A)| \le |W| = |A|$ so that $|\mathfrak{S}(A)| = |A|$. Since A is maximal, for each g in G a multiple of g is in $\mathfrak{S}(A)$. Thus to each element g of G is associated a pair (n_g, a_g), where n_g is an integer such that $n_g g = a_g$ is an element of $\mathfrak{S}(A)$. The cardinality of this set of pairs is equal to $|A|$ since $|A|$ is infinite. Furthermore, if

g and h are distinct elements of G, then the pair (n_g, a_g) is distinct from (n_h, a_h); for $n_g g = n_h h$ with $n_g = n_h$ implies that $n_g(g - h) = 0$ and hence that $g = h$ since G is torsion free.   Thus $|G| \le |A|$ and therefore $|G| = |A|$ as was to be shown.

II.4.d. Lemma.   *Let G be an abelian group and T its torsion subgroup. To each independent set of elements of infinite order of G (respectively G/T) can be associated an independent set of elements of infinite order of G/T (respectively G) of the same cardinality.*

The proof of the above lemma is immediate and is left to the reader. The results of the above lemmas give immediately the following theorem, the details of proof being left to the reader for an exercise.

II.4.e. Theorem.   *Two maximal independent sets of elements of infinite order of an abelian group have the same cardinality.*

In view of the above theorem we are now able to define torsion-free rank as follows.

II.4.f. Definition.   The **torsion-free rank** of an abelian group G is the cardinality of a maximal independent set of elements of infinite order.   It will be denoted by $r_0(G)$.

In the remainder of this section the sets defined below will play an important role.

II.4.g. Definition.   Let G be an abelian group and let p^t be a power of a prime p; an independent set A of elements of order p^t, such that $\mathfrak{S}(A) \cap p^t G = 0$ is a **pure independent p^t-set** of G.

Our immediate goal is to show that any two maximal pure independent p-sets of an abelian group have the same cardinality.   We begin with a very useful lemma.

II.4.h. Lemma. *Let D and M be subgroups of an abelian group G, such that $D \cap M = 0$, and let p be a prime. If there is an element $y \in G$, $y \notin D + M$, such that $py \in M$, then $\mathfrak{S}(M, y) \cap D = 0$.*

Proof. Let $d = m + hy$ be in $D \cap \mathfrak{S}(M, y)$, $d \in D$, $m \in M$, and h an integer. If h is prime to p, then there are integers k and r so that $rh = kp + 1$; hence $rd = rm + kpy + y$ so that $y \in D + M$ contrary to hypothesis. We conclude that p divides h, and hence that hy is in M, and $d = 0$. Thus $\mathfrak{S}(M, y) \cap D = 0$, as was to be shown.

II.4.i. Theorem. *Let G be an abelian group and, for $i = 1, 2$, let B_i be a maximal pure independent p-set; then $|B_1| = |B_2|$.*

Proof. It is sufficient to assume that G is a p-group since all the p-elements of G are in the p-component of G. Let M be a subgroup of G containing pG maximal in that all elements of M of order p are in pG. Since $\mathfrak{S}(B_i) \cap pG = 0$ and since all elements of $\mathfrak{S}(B_i)$ have orders less than or equal to p, it follows that $\mathfrak{S}(B_i) \cap M = 0$. Let D_i denote $\mathfrak{S}(B_i)$; if there is an element $y \in G$, $y \notin D_i + M$, then $py \in pG \subseteq M$ and hence, by II.4.h, $\mathfrak{S}(M, y) \cap D_i = 0$. By the maximality of M there is a $z \in \mathfrak{S}(M, y)$ of order p such that $z \notin pG$ and hence $z \notin M$. Therefore, since $\mathfrak{S}(M, y)/M$ has order p, $\mathfrak{S}(M, y) = M \oplus (z)$. Then $\mathfrak{S}(D_i, z) = D_i \oplus (z)$ and $\mathfrak{S}(D_i, z) \cap M = 0$ so that the existence of the set $B_i \cup \{z\}$ is in contradiction to the maximality of B_i. We conclude that $G = M \oplus D_i$ and therefore that $D_i \cong G/M$. Thus $|B_1| = |B_2|$ and the theorem is proved.

In view of II.4.i the pure p-rank may be defined as follows.

II.4.j. Definition. *If p is a prime, the **pure p-rank** of an abelian group G, denoted by $r_p(G)$, is the cardinality of a maximal pure independent p-set.*

As an immediate consequence of the above definition, we have the following easily proved proposition, which justified introducing the notion of pure p-rank.

II.4.k. Proposition.   *If B is the subset of elements of order p of a basis of an abelian group G, then $|B| = r_p(G)$.*

II.4.l. Definition.   The **p-rank** of an abelian group G (cf. [F]) is the cardinality of a basis of the subgroup of G of elements whose orders are less than or equal to p.

Thus the p-rank of G is the maximum of the $r_p(H)$ with H ranging over all the subgroups of G; and hence the p-rank is never less than the pure p-rank.   If $n > 1$ and $G = C_{p^n}$, or if $G = C_{p^\infty}$, then $r_p(G) = 0$ even though the p-rank is 1.   Accordingly we make the following further definitions.

II.4.m. Definitions.   If p is a prime and t is an integer greater than 1, the **pure p^t-rank** of an abelian group G, denoted by $r_{p^t}(G)$, is defined to be the pure p-rank of $p^{t-1}G$.

The pure p^t-rank of the cyclic group C_{p^n} is 1 or 0, according as n is equal to t or not.

In view of II.4.k we have the following proposition.

II.4.n. Proposition.   *Let B be a basis of an abelian p-group G, and let $B = \bigcup_{n=1}^{\infty} B_n$, where for each n, B_n contains only elements of order p^n; then $|B_n| = r_{p^n}(G)$ for each n.*

From II.4.n and II.4.e we deduce immediately the following theorem.

II.4.o. Theorem.   *If a basis of an abelian group G contains only elements of prime power or infinite order, then it contains $r_0(G)$ elements of infinite order and $r_{p^t}(G)$ elements of order p^t for each prime power p^t.*

Thus if a group is a direct sum of cyclic groups, the set of its torsion-free and pure p^t-ranks is in fact a complete set of invariants.

We shall sometimes speak of the **type** of a finite abelian p-group as the sequence $(m_1, \cdots, m_k)$ if the group has a basis whose elements have orders $p^{m_1}, \cdots, p^{m_k}$.

We conclude this section with a proposition which could be used to give an alternative definition of pure p^t-rank.

II.4.p. Proposition. *Let B be a maximal pure independent p^t-set of a group G; then $|B| = r_{p^t}(G)$.*

Proof. Let D be a maximal pure independent p-set of $p^{t-1}G$ containing $p^{t-1}B$. Then $|D| = r_{p^t}(G)$. Choose a set Q of G containing B so that $p^{t-1}Q = D$ and so that for each $d \in D$ there is only one $q \in Q$ with $p^{t-1}q = d$. Then $|Q| = |D|$, and Q is an independent set since D is independent. Furthermore $\mathfrak{S}(Q) \cap p(p^{t-1}G) = 0$. Thus $B = Q$ by the maximality of B, and $|B| = r_{p^t}(G)$, as was to be shown.

II.4.q. Exercise. *Show that an abelian group G is locally cyclic if and only if $r_0(H) + r_{p^t}(H) \le 1$ for each prime power p^t and each subgroup H of G. In particular, a torsion abelian group is locally cyclic if and only if it has at most one subgroup of order p for each p.*

II.4.r. Exercise. *Let G be an ascending union of its subgroups G_n, $n = 1, 2, \cdots$; if the torsion-free ranks (or the pure p^t-ranks for a fixed prime power p^t) of the G_n are bounded by an integer k, show that the torsion-free rank (or pure p^t-rank) is also bounded by k.*

II.4.s. Exercise. *If an abelian group G is a direct sum of cyclic groups and has an infinite p-component G_p for some prime p, show that the p-rank of G is $|G_p|$.*

We shall see (cf. II.5.r below) that the p-rank of a p-group G can be uncountable, although the p^t-rank is 1 for each t.

5. Pure subgroups; direct sums of cyclic p-groups

The first goal of this section is to give Kulikov's criterion for a p-group to be a direct sum of cyclic subgroups. From this we derive Prüfer's theorems that abelian p-groups of finite exponent and countable abelian p-groups without elements of infinite height are direct sums of cyclic subgroups; and also that a subgroup of a direct sum of cyclic p-groups is a direct sum of cyclic subgroups. The notion of purity is introduced in order to develop this part of the theory. The section concludes with some theorems giving conditions under which a pure subgroup is a direct summand.

II.5.a. Definition. A subgroup H of the abelian group G is **pure** in G (also **serving** or **isolated**) if for each natural number n, $nG \cap H = nH$.

Some elementary facts about pure subgroups are given in the following propositions. The proofs are easy and are left to the reader.

II.5.b. Proposition. *Let H be a subgroup of an abelian group G; then H is pure in G if and only if for each h in H and each integer n, the equation $nx = h$ has a solution in H if it has a solution in G.*

In view of II.5.b, the torsion subgroup H of an abelian group G is pure in G; the solution of the equation $nx = h$, with h in H and n an integer, is in fact in H.

II.5.c. Proposition. *Let G be a group and p a prime; a p-subgroup H of G is pure in G if and only if $p^k G \cap H = p^k H$ for each natural number k.*

The proof of II.5.c depends on the fact that if the element g of G has p-power order and if n is prime to p, then the equation $nx = g$ has a solution in (g).

II.5.d. Proposition.   *Let G be an abelian group and let $H < K < G$. If H is pure in K and K is pure in G, then H is pure in G.   Furthermore, if H is pure in G, then H is pure in K.*

Note that II.5.d is still true if each expression "pure in" is replaced by "direct summand of."

II.5.e. Proposition.   *An ascending union of pure subgroups of an abelian group G is a pure subgroup of G.*

The analogous result for direct summands is false, as we see from II.5.g below.

II.5.f. Proposition.   *A direct summand of an abelian group G is a pure subgroup of G.*

It follows from II.5.g below that the converse of II.5.f is not true.

II.5.g. Exercise.   *Let $G = \mathsf{P}_{i=1}^{\infty}(a_i)$ with each $(a_i) \cong C_\infty$, and let H be the subgroup $\sum_{i=1}^{\infty}(a_i)$ of G.   Show that H is pure in G but not a direct summand of G.   Hint: Note that if a is the element $(\cdots, 2^i a_i, \cdots)$ of G, then for each natural number n there is a solution to the equation $2^n(x + H) = a + H$ in G/H.   On the other hand, for no g in G is there a solution to the equation $2^n x = g$ in G for every n.   Note also that if for each n, $H_n = \sum_{i=1}^{n}(a_i)$, then H_n is a direct summand of G and $H = \bigcup_{i=1}^{\infty} H_n$.*

II.5.h. Exercise.   *Show that the subgroup generated by a pure independent p^t-set is a pure subgroup; show also that if a pure subgroup has a basis, then the basis is the union of pure independent p^t-sets, one for each natural number t.*

The following three lemmas will readily give Kulikov's theorem.

II.5.i. Lemma.   *Let G be an abelian p-group.   A subgroup D of G is a direct sum of cyclic subgroups and is a pure subgroup of G if and only if it is the direct sum of subgroups D_n, $n = 1, 2, \cdots$, where each D_n is generated by a pure independent p^n-set.*

Proof. Suppose first that for each n, D_n is generated by a pure independent p^n-set. Let $V_0 = 0 = D_0$ and for $n > 0$ define V_n inductively to be $\mathfrak{S}(V_{n-1}, D_n)$. Then we shall prove the following sets of assertion for each n:

(n^*) $V_n = V_{n-1} \oplus D_n$ (*and consequently* $V_n = \sum_{i=1}^{n} D_i$).

(n^{**}) $V_n \cap p^n G = 0$.

(1^*) and (1^{**}) are true by hypothesis. We proceed by induction on n, assuming that for $n > 1$, $((n-1)^*)$ and $((n-1)^{**})$ are true. Then if x were an element of order p of $V_{n-1} \cap D_n$, x would be in $p^{n-1} D_n$ which is contrary to $((n-1)^{**})$; accordingly we conclude that (n^*) is true. To show that (n^{**}) is true we note that if $p^n y$ were an element of order p of $V_n \cap p^n G$, then $p^n y = v + p^{n-1} d$ with $v \in V_{n-1}$, $d \in D_n$; thus $v = 0$ by $((n-1)^{**})$ and $p^n y = p^{n-1} d$. But then $p^n y = 0$ by the hypothesis on D_n and this is contrary to the fact that $p^n y$ has order p.

We conclude that $V_n \cap p^n G$ has no element of order p and hence (n^{**}) follows.

From (n^{**}), we deduce that V_n is pure in G, and hence, in view of II.5.c, D is pure in G; in view of all the equations (n^*), D has a basis, which is the union of bases, one for each D_n.

Conversely, if D is a pure subgroup of G and a direct sum of cyclic subgroups, let D_n be the subgroup generated by the basis elements of order p^n of a fixed basis of D. Then D_n is a direct sum of cyclic subgroups of order p^n and is pure in D; hence by II.5.d, D_n is pure in G, so that $D_n \cap p^n G = 0$. This proves the lemma.

II.5.j. Lemma. *Let an abelian p-group G contain subgroups C_m such that $C_m \cap p^m G = 0$, $m = 1, 2, \cdots$; suppose that $C_m \leq C_{m+1}$, and let $C = \bigcup_{m=1}^{\infty} C_m$. Then G contains a pure subgroup D which is a direct sum of cyclic subgroups and which contains $C(p)$ ($C(p)$ is the subgroup of C generated by its elements of order p).*

Proof. For each pair of natural numbers n, m, we choose a pure independent p^n-set Y_{nm} so that $Y_{nm+1} \geq Y_{nm}$ and so that if D_{nm} denotes $\sum_{y \in Y_{nm}} (y)$, then Y_{nm} is maximal in that $p^{n-1} D_{nm} \leq C_m$. Thus $\bigcup_{m=1}^{\infty} Y_{nm}$ is a pure independent p^n-set and is a basis for the subgroup D_n that it generates. By Lemma II.5.i, the subgroup D

generated by all the D_n is pure in G and is a direct sum of cyclic groups.

To show that D contains $C(p)$, we assume the contrary is true and that for a fixed m there is an element $c \in C_m$, $c \notin D$. Then $Y_{1m} \cup \{c\}$ cannot be a pure independent p-set in view of the maximality of Y_{1m}. Accordingly there is an element g of order p^n for some n, so that $p^{n-1}g$ is in C_m but not in D. Since $C_m \cap p^m G = 0$, we may assume that g is chosen so that n is maximal. We consider $Y = Y_{nm} \cup \{g\}$ and note that $(g) \cap D_{nm} = 0$ since $p^{n-1}g$ is not in D_{nm}. Thus Y is an independent set. Clearly every element of Y has order p^n and $p^{n-1}\mathfrak{S}(Y) \le C_m$. Furthermore, $Y \cap p^n G = 0$; for if h were an element of order p in $Y \cap p^n G$, then $h = p^n x$ for some x in G and h is in C_m contrary to the maximality of n. Thus the existence of Y contradicts the maximality of Y_{nm}. We conclude that $D \ge C(p)$ as the lemma asserts.

II.5.k. Lemma. *If the pure subgroup H of the abelian p-group G contains $G(p)$, then $H = G$.*

Proof. Since G is a p-group, $G = \bigcup_{n=1}^{\infty} G(p^n)$. Suppose the lemma not true and let m be minimal so that there is an element $g \in G(p^m)$, $g \notin H$. Then $p^{m-1}g \in G(p) \le H$. By the purity of H there is an $h \in H$ so that $p^{m-1}g = p^{m-1}h$ and hence $g - h \in G(p^{m-1})$. But $g - h \notin H$ (since $g \notin H$) contrary to the minimality in the choice of g. We conclude that the lemma is true.

Lemmas II.5.j and II.5.k immediately give Kulikov's criterion for a p-group to be a direct sum of cyclic subgroups.

II.5.l. Theorem (*Kulikov*). *Let G be an abelian p-group; then G is a direct sum of cyclic subgroups if and only if G has subgroups C_n, so that $G = \bigcup_{n=1}^{\infty} C_n$, $C_n \le C_{n+1}$, and $C_n \cap p^n G = 0$.*

It should be observed that if $G = \bigcup_{n=1}^{\infty} C_n$, $C_n \le C_{n+1}$, $C_n \cap p^n G = 0$, then any subgroup H of G satisfies the same hypotheses with $C_n \cap H$

in place of C_n. Hence a subgroup of a direct sum of cyclic p-sub-groups is also a direct sum of cyclic subgroups. From this and II.1.d, we have immediately the following proposition.

II.5.m. Proposition.   *A subgroup of a direct sum of periodic cyclic subgroups is also a direct sum of cyclic groups.*

The above is a special case of Theorem II.6.a in the next section.

If G is an abelian p-group of finite exponent, then for some natural number n, $p^n G = 0$, and hence $G \cap p^n G = 0$; accordingly in view of II.1.d we have the following immediate consequences of Theorem II.5.1.

II.5.n. Theorem (*Prüfer*).   *An abelian group of finite exponent is a direct sum of cyclic groups.*

II.5.o. Definition.   An element $x \neq 0$ of an abelian group G has **p-height n** if $x \in p^n G$, $x \notin p^{n+1} G$. If $x \in \bigcap_{n=1}^{\infty} p^n G$, then x has **infinite p-height**.

In view of the comment after II.5.c it follows that if m is prime to p, then an element of order m has infinite p-height. Furthermore, if θ is a homomorphism of G, and if $g\theta \neq 0$, then the p-height of $g\theta$ in $G\theta$ is at least as great as the p-height of g in G.

II.5.p. Theorem (*Prüfer*).   *Let G be a countable abelian p-group. Then G is a direct sum of cyclic subgroups if and only if G has no elements of infinite p-height.*

Proof.   Since G is countable, it is an ascending union of finitely generated subgroups G_n each of which is finite since it is a finitely generated abelian periodic group. If G has no elements of infinite height, then there is a bound m_n on the p-heights of the elements of G_n; hence $G_n \cap p^{m_n} G = 0$. Then by relabeling (and repeating if necessary) the G_n, G and the set of G_n satisfy the hypotheses of

Theorem II.5.1; hence G is a direct sum of cyclic subgroups as was asserted. The proof of the converse is immediate and is left to the reader.

That countability is a necessary hypothesis in Theorem II.5.p is a consequence of the following two exercises.

II.5.q. Exercise. *If K is a countable subgroup of the abelian group G, and if there is an uncountable subset H of G, so that for $h \in H$, $h + K$ has infinite p-height in G/K, then G is not a direct sum of cyclic subgroups.*

II.5.r. Exercise. *Let G be the torsion subgroup of $P_{n=1}^{\infty} (a_n)$, a_n of order p^n. Show that $\{a_n\}$ is a maximal pure independent p^n-set for each n. Also show that G is a p-group with no elements of infinite p-height, but that G is not a direct sum of cyclic subgroups. (Consider the uncountable subset of elements (functions) f of G with $f(1) = f(2) = 0$, $f(n) = p^{n-1}a_n$ or $p^{n-2}a_n$ for $n > 2$.)*

The next theorem gives a condition under which a pure subgroup is a direct summand. We deduce from it that if an abelian group has an element of p-power order and finite p-height, then it has a finite direct summand.

II.5.s. Theorem. *A pure subgroup of finite exponent of an abelian group is a direct summand.*

Proof. Suppose H is a pure subgroup of finite exponent of the abelian group. By Theorem II.5.n, H has a basis, the elements of which may be taken to have prime power order. If p^k is the largest of these prime powers, let D be the subgroup generated by the elements of order p^k of this basis. Then $D \neq 0$, and D is pure in H and hence in G; it follows that $D \cap p^k G = 0$. Now by Theorem I.7.c there is a subgroup M of G containing $p^k G$, and maximal with respect to the property that its intersection with D is 0. We shall show that $G = M \oplus D$.

If there were an element of G not in $M+D$, then there would be such an element x, so that for some prime q, $qx=d+m$, $d \in D$, $m \in M$. If $q \neq p$, there is, in view of the remark following II.5.c, a $d*$ in D so that $d=qd*$; then $q(x-d*)=m$ would be in M. If $q=p$, then $p^k x=p^{k-1}d+p^{k-1}m$ with $p^k x \in p^k G \leq M$. It follows that $p^{k-1}d=0$, since $M \cap D=0$, and from the form of D, there is a $d*$ in D so that $d=pd*$. Thus again $p(x-d*)=m$ is in M. In either case, q equal to p or not, if $y=x-d*$, then $y \notin M+D$, $qy \in M$, and we have a contradiction to the maximality of M in view of Lemma II.4.h. We conclude that $G=D \oplus M$.

Since $G=D \oplus M$ and $D \leq H$, it follows that $H= D \oplus(M \cap H)$. Furthermore, $M \cap H$ has no elements of order p^k, and hence has a lower exponent than H. Finally, $M \cap H$ is pure in M; for if n is any natural number, then $nM \cap (M \cap H)=nM \cap H=nM \cap nH=nM \cap (nD+n(M \cap H))=n(M \cap H)+(nM \cap nD)=n(M \cap H)$. By an induction argument on the exponent, we can assume that there is a subgroup S, so that $M=(M \cap H) \oplus S$. Hence $G=H \oplus S$, as was to be shown.

The following examples show that the pure subgroup H must have finite exponent for the conclusion of Theorem II.5.s to be true, and that even if the p-components of H have finite exponent, H need not be a direct summand.

II.5.t. Example. Let $G=\sum_{n=1}^{\infty} (x_n)$, $(x_n) \cong C_{p^n}$, p a prime. Then $H= \mathfrak{S}(x_n - px_{n+1}, n=1, 2, \cdots)$ is pure in G, but not a direct summand of G; for G/H is p-quasicyclic and G has no elements of infinite height.

II.5.u. Example. Let $G=\mathsf{P}_{n=1}^{\infty} (x_n)$, $(x_n) \cong C_{p^n}$, p_n the nth prime number in the usual ordering. Then $H=\sum_{n=1}^{\infty} (x_n)$ is the torsion subgroup of G, and hence pure in G; but every element of G/H has infinite p-height for all primes p.

The following is often of interest in connection with the decomposability of abelian groups.

II.5.v. Theorem. *Let G be an abelian group, and p a fixed prime. If G has an element of p-power order and finite p-height, then G has a finite cyclic direct summand.*

Proof.   Let k be minimal so that there is a $g \in G$ of order p^k and p-height zero.   If (g) were not pure in G, there would be an element h so that $p^k h = p^{k-1} g$.   But then $ph - g$ would have order p^{k-1} and p-height zero contrary to the minimality of k.   We conclude that (g) is pure in G.   It follows from II.5.s that (g) is a direct summand of G.

II.5.w. Exercise. *Show that the only indecomposable periodic abelian groups are subgroups of p-quasicyclic groups.*

We conclude this section with a proposition that gives another condition under which a pure subgroup is a direct summand.

II.5.x. Proposition. *If H is a pure subgroup of an abelian group G and if G/H has a basis, then H is a direct summand of G.*

Proof.   Let $\{\bar{y}_\alpha\}$ be a basis of G/H.   In view of the purity of H it is easy to check that we may choose elements x_α of G such that for each α, $\bar{y}_\alpha = x_\alpha + H$ and such that x_α has the same order in G as $\bar{y}_\alpha$ has in G/H.   Then the set of x_α is an independent set; for if $\sum n_\alpha x_\alpha = 0$, then $\sum n_\alpha \bar{y}_\alpha = 0$ and hence $n_\alpha \bar{y}_\alpha = 0$ since $\{\bar{y}_\alpha\}$ is a basis of G/H.   In view of the choice of the x_α, this implies that $n_\alpha x_\alpha = 0$ and hence the x_α are independent.   It is clear that if K is the subgroup generated by the x_α, then $H \cap K = 0$ and $G = H + K$ so that $G = H \oplus K$ and the lemma is proved.

II.5.y. Corollary. *Let H be a subgroup of an abelian group G so that each of H and G/H has a basis.   If H is pure in G, then G has a basis.*

6. Direct sums of cyclic groups; free abelian groups

In this section we prove that a subgroup of a direct sum of cyclic groups is also a direct sum of cyclic groups.   Two special cases have already been proved in Sections II.3 and II.5.   We also give some theorems about free abelian groups.

II.6.a. Theorem. *If G is a direct sum of cyclic groups, then any subgroup H of G is also a direct sum of cyclic groups.*

Proof. Let M be a fixed basis of G and let T be the elements of finite order of M. Then $\mathfrak{S}(T)$ is the torsion subgroup of G, $\mathfrak{S}(T) \cap H$ is the torsion subgroup of H, and $\mathfrak{S}(T) \cap H$ has a basis K in view of II.5.m. Now the pair (T, K) is connected by the relation $\mathfrak{S}(T) \cap H = \mathfrak{S}(K)$. We consider the set of all pairs (N, Y), with $M \supseteq N \supseteq T$, and Y an independent subset of H, $Y \supseteq K$, and $\mathfrak{S}(N) \cap H = \mathfrak{S}(Y)$. We let this set be partially ordered as follows: $(N, Y) \leq (N_1, Y_1)$ if $N \subseteq N_1$, $Y \subseteq Y_1$. It is clear that the set is inductive and hence there is a maximal element (N, Y). We shall show that $N = M$.

Suppose $N \neq M$; then there is an $m \in M$, $m \notin N$. Consider elements $z \in H$, $z = qm + x$, q integral, $x \in \mathfrak{S}(N)$. By the maximality of (N, Y), $\mathfrak{S}(N \cup \{m\}) \cap H \neq \mathfrak{S}(Y)$ while $\mathfrak{S}(N) \cap H = \mathfrak{S}(Y)$. Hence there must be a $z = qm + x$ in H with $q \neq 0$; suppose z is chosen so that q is minimal positive. From the facts that m has infinite order and $N \cup \{m\}$ is an independent set, it follows that $Y \cup \{z\}$ is an independent set. Since q is minimal, $\mathfrak{S}(N \cup \{m\}) \cap H = \mathfrak{S}(Y \cup \{z\})$ contrary to the maximality of the pair (N, Y). We conclude that $M = N$ and hence that $\mathfrak{S}(N) \cap H = H$. Consequently Y is a basis for H, and H is a direct sum of cyclic groups as was to be shown.

If F is a torsion-free abelian group with a basis B, then (cf. I.8.n) the natural extension to F of any mapping of B into an arbitrary abelian group is a homomorphism. Accordingly we make the following definition.

II.6.b. Definition. A **free abelian group** is a torsion-free abelian group with a basis, i.e., a direct sum of infinite cyclic groups.

The following characterization of free abelian groups is of importance in cohomology theory. It is essentially a reformulation of the fact that a free abelian group is a reduced free group in the variety of abelian groups, and hence that any mapping of a basis is the restriction of a homomorphism.

II.6.c. Theorem. *An Abelian group F is free if and only if, whenever there is a homomorphism θ from an abelian group G onto a group H, and a homomorphism ϕ from F into H, then there is a homomorphism ψ of F into G so that $\psi\theta = \phi$. This is indicated in Figure 2.*

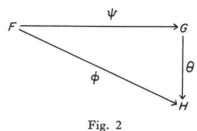

Fig. 2

We give the following hint and leave the proof to the reader: For one part of the proof let $F = \sum_{\alpha \in A} (f_\alpha)$; then for each $f_\alpha\phi$ in H, choose an element g_α in G so that $g_\alpha\theta = f_\alpha\phi$, and define ψ so that the g_α chosen is $f_\alpha\psi$. For the other part of the proof, let $H = F$, let G be free, and let ϕ be the identity map.

In view of II.6.a, subgroups of free abelian groups are free abelian groups. We shall see later (Chapter V) that an analogous theorem holds in the variety of all groups; namely that subgroups of free groups are free groups.

We conclude this section with a study of torsion-free abelian groups all of whose subgroups of finite torsion-free rank are free abelian. The results below also have analogues in the variety of all groups; but the analogues will not be given in this book.

II.6.d. Theorem. *(Pontryagin). A countable torsion-free abelian group G is free abelian if and only if its subgroups of finite rank are free abelian.*

Proof. Since subgroups of free abelian groups are free abelian, it is only necessary to prove that G is free abelian if its subgroups of finite rank are free abelian. To do this we observe first that if for some integer k, R_k is a subgroup of torsion-free rank k, then it follows from II.4.r (with Zorn's Lemma) that R_k is contained in a maximal subgroup B_k of torsion-free rank k. Let the elements of G be well-ordered, let R_1 contain the first element, and for each k let a_k be the first element not in B_k. Then $\mathfrak{S}(B_k, a_k)$ has torsion-free rank $k+1$

and is contained in a maximal subgroup B_{k+1} of torsion-free rank $k+1$. By II.3.h, a basis $\{b_1, \cdots, b_{k+1}\}$ may be chosen for B_{k+1}, so that there are integers $c_1, \cdots, c_k$ with $\{c_1 b_1, \cdots, c_k b_k\}$ a basis for B_k. In view of the maximality of B_k, all the c_i are 1 and $\{b_1, \cdots, b_k\}$ is a basis for B_k. Then the union of all the b's so chosen, $\{b_1, b_2, \cdots\}$ is an independent set which generates G. Thus G has a basis; since G is torsion-free, G is free abelian as the theorem asserts.

II.6.e. Theorem (*Baer, Specker*).   *The group $G = \mathsf{P}_{i=1}^{\infty}(x_i)$ with $(x_i) \cong C_\infty$, is not free abelian; but its subgroups of countable rank are free.*

Proof. We prove first that subgroups of finite rank are free. Let H be a subgroup of rank n, and suppose, without loss of generality, that there are elements h in H so that (using the functional notation for an element of the cartesian product) $h(1) = dx_1$ with d a non-zero integer. Let h be chosen from among such elements so that d is minimal, $d \neq 0$. If $D = \mathsf{P}_{i=2}^{\infty}(x_i)$, then G is isomorphic both to D and to $D \oplus (h)$. Furthermore $D \oplus (h)$ contains H, $H = (h) \oplus H \cap D$, and the rank of $H \cap D$ is $n-1$. Then if $n=1$, H is cyclic, and an induction argument on n allows us to conclude that $H \cap D$ is free abelian on $n-1$ generators; hence H is free abelian on n generators. In view of II.6.d, the countable subgroups of G are free abelian as the theorem asserts.

To prove that G itself is not free, we consider the uncountable set of elements f of G, with $f(n) = c_n x_n$, where $c_1 = 1$ and $c_n = c_{n-1} p^r$ $(r = 1, 2)$, p a fixed prime. Then if $K = \sum_{i=1}^{\infty}(x_i)$, for all f not in K, $f + K$ has infinite p-height in G/K. It follows from II.5.q that G is not free abelian.

7. Divisible groups

In this section divisible abelian groups are characterized as direct sums of copies of the additive group of rationals and p-quasicyclic groups. It is seen that a divisible subgroup is always a direct summand of any abelian group containing it; and that any abelian group is a subgroup of a divisible group.

II.7.a. Definition. An abelian group G is **divisible** (**complete** in the terminology of some authors) if $G = nG$ for every positive integer n.

We list some immediate consequences of this definition.

(i) *The abelian group G is divisible if and only if one of the following equivalent conditions holds for each prime p:*
   (a) *$G = pG$;*
   (b) *each element of G has infinite p-height;*
   (c) *G has a generating set M so that the equation $px = m$ has a solution x in G for each $m \in M$.*

(ii) *Any homomorphic image of a divisible group is divisible.*

(iii) *The subgroup generated by any set of divisible subgroups of a group is divisible.*

(iv) *For each natural number t, the p^t-rank of a divisible group is zero.*

In view of (i) above and II.1.h, we have the following.

II.7.b. Proposition. *An abelian group is divisible if and only if it is equal to its Frattini subgroup.*

It is clear that the group of additive rationals is divisible, and that any p-quasicyclic group is divisible. We leave it to the reader to show the following basic fact (cf. I.5.i and I.5.k).

II.7.c. Proposition. *If g is a torsion-free element of a divisible group G, there is a subgroup Q of G containing g with Q isomorphic to the group of additive rationals; if h is an element of p-power order for some prime p, then there is a p-quasicyclic subgroup T of G containing h. If further $G = H \oplus K$ and g is in K, then Q may be chosen in K; if h is in K, then T may be chosen in K.*

II.7.d. Theorem (*Baer*). *If D is a divisible subgroup of an abelian group G and if K is a subgroup such that $K \cap D = 0$, then D has a direct complement M containing K.*

Proof. Let M be a subgroup maximal in that it contains K and so that $M \cap D = 0$, as in Theorem I.7.c, and suppose that there is an element of G not in $M + D$. Then a multiple of such an element must be in $M + D$; therefore without loss of generality such an element x may be chosen so that for some prime p, $px = m + d$, $d = pd^*$, d^* in D, m in M. Then if $y = x - d^*$, $\mathfrak{S}(M, y) \cap D = 0$ by II.4.h and we have a contradiction to the maximality of M. We conclude that $G = M \oplus D$, as the theorem asserts.

In view of (iii) above, an abelian group has a unique maximal divisible subgroup. In case the maximal divisible subgroup of an abelian group is 0, the group is said to be **reduced**. Then II.7.d has the following corollary.

II.7.e. Corollary. *An abelian group is the direct sum of its maximal divisible subgroup and a reduced group.*

The description of the structure of divisible groups is included in the following theorem.

II.7.f. Theorem. *The maximal divisible subgroup D of an abelian group G is a direct sum of subgroups, each isomorphic either to the group of additive rationals or to a p-quasicyclic group. Furthermore $G = D \oplus R$ where R is reduced.*

Proof. Let $\mathscr{B}$ be a maximal set of subgroups H of G, each H isomorphic either to the group of additive rationals or to a p-quasicyclic group, and such that the subgroup M generated by all the subgroups H of $\mathscr{B}$ is their direct sum $\sum_{H \in \mathscr{B}} H$. By (iii), M is divisible and it follows from II.7.d that M has complements Q and R, respectively in D and G; that is, $D = M \oplus Q$ and $G = M \oplus R$. In view of II.7.c and the maximality of $\mathscr{B}$, $Q = 0$ so that $D = M$ and $G = D \oplus R$. Then by the maximality of D, R is reduced and the theorem is proved.

II.7.g. Exercise. *Show that the additive group of real numbers is a direct sum of copies of the group of additive rationals (i.e., the real*

numbers have a Hamel basis), and that the additive group of real con-
tinuous (or differentiable) functions on the interval [0, 1] *is isomorphic to*
the additive group of real numbers.

In view of Theorem II.7.f, many of the problems of abelian group
theory can quickly be reduced to problems of reduced groups.   On
the other hand, the study of abelian groups is the study of subgroups
of divisible groups in view of the following theorem.

II.7.h. Theorem.   (*Kulikov*).   *Every abelian group G is a subgroup*
of a divisible group.

Proof.   Express G as a factor group F/R where F is a free abelian
group with basis elements x_α for α in some index set A.   For each α
in A, let R_α be a subgroup isomorphic to the group of additive
rationals and let $T = \sum_{\alpha \in A} R_\alpha$.   There is an isomorphism θ of F into
T with $x_\alpha \theta$ in R_α for each α.   Then $T/R\theta$ is divisible and contains a
copy of $F/R = G$, as the theorem asserts.

The following is a characterization of divisible abelian groups dual
in a sense to that given for free abelian groups in Theorem II.6.c.

II.7.i. Theorem.   *The abelian group D is divisible if and only if,*
whenever there is an isomorphism θ of a group H into the abelian group
G, and a homomorphism ψ of H into D, there is a homomorphism φ of G
into D with θφ = ψ.   This may be diagrammed as shown in Figure 3.

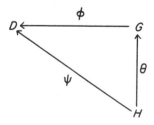

Fig. 3

We give the following hint and leave the proof to the reader: Prove that a homomorphism ψ from a subgroup H of G into a divisible group D can be extended to a homomorphism of G into D, by considering the set of pairs (B, ψ), B a subgroup of G containing H, ψ a homomorphism of B into D; and partially order this set by the relation $(B, \psi) \leq (B', \psi')$ if $B \leq B'$ and ψ' extends ψ.

8. Basic subgroups

Not every abelian p-group (p a prime), even without elements of infinite p-height, has a basis.   On the other hand, every abelian p-group has at least one basic subgroup as defined below.   In this section we shall show that a basic subgroup is a maximal pure subgroup with a basis, that the p^t ranks of an abelian p-group and each of its basic subgroups are equal, and that the quotient of an abelian p-group by a basic subgroup is divisible.

II.8.a. Definition.   For each natural number n, let B_n be a maximal pure independent p^n-set of an abelian p-group G; the subgroup generated by all the B_n is a **basic subgroup** of G.

Since the empty set generates the group 0, it follows that every abelian p-group has at least one basic subgroup.

II.8.b. Examples.   A divisible p-group always has 0 as a basic subgroup; a p-group with a basis is always its own basic subgroup.   If G is the group of II.5.r, then its subgroup $\mathfrak{S}(a_n, n = 1, 2, \cdots)$ is a basic subgroup.

In view of II.4.p we have immediately the following proposition.

II.8.c. Proposition.   *For each t, the p^t-rank of a basic subgroup of an abelian group G is equal to the p^t-rank of G.*

In view of II.5.i, it is easy to deduce the following proposition. The proof is left to the reader.

II.8.d. Proposition. *A subgroup of an abelian p-group is a basic subgroup if and only if it is a maximal pure subgroup which has a basis.*

Our next goal is a characterization of basic subgroups which is used as the definition in [K] and [F]. We begin with two lemmas.

II.8.e. Lemma. *If B is a basic subgroup of an abelian p-group, then G/B is divisible.*

Proof. Suppose that for each natural number n there is a maximal pure independent p^n-set B_n, such that $\bigcup_{n=1}^{\infty} B_n$ is a basis for B. We wish to show that for every $x \notin B$, there is a $y \in G$ so that $py + B = x + B$ If this were not so, let x be chosen to have least order p^n from among the elements for which it is not so; that is, for each z of order less than p^n, there is a y so that $py + B = z + B$. Then $\mathfrak{S}(x, B_n) = (x) + \mathfrak{S}(B_n)$ in view of the minimality of n; otherwise $p^{n-1}x - p^{n-1}b = 0$ with $b \in \mathfrak{S}(B_n)$, and there is a y so that $py + B = x - b + B$ or $py + B = x + B$, contrary to the choice of x. But then by the maximality of B_n, $\mathfrak{S}(x, B_n) \cap p^n G \neq 0$; that is, there is a $w \in G$ and a $b_n \in B_n$ so that $p^{n-1}(x + b_n) = p^n w$, or $p^{n-1}(x + b_n - pw) = 0$. Consequently, there is a y so that $x + b_n - pw + B = py + B$, or $x + B = p(w + y) + B$, again contrary to the choice of x. We conclude that G/B is divisible as the lemma asserts.

II.8.f. Lemma. *If B is a pure subgroup of an abelian p-group G, if G/B is divisible, and if B has a basis, then B is a basic subgroup of G.*

Proof. In view of II.5.h, B has a basis which is the union $\bigcup_{n=1}^{\infty} B_n$ of pure independent p^n-sets. If some B_n is not maximal, there is a maximal pure independent p^n-set M_n containing B_n properly. It follows that the p^n-rank of the divisible group G/B is not zero, contrary to (iv) of Section 7.

Basic subgroups may now be characterized as follows.

II.8.g. Theorem. *A subgroup B of the abelian p-group G, p a prime, is a basic subgroup of G if and only if B is a pure subgroup of G, B has a basis, and G/B is divisible.*

In view of II.8.g, both H and G of Example II.5.t are basic subgroups of G; it follows that the factor groups of a group by different basic subgroups need not be isomorphic.

We conclude this section with some exercises which develop further facts about basic subgroups.

II.8.h. Exercise (*Kulikov*). *Show that an abelian p-group has only one basic subgroup if and only if it is either a divisible group or a group of finite exponent.*

II.8.i. Exercise. *Show that a basic subgroup of a basic subgroup of an abelian group G is a basic subgroup of G.*

II.8.j. Exercise. *Show that the group of II.5.t has an uncountable number of basic subgroups.*

Chapter *III*

SOME IMPORTANT SUBGROUPS, MAPPINGS, CONSTRUCTIONS, AND FAMILIES OF GROUPS

This chapter continues the study of fundamental notions of group theory. Each subset of a group distinguishes certain subgroups such as its normalizer and centralizer, and certain subsets such as its conjugate class; these are of great interest for non-abelian groups and are defined here. The study of homomorphisms is continued and the automorphism groups of cyclic groups are described completely. It is shown how a given set of endomorphisms leads to the notions of operator group, module, and vector space. The construction of the semi-direct product and that of the wreath product are described here; it is seen how the semi-direct product is useful in the classification of groups (for instance, of order p^3), and some interesting general theorems are obtained by means of the wreath product. A study is made of the normal structure of groups; the various notions relating to normal and composition series and systems are introduced, and the Jordan—Hölder and Schreier theorems are proved. The chapter concludes with proofs that almost all the alternating groups and projective unimodular groups are simple.

1. Commutators, conjugates, center, centralizer, normalizer, and related topics

In a non-abelian group there are elements x and y which do not commute; that is, $xy \neq yx$. In such a case the elements of the form

$x^{-1}y^{-1}xy$ and $y^{-1}xy$ are of special importance in the further study of the group structure.   We begin with some terminology.

III.1.a. Definitions.   If x and y are elements of a group G, the element $x^{-1}y^{-1}xy$ is the **commutator** of x and y; it is denoted by $[x, y]$.   The element $y^{-1}xy$ is the **conjugate** (or **transform**) of x by y; it is denoted by x^y.   If S is any subset of G, the **conjugate of S by x** is the set of all s^x, $s \in S$; it is denoted by S^x.   If S and T are subsets of G, then S^T denotes the set of all s^t, $s \in S$, $t \in T$.   If $S^G = S$, then S is a **normal** subset of G.   If s is an element of G, then $\{s\}^G$ or, more briefly, s^G is the **conjugate class** of s.   If S is a subgroup or subset of G, then as x ranges over all the elements of G, the set of all conjugates S^x of S is the **conjugate class** of S.

If x is a fixed element of a group G, the map α_x defined by the equation $g\alpha_x = g^x$ for $g \in G$ is of special importance.   It is a one-one isomorphism of G onto G as the reader may readily check.   Such a map is called an **inner automorphism.**   A group G is abelian if and only if α_x is the identity map for each $x \in G$.

We shall say that two elements x and y of a group G are **conjugate** if there is a $z \in G$ so that $x = y^z$; the reader should verify that this notion leads to an equivalence relation on G, and hence that G is the disjoint union of its conjugate classes.   A group G is abelian if and only if each conjugate class has only one element.

III.1.b. Exercise.   *If S is a normal subset of a group G, show that $\mathfrak{S}(S)$ is the normal closure of S in G (cf. I.3.q).   If H is a subgroup of G, show that the intersection of all the conjugates of H is a normal subgroup of G.*

III.1.c. Definitions.   If S and T are subsets of a group G, then $[S, T]$ will denote $\mathfrak{S}([s, t],\ s \in S, t \in T)$; this subgroup is the **commutator** of S and T.   In particular, $[G, G]$ is the **commutator subgroup** or **derived group** of G; it will usually be denoted by G'. The **second derived group** of G is $[G', G']$ which will be denoted by G'' or $G^{(2)}$; the **third derived group** is $[G'', G''] = G'''$ or $G^{(3)}$ and so on.

Since $[x, y]^{-1} = [y, x]$, it follows that $[S, T] = [T, S]$, and that the subgroup G' is the semigroup generated by the commutators of G.

The fact that a subgroup of a group is normal may be expressed in terms of commutators in view of the following proposition.

III.1.d. Proposition. *If H is a subgroup of the group G, then H is normal in G if and only if $[G, H] \leq H$. If H is normal in G and $H \leq M \leq G$, then H is normal in M. If H and K are normal subgroups of G, then $[H, K]$ is also a normal subgroup of G.*

The proof is direct and is left to the reader.

The commutator subgroup of a group G can be characterized as that normal subgroup which is in the kernel of every homomorphism of G with abelian image in view of the following theorem.

III.1.e. Theorem. *If M is a normal subgroup of G and if G/M is abelian, then $M \geq G'$. Conversely, if M is any subgroup of G containing G', then M is normal in G and G/M is abelian.*

Proof. If M is normal in G and G/M is abelian, then

$$M = x^{-1}My^{-1}MxMyM = x^{-1}y^{-1}xyM$$

and hence $[x, y] \in M$ for all $x, y \in G$. It follows that $G' \leq M$.

Conversely, if $M \geq G'$, then $[G, M] \leq [G, G] = G' \leq M$ so that M is normal in G by III.1.d. Then $x^{-1}My^{-1}MxMyM = x^{-1}y^{-1}xyM = M$ and G/M is abelian.

III.1.f. Corollary. *If $G = \mathfrak{G}(M \mid R)$, then the abelian factor group G/G' is isomorphic to $\mathfrak{G}(M \mid R, [m, n])$ with $m, n \in M$.*

III.1.g. Exercise. *Show that the knot group of I.5.o. has an infinite cyclic homomorphic image and is therefore non-trivial.*

We now introduce two important subgroups determined by a given subset of a group G.

III.1.h. Definitions. If M is a subset of a group G, the set of elements c such that $m^c = m$ for all $m \in M$ is the **centralizer** of M; it is denoted by $\mathfrak{C}(M)$; if $c \in \mathfrak{C}(M)$, c **centralizes** M.   In particular, the **center** of G is $\mathfrak{C}(G)$; it will also be denoted by $\mathfrak{Z}(G)$.   The set of elements n, such that $M^n = M$, is the **normalizer** of M; it is denoted by $\mathfrak{N}(M)$; if $n \in \mathfrak{N}(M)$, n **normalizes** M.   If H is a subgroup of G, $\mathfrak{C}_H(M)$ will denote $\mathfrak{C}(M) \cap H$, and $\mathfrak{N}_H(M)$ will denote $\mathfrak{N}(M) \cap H$. If $g \in G$, $\mathfrak{C}(\{g\})$ will be written $\mathfrak{C}(g)$; the notation $\mathfrak{N}(g)$ for $\mathfrak{N}(\{g\})$ is unnecessary since $\mathfrak{N}(\{g\}) = \mathfrak{C}(g)$.

Some of the important properties of centralizer and normalizer are given in the following propositions.   The proofs are direct and are left to the reader.

III.1.i. Proposition.   *If M is a subset of a group G, then $\mathfrak{C}(M)$ and $\mathfrak{N}(M)$ are subgroups of G.   If M is a subgroup of G, then $\mathfrak{N}(M) \geq M$.*

III.1.j. Proposition.   *If M is a normal subset of a group G, then $\mathfrak{C}(M)$ is normal in G.   In particular, $\mathfrak{C}(M)$ is normal in $\mathfrak{N}(M)$, and $\mathfrak{Z}(G)$ is normal in G.*

III.1.k. Proposition.   *An element z of a group G is in the center of G if and only if $zm = mz$ for each m in any given generating set of G, or if and only if z is the only element in the conjugate class of z.*

It should be noted that the following three conditions are equivalent for the group G:

(1) G is abelian.
(2) $G' = 1$.
(3) $\mathfrak{Z}(G) = G$.

That $M^x \leq M$ does not imply that $M^x = M$ may be seen from the following example.

III.1.l. Example.   Let G be the group

$$\mathfrak{G}(x, a_n, n = 1, 2, \cdots \mid a_{n+1}{}^2 = a_n, \ x^{-1}a_{n+1}x = a_n, \ n = 1, 2, \cdots),$$

and let $M = \mathfrak{G}(a_n)$; then $M^x < M$ but $M^x \neq M$.

III.1.m. Exercise. *If M is a normal subgroup of order 2 of a group G, show that M is in the center of G.*

III.1.n. Exercise. *If n is even, show that the dihedral group D_{2n} of I.5.m has center of order 2.*

III.1.o. Exercise. *If G is a group so that $G/3(G)$ is locally cyclic, show that $G/3(G) = 1$ and hence that G is abelian.*

The next proposition gives a relation of fundamental importance. The verification is direct and is left for the reader.

III.1.p. Proposition. *If S is a subset of a group G, the conjugates of S are in one-one correspondence with the cosets of $\mathfrak{N}(S)$ in G. In particular, if $s \in G$, $|s^G| = |G{:}\mathfrak{C}(s)|$.*

As an immediate corollary to III.1.p and III.1.k we have the important "class equation" of the following theorem.

III.1.q. Theorem. *Let G be a finite group; for $i = 1, 2, \cdots, k$, let C_i be those conjugate classes of G with $|C_i| > 1$, and pick one element g_i from each C_i. Then $|G| = |3(G)| + \sum_{i=1}^{k} |G{:}\mathfrak{C}(g_i)|$.*

III.1.r. Corollary. *Let p be a prime and n a positive integer; then a group of order p^n has a non-trivial center.*

Proof. The numbers $|G|$ and $|G{:}\mathfrak{C}(g_i)|$ are positive powers of p; hence so also is $|3(G)|$.

III.1.s. Corollary. *If p is a prime, a group of order p^2 is abelian and hence is isomorphic either to C_{p^2} or $C_p \times C_p$. In particular, the Klein four-group K_4 (cf. I.6.b) and C_4 are the only groups of order 4.*

We say that a group satisfies the **normalizer condition** if each of its proper subgroups is different from its normalizer, and then we have the following theorem as an easy consequence of III.1.r.   The proof is a good exercise for the reader.

III.1.t. Theorem.   *If p is a prime, then a group of order p^n is different from its derived group, satisfies the normalizer condition, and has subgroups of each order p^m with $0 \le m \le n$.*

III.1.u. Proposition.   *If a group has a proper subgroup of finite index, then it has a proper normal subgroup of finite index.*

Proof.   Let H be a subgroup of finite index in G and let K be the intersection of the conjugates of H.   In view of III.1.p, there are only a finite number of conjugates of H in G and hence, by I.2.k, K has finite index in G; K is normal in G by III.1.b.

III.1.v. Exercise.   *Let H be a proper subgroup of the finite group G; use III.1.p to show that $\bigcup_{g \in G} H^g$ is a proper subset of G.*

It will be seen in Chapter V that finiteness is a necessary hypothesis for the assertion of III.1.v to be true.

We conclude this section with the important notion of weak closure.

III.1.w. Definitions.   If Q and P are subgroups of a group G, then the **weak closure** of Q in P is the subgroup generated by all the conjugates of Q lying in P.   If $Q \le P$ and if for $g \in G$, $Q^g \le P$ implies that $Q^g = Q$, then Q is **weakly closed** in P.   If Q contains the weak closure in P of each of its cyclic subgroups, then Q is **strongly closed** in P.

We list some elementary consequences of the definitions of III.1.w, leaving the proofs to the reader.

III.1.x. Proposition.   *Let G be a group with subgroup P and let Q be a weakly closed subgroup of P; then Q is normal in P.   If R is a subgroup of G, the weak closure of R in G is the normal closure of R.*

A subgroup of a group is always its own weak closure in itself, but it need not be weakly closed in itself as the subgroup M of Example III.1.1 illustrates. On the other hand, there are conditions under which the weak closure of a subgroup is weakly closed. That this is true in a finite group is a special case of the following proposition.

III.1.y. Proposition. *Let Q and P be subgroups of the group G, and suppose that either Q satisfies the minimum condition for subgroups or that $|G:\mathfrak{N}(Q)|$ is finite; then Q is weakly closed in P if and only if Q is its own weak closure in P.*

III.1.z. Proposition. *If Q and P are subgroups of the group G, then the number of right cosets of P contained in PxQ is $|Q:(x^{-1}Px \cap Q)|$. If Q is weakly closed in P, then this number is 1 if and only if $x \in \mathfrak{N}(Q)$.*

2. Endomorphisms and automorphisms

Homomorphisms have already been introduced and studied in Chapter I. In this section the study of homomorphisms of a group into itself is undertaken in more detail. In particular, the automorphism groups of the cyclic groups are determined.

III.2.a. Definitions. A homomorphism of a group G into G is an **endomorphism**; a one-one homomorphism of G onto G is an **automorphism**. The automorphism α_z of G induced by conjugation by the fixed element z of G, i.e., $g\alpha_z = g^z$, $g \in G$ (cf. Section 1), is an **inner automorphism**. The sets of endomorphisms, automorphisms and inner automorphisms will be denoted, respectively, by $\mathfrak{E}(G)$, $\mathfrak{A}(G)$, and $\mathfrak{I}(G)$.

The important elementary facts about $\mathfrak{A}(G)$ and $\mathfrak{I}(G)$ are given in the next three propositions.

III.2.b. Proposition. *If G is a group and $\mathfrak{I}(G)$ is the set of inner automorphisms of G, then $\mathfrak{I}(G)$ is a group under composition of mappings; and $\mathfrak{I}(G) \cong G/\mathfrak{Z}(G)$ with $\mathfrak{Z}(G)$ the center of G.*

Proof. Since $g\alpha_z\alpha_y = g\alpha_{zy}$ for all g, z, y in G, it follows from Proposition I.3.e that if θ is the map from G onto $\Im(G)$ defined by the equation $z\theta = \alpha_z$, $z \in G$, then θ is a homorphism, and $\Im(G)$ is a group. Since the center $\Im(G)$ is the kernel of θ, it follows that $\Im(G) \simeq G/\Im(G)$. This proves the proposition.

When $\Im(G) = 1$, then $G \simeq \Im(G)$ and G can be identified with $\Im(G)$; in this sense G is a subgroup of $\mathfrak{A}(G)$ when $\Im(G) = 1$.

III.2.c. Proposition. *If G is a group and $\mathfrak{A}(G)$ is the set of all automorphisms of G, then $\mathfrak{A}(G)$ is a group under composition of mappings; if $\Im(G)$ is the group of inner automorphisms, then $\Im(G)$ is a normal subgroup of $\mathfrak{A}(G)$.*

Proof. The set of one-one mappings of any set onto itself is a group. Hence to show that $\mathfrak{A}(G)$ is a group we need only show that if β, $\gamma \in \mathfrak{A}(G)$, then $\beta\gamma$ is a homomorphism of G. This is shown as follows. If $g, h \in G$, then $(gh)(\beta\gamma) = ((gh)\beta)\gamma = ((g\beta)(h\beta))\gamma = (g\beta)\gamma(h\beta)\gamma = g(\beta\gamma)h(\beta\gamma)$.

To show that $\Im(G) \triangleleft \mathfrak{A}(G)$ we note that if $\gamma \in \mathfrak{A}(G)$, $\alpha_z \in \Im(G)$, then $\gamma^{-1}\alpha_z\gamma = \alpha_{(z\gamma)}$, since for $g \in G$, $g(\gamma^{-1}\alpha_z\gamma) = (z^{-1}(g\gamma^{-1})z)\gamma = (z^{-1}\gamma)g(z\gamma) = g\alpha_{(z\gamma)}$.

III.2.d. Proposition. *If the center of a group G is trivial, and if G is considered to be a subgroup of $\mathfrak{A}(G)$ as above, then the centralizer of G in $\mathfrak{A}(G)$ is trivial, and in particular $\mathfrak{A}(G)$ has trivial center.*

The proofs of III.2.d, and also III.2.e below are left to the reader.

III.2.e. Proposition. *If A and B are subgroups of a group G and θ is in $\mathfrak{A}(G)$, then $(A \cap B)\theta = A\theta \cap B\theta$.*

Before discussing the structure of $\mathfrak{E}(G)$, it is convenient to define the sum of two endomorphisms and the negative of an endomorphism. If θ and ϕ are two endomorphisms of a group G, then their sum $\theta + \phi$ may be defined by the equation $g(\theta + \phi) = (g\theta)(g\phi)$, $g \in G$. The sum

$\theta + \phi$ is, in general, not an endomorphism, but if $G\theta$ and $G\phi$ are both contained in an abelian subgroup of G, then $(gh)(\theta + \phi) = (gh)\theta(gh)\phi$ $= g\theta\, h\theta\, g\phi\, h\phi = g(\theta + \phi)\, h(\theta + \phi)$; so that in this case $\theta + \phi$ is an endomorphism. The zero endomorphism is the endomorphism mapping each g of G onto 1; and the negative of the endomorphism θ is the mapping $-\theta$ defined by the equation $g(-\theta) = (g\theta)^{-1}$ for each g in G.

The basic elementary facts about $\mathfrak{E}(G)$ may now be stated as follows, the direct verifications being left to the reader.

III.2.f. Proposition.   *If G is a group, then the set of all endomorphisms $\mathfrak{E}(G)$ is a semigroup under composition of mappings.   The subset of those elements of $\mathfrak{E}(G)$ mapping into a fixed abelian subgroup is a ring.   In particular, if G is abelian, $\mathfrak{E}(G)$ is a ring and $\mathfrak{A}(G)$ is the group of units of $\mathfrak{E}(G)$.*

If θ is an endomorphism of a cyclic group G, then θ is completely determined by the image under θ of any generator of G.   Thus if G is the additive group of integers (or integers mod n), then θ may be described as a multiplication by an integer (or an integer mod n), and we have the following.

III.2.g. Proposition.   *If n is a natural number, $\mathfrak{E}(C_n)$ is isomorphic to the ring of integers mod n; $\mathfrak{E}(C_\infty)$ is isomorphic to the ring of integers.*

Let G be a torsion-free locally cyclic group, i.e., a subgroup of the additive group of rationals in view of II.2.k.   An endomorphism θ of G may be described as a multiplication by an appropriate rational number and we have the following proposition, the proof being left to the reader.

III.2.h. Proposition.   *If G is a subgroup of the additive group of rationals, then $\mathfrak{E}(G)$ is isomorphic to the subring of rationals whose denominators are divisible only by those primes p for which the value $v_p(G)$ is $-\infty$; and $\mathfrak{A}(G)$ is the subset of $\mathfrak{E}(G)$ of rationals whose numerators as well as denominators are divisible only by those p for which $v_p(G) = -\infty$.*

III.2.i. Corollary.   *The automorphism group of the group of additive rationals is the set of non-zero elements of the field of rational numbers.*

III.2.j. Proposition.   *If G is a p-quasicyclic group, then $\mathfrak{E}(G)$ is the ring of p-adic integers.*

The reader is referred to [K], vol. 1, p. 154, for the proof of III.2.j.

An important goal of this section is to give the structure of the automorphism group of a cyclic group of prime power order p^n. In view of III.2.g, we are studying the structure of the group of units in the ring of integers mod p^n. The first step in this direction is given in the following proposition.

III.2.k. Proposition.   *If p^n is a prime power, $1+p$ is a unit of order p^{n-1} in the ring of integers mod p^n if p^n is odd or 2 or 4. In the ring of integers mod 2^n with $n > 2$, 5 is a unit of order 2^{n-2}.*

Proof.   The first statement follows from the fact that if p is odd, then $(1+p)^{p^{n-1}} = 1 \bmod p^n$ while $(1+p)^{p^{n-2}} \neq 1 \bmod p^n$. Similarly, the second statement follows from the facts that $(1+2^2)^{2^{n-2}} = 1 \bmod 2^n$ and $(1+2^2)^{2^{n-3}} \neq 1 \bmod 2^n$.

III.2.l. Proposition.   *If p is a prime, then the group of units of the ring of integers mod p is cyclic of order $p-1$.*

Proof.   If p is a prime, then the ring of integers mod p is a field. The group of units of this field can contain at most one subgroup of order n, for any natural number n; for otherwise it would have more than n elements satisfying the equation $x^n = 1$, which is impossible in a field. From this and Exercise II.4.q we conclude that the group of units of the ring of integers mod p is cyclic of order $p-1$.

III.2.m. Theorem.   *If p is a prime, the automorphism group of the cyclic group of order p^n is cyclic of order $p^n - p^{n-1}$ except when $p = 2$ with $n > 2$; in the case where $p = 2$ with $n > 2$, it is the direct product of a cyclic group of order 2^{n-2} with a cyclic group of order 2.*

Proof. The cyclic group of order p^n has one maximal subgroup of order p^{n-1}. Accordingly there are $p^n - p^{n-1}$ elements of order p^n, and hence $p^n - p^{n-1}$ automorphisms of the group; for the natural extension of the map sending any generator of order p^n into any one of the $p^n - p^{n-1}$ elements of order p^n is an automorphism.

In view of III.2.g, it is enough to show that the group of units of the ring of integers mod p^n has a cyclic group of order $p^n - p^{n-1}$, except when $p = 2$ with $n > 2$, and that in that case it has disjoint cyclic subgroups of order 2^{n-2} and 2. The latter statement is true since 5 is a unit of order 2^{n-2} by III.2.k; furthermore, -1 is a unit of order 2, not in the subgroup generated by 5, since all powers of 5 are congruent to 1 mod 4, whereas -1 is not. Thus the exceptional part of the theorem is proved.

We turn now to the general case. It follows from III.2.1 that mod p there is an integer k of order $p-1$. If k has order m mod p^n, then $p-1$ divides m; for if $m = r(p-1) + s$, $s < p-1$, then $k^s = 1$ mod p whence $s = 0$. Hence a power of k has order $p-1$. By III.2.k, $1+p$ has order p^{n-1}; therefore $1+p$ and the above power of k generate a cyclic group of order $p^n - p^{n-1}$ in the ring of integers mod p^n. The main statement of the theorem follows from this and the proof is complete.

In order to describe the structure of the automorphism group of any cyclic group it is convenient first to introduce the notion of characteristic subgroup.

III.2.n. Definition. A subgroup (or subset) H of a group G is **characteristic** in G if $H\theta \leq H$ for every automorphism θ of G.

We list some elementary facts about characteristic subgroups; the verifications are direct and are left to the reader.

    (i) *If H is a characteristic subgroup (or subset) of a group G and θ is any automorphism of G, then $H\theta = H$.*

    (ii) *A characteristic subgroup (subset) is a normal subgroup (subset).*

    (iii) *A fully invariant subgroup is characteristic.*

    (iv) *The intersection of characteristic subgroups (or subsets) is characteristic.*

(v) *The subgroup generated by a set of characteristic subgroups (or subsets) is characteristic.*

(vi) *The subgroups mG and $G(m)$ introduced in Section II.1 are characteristic subgroups.*

(vii) *If H and K are characteristic subgroups (or subsets) of G, then $[H, K]$ is characteristic in G; in particular G', G'', and G''' are characteristic in G.*

(viii) *The center of a group is a characteristic subgroup.*

(ix) *The Frattini subgroup of a group is a characteristic subgroup.*

(x) *A characteristic subgroup of a characteristic (normal) subgroup of a group is characteristic (normal) in the whole group.*

III.2.o. Proposition. *If a group G is a direct product or cartesian product of some of its subgroups G_α for α in some index set A, i.e., $G = \prod_{\alpha \in A} G_\alpha$ or $G = \mathsf{P}_{\alpha \in A} G_\alpha$, then there is an isomorphism of $\mathsf{P}_{\alpha \in A} \mathfrak{A}(G_\alpha)$ into $\mathfrak{A}(G)$ which is an isomorphism onto $\mathfrak{A}(G)$ if and only if G_α is a characteristic subgroup of G for each $\alpha \in A$.*

We can now give a theorem which with III.2.m gives the structure of the automorphism group of any finite cyclic group.

III.2.p. Theorem. *If $n = \prod_{i=1}^{k} p_i{}^{m_i}$ where the p_i are distinct primes, then the automorphism group of the cyclic group of order n is the direct product of the automorphism groups of the cyclic groups of order $p_i{}^{m_i}$, for $i = 1, 2, \cdots, k$.*

Proof. By Theorem I.6.h, $C_n \cong \prod_{i=1}^{k} C_{p_i{}^{m_i}}$. Since each $C_{p_i{}^{m_i}}$ is characteristic in C_n by property (vi) above, the theorem follows directly from III.2.o.

III.2.q. Theorem. *The automorphism group of an infinite cyclic group is a cyclic group of order 2.*

Proof. If x is a generator of the infinite cyclic group, then x^{-1} is the only other generator; and the theorem follows.

We conclude this section with some remarks on locally cyclic groups.

III.2.r. Proposition. *Let G be an ascending union $\bigcup_{n=1}^{\infty} G_n$ of characteristic subgroups G_n with $G_n \le G_{n+1}$; then $\mathfrak{A}(G)$ is abelian if each $\mathfrak{A}(G_n)$ is abelian, and $\mathfrak{A}(G)$ has no element of order p if no $\mathfrak{A}(G_n)$ has an element of order p.*

III.2.s. Corollary. *If p is an odd prime, then $\mathfrak{A}(C_{p^\infty})$ has no element of order p.*

The situation in the case $p = 2$ is given in the following proposition, the proof being left to the reader as an exercise.

III.2.t. Proposition. *The only non-trivial automorphism of 2-power order of C_{2^∞} maps each element onto its inverse.*

In view of II.2.k, the automorphism group of a locally cyclic group may be described in terms of the results of this section. In particular, we observe the following, which will be needed in III.2.v.

III.2.u. Proposition. *If G is a locally cyclic group, then $\mathfrak{A}(G)$ is abelian.*

III.2.v. Theorem. *(cf. [Z]). If G is a group such that both G'/G'' and G''/G''' are locally cyclic, then $G'' = G'''$.*

Proof. Let H denote G/G'''; then, as is easy to see, $H' = G'/G'''$ and $H'' = G''/G'''$, so that H'/H'' and H'' are locally cyclic. Since H'' is a normal subgroup of H, the centralizer $\mathfrak{C}(H'')$ of H'' is also normal in H, and the group of inner automorphisms of H induces a group of automorphisms of H'', which is isomorphic to $H/\mathfrak{C}(H'')$. It follows from III.2.u that this group is abelian so that $H' \le \mathfrak{C}(H'')$ and therefore H'' is in the center of H'. But then $H'/\mathfrak{Z}(H')$ is locally cyclic since $H'/\mathfrak{Z}(H')$ is a factor group of H'/H'', and by III.1.o, H' is abelian. Thus $H'' = 1$ and $G'' = G'''$, as the theorem asserts.

3. Operator groups, modules, and vector spaces

A given set of endomorphisms of a group distinguishes certain subgroups of the group, namely, those subgroups each of which is mapped into itself by each endomorphism of the given set. The study of such distinguished subgroups (depending on the given set of endomorphisms) is of extreme importance and includes the study of module theory and vector space theory. Since two distinct endomorphisms of a group may be identical when restricted to a subgroup, it is convenient to consider sets of "operators" to each of which corresponds an endomorphism of the group, rather than to consider the sets of endomorphisms themselves. Thus we make the following definitions.

III.3.a. Definitions. Let G be a group and Σ a set; suppose there is given a mapping from Σ to $\mathfrak{E}(G)$, that is, to each $\sigma \in \Sigma$ there is associated an endomorphism of G also denoted by σ. Then G is a Σ-**group** and the elements of Σ are **operators**. A subgroup H of G is a Σ-**subgroup (operator subgroup)** if $H\sigma \leq H$ for all $\sigma \in \Sigma$. A subset M of a Σ-group G is a set of Σ-**generators** if G is the subgroup generated by all m and $m\sigma$, $m \in M$, $\sigma \in \Sigma$; if M contains exactly one element, then G is Σ-**cyclic**.

III.3.b. Examples. If G is a group, the $\mathfrak{J}(G)$-subgroups of G are the normal subgroups, the $\mathfrak{A}(G)$-subgroups are the characteristic subgroups, and the $\mathfrak{E}(G)$-subgroups are the fully invariant subgroups.

If ϕ is a group homomorphism from a Σ-group G onto a group $\bar{G}$, and if the kernel K of ϕ is a Σ-subgroup of G, then there is a natural way to make $\bar{G}$ into a Σ-group by associating to $\sigma \in \Sigma$ the map sending $g\phi$ into $g\sigma\phi$ for $g \in G$; this map is well defined, since K is a Σ-subgroup, and is readily seen to be an endomorphism. Thus $g\phi\sigma = g\sigma\phi$. Accordingly we make the following definition.

III.3.c. Definition. A group homomorphism ϕ from a Σ-group G to a Σ-group $\bar{G}$ is a Σ-**homomorphism** if it commutes with the operators; that is, if for $g \in G$, $\sigma \in \Sigma$, $g\sigma\phi = g\phi\sigma$.

It is clear that the kernel of a Σ-homomorphism is a Σ-subgroup and that if the kernel of a homomorphism of a Σ-group is a Σ-subgroup and if the image is a Σ-group in the natural way as described above, then the homomorphism is a Σ-homomorphism.

III.3.d. Definition.   If G is a Σ-group with G an abelian group and Σ a ring, if $g(\sigma + \tau) = g\sigma + g\tau$ and $g(\sigma\tau) = (g\sigma)\tau$ for $g \in G$, σ, $\tau \in \Sigma$, then G is a **right Σ-module** and the Σ-subgroups of G are the **right Σ-submodules**.   One defines similarly **left Σ-module** by the equations $(\sigma + \tau)g = \sigma g + \tau g$, $(\sigma\tau)g = \sigma(\tau g)$ and $\sigma(g_1 + g_2) = \sigma g_1 + \sigma g_2$.   It is easy to check that such a left Σ-module is anti-isomorphic (in fact, isomorphic when Σ is commutative) to the above right Σ-module.

We shall generally use the terms module and submodule for right Σ-module and right Σ-submodule.

III.3.e. Definition.   If in a Σ-module G, Σ is a division ring and if $g1 = g$ for $1 \in \Sigma$, $g \in G$, then G is a **right vector space over** Σ, and the submodules are the **subspaces**.

III.3.f. Definition.   If V is a vector space over a field Σ, the Σ-homomorphisms are the **linear transformations** and the Σ-automorphisms are the **non-singular** linear transformations.

We summarize some of the elementary theory of vector spaces which will be of interest in the sequel.   The reader may prove these facts directly or refer to any book on linear algebra (cf. [J], for instance).

III.3.g. Proposition.   *A vector space V over a division ring Σ has a basis; that is, there is a subset A of nonzero elements of V so that V is the direct sum of the Σ-cyclic subgroups generated by the elements of A. Furthermore, each basis of a subspace U of V is part of a basis of V; thus there is a subspace W so that $V = U \oplus W$ (i.e., each subspace U has a complement W in V).*

III.3.h. Proposition. *Any two bases of a vector space have the same cardinality. The common cardinality is called the* **dimension** *of the space.*

That there are vector spaces of arbitrary cardinality follows immediately from the following.

III.3.i. Proposition. *If Σ is a ring, then its underlying additive group Σ^+ is a Σ-module, the endomorphism corresponding to the element σ of Σ being the right multiplication ρ_σ (cf. Section I.1). Similarly the direct sum of an arbitrary number of copies of Σ^+ is also a Σ-module.*

III.3.j. Proposition. *A mapping ϕ of a basis of a vector space V over a division ring Σ into V has a unique extension to a Σ-endomorphism (also called ϕ) of the additive group of V. In fact, if A is the basis of V and v is a finite sum $\sum_{e_\alpha \in A} e_\alpha \sigma_\alpha$, then $v\phi = \sum_{e_\alpha \in A} (e_\alpha \phi)\sigma_\alpha$.*

It follows from III.3.j that when Σ is a field the mapping ϕ defined on a basis of V extends in fact to a linear transformation of V. Accordingly we make the following definition.

III.3.k. Definition. If ϕ is any mapping of a basis of a vector space V over a division ring Σ into V, then the extension of ϕ to V is a **linear transformation** of V.

Thus a linear transformation may be described simply by its action on a basis and this is conveniently written in matrix form. In particular, if $\{e_1, \cdots, e_n\}$ is a basis of the finite dimensional vector space V over Σ and if η is a linear transformation of V with $e_j\eta = \sum_{i=1}^{n} e_i a_{ij}$ for $j = 1, \cdots, n$, then relative to this basis the linear transformation is described by the n by n matrix

$$(a_{ij}) = \begin{pmatrix} a_{11} & \cdots & a_{1n} \\ a_{21} & \cdots & a_{2n} \\ \vdots & & \\ a_{n1} & \cdots & a_{nn} \end{pmatrix}$$

III.3.1. Proposition. *The set of all linear transformations of an n-dimensional vector space over a division ring Σ is a ring which is isomorphic to the ring of all n by n matrices with coefficients in Σ.*

If G is an abelian group and if, for each integer n, μ_n is defined by the equation $g\mu_n = g^n$, $g \in G$, n an integer, then μ_n is an endomorphism. If M is the set of all such μ_n as n ranges over the integers, then each subgroup of G is always an M-group and μ_n commutes with every endomorphism of G. We may thus interpret an elementary abelian p-group as a vector space over the field of p elements as follows.

III.3.m. Example.   If for the fixed prime p, the group G is a direct sum of cyclic groups of order p, then the set M of endomorphisms $\mu_1, \cdots, \mu_p$ is a field and hence G is a vector space over M.

The proof of the next proposition is a good exercise for the reader.

III.3.n. Proposition. *If for the prime p, G is an elementary abelian p-group of order p^n (i.e., $G = \sum_{i=1}^{n} (a_i)$ with $(a_i) \simeq C_p$), then*

$$|\mathfrak{A}(G)| = (p^n - 1)(p^n - p) \cdots (p^n - p^{n-1}) = p^{n(n-1)/2} \prod_{i=1}^{n} (p^i - 1).$$

4. Semi-direct products

In this section we see how to construct extensions of a given group by means of groups of automorphisms. We then use the information so obtained to describe completely all types of groups of certain orders. We begin with the fact that a group G is isomorphic (cf. I.3.c) to its group ρ_G of right multiplications under the isomorphism ρ with $g\rho = \rho_g$ for $g \in G$. Then if Σ is a sub-semigroup of $\mathfrak{E}(G)$, both ρ_G and Σ are sets of maps of G into itself, and hence they generate a sub-semigroup K of the semigroup of all maps of G into itself. This semigroup is the **holomorph of G with Σ**. When Σ is a group, then the holomorph is a subgroup of the group of permutations of G.

For $x \in G$, $\rho_g \in \rho_G$, and $\sigma \in \Sigma$, $x\rho_g\sigma = x\sigma g\sigma = x\sigma\rho_{g\sigma}$; hence $\rho_g\sigma = \sigma\rho_{g\sigma}$, and $K = \Sigma\rho_G$. Thus when K is a group, ρ_G is normal in K. It follows that if $\tau \in \Sigma$ and if $\rho_h \in \rho_G$, then $\sigma \rho_g \tau \rho_h = \sigma \tau \rho_{gt} \rho_h$, and therefore each element of K has the general form $\sigma \rho_g$.   Furthermore, $1 \rho_g = g$ for $1 \in G$, while $1\sigma = 1$; hence $\rho_G \cap \Sigma$ is non-null if and only if $\rho_1 \in \Sigma$, and then ρ_1 is the identity of K.

The above properties of the holomorph are sufficient to enable one to give a general construction for a semigroup, from two given groups in the following fashion.   Suppose G is a group, S a semigroup, and ϕ a homomorphism from S into $\mathfrak{E}(G)$.   Let K be the set of pairs (s, g), $s \in S$, $g \in G$.   For (s, g) and (t, h) in K define the product of (s, g) with (t, h) to be $(st, g(t\phi)h)$.   It is left to the reader to verify that K is a semigroup.   If, in addition, S is a group and $S\phi$ is a subgroup of $\mathfrak{A}(G)$, then K is a group with identity $(1, 1)$; and the inverse of (s, g) is $(s^{-1}, g^{-1}(s^{-1}\phi))$.

III.4.a. Definition.   The group K constructed above from the groups G and S is a **semi-direct product** of G with S depending on ϕ.   The subgroup of K consisting of the elements $(1, g)$ is isomorphic to G and will be identified with G; similarly, the subgroup of elements $(s, 1)$ is isomorphic to S and will be identified with S.

We now introduce the notion of "split extension" which is related to the semi-direct product in much the same way that the internal direct product is related to the external direct product.

III.4.b. Definition.   The group K is a **split extension** of its subgroup G by its subgroup S (notation: $K = [G]S$) if G and S are complementary subgroups of K and if $G \triangleleft K$.

If $G \triangleleft K$, the group K is merely an **extension** of G by K/G.

The connection between the semi-direct product and split extension is emphasized in the following proposition, the proof of which should now be obvious.

III.4.c. Proposition.   *The group K is a semi-direct product of G with S if and only if it is a split extension of G by S.*

If $G = K \times S$, then G is a split extension $[K]S$; thus non-isomorphic groups may appear the same when written as split extensions.   For instance, both $C_4 \times C_2$ and D_8 (cf. III.4.d below) are split extensions $[C_4]C_2$. Thus the structure of the split extension depends not only on the components but also on the group of automorphisms induced by S on G, that is, it depends also on the homomorphism ϕ.

The following propositions are designed to give the classification of certain types of groups. The proofs are left to the reader.

III.4.d. Proposition. *The dihedral groups D_{2n} and D_∞ (cf. I.5.m) are split extensions $[C_n]C_2$ and $[C_\infty]C_2$, respectively.*

In view of I.3.k, a group of order 6 is a split extension $[C_3]C_2$. Since $\mathfrak{A}(C_3) \cong C_2$ (cf. III.2.m), there are only two possibilities for the homomorphism ϕ in the construction of the semi-direct product of C_3 with C_2. Accordingly we have the following proposition.

III.4.e. Proposition. *A group of order 6 is a split extension $[C_3]C_2$. It is either abelian and isomorphic to $C_3 \times C_2$ (i.e., isomorphic to C_6), or it is non-abelian and isomorphic to D_6 (i.e., isomorphic to S_3 (cf. I.5.m)).*

III.4.f. Proposition. *If p and q are prime numbers there is a non-abelian split extension of the form $[C_p]C_q$ if and only if q divides $p-1$; and when this is the case the split extension is uniquely determined (up to isomorphism).*

If we anticipate Cauchy's theorem (IV.1.f) we know that a group G of order pq, with p and q distinct primes, has a subgroup A of order p and a subgroup B of order q. If A is not normal in G, $A = \mathfrak{N}(A)$, and hence there are only $q-1$ elements not in A or its conjugates. Thus B is normal in G if A is not, and hence G is a split extension either $[A]B$ or $[B]A$.

In view of the above remarks together with III.4.f and III.1.s, we have the following description of groups of order pq.

III.4.g. Proposition. *Let p and q be prime numbers and let G be a group of order pq. Then G is either abelian having one of the forms*

C_{pq} or $C_p \times C_q$ (*these are identical if* $p \neq q$), *or else G is the non-abelian split extension* $[C_p]C_q$ *with q dividing* $p-1$.

We have seen that a group of order pq is either cyclic or a split extension. We now introduce a very important group which is not a split extension of any of its non-trivial subgroups. It is needed to give a complete classification of groups of order 8, as well as for the study of many other classes of groups.

III.4.h. Definition. The **quaternion group of order 8** Q_8 is defined to be $\mathfrak{G}(a, b \mid a^2 = b^2 = [a, b], a^4 = 1)$.

We list some important facts about the quaternion group of order 8, and give the classification of groups of order p^3, leaving the proofs as exercises for the reader.

III.4.i. Proposition. *The quaternion group of order* 8 *is isomorphic to a factor group of a split extension of a* C_4 *by a* C_4; *this factor group has six elements of order 4, only one element of order two, and hence cannot be expressed as a split extension of any of its non-trivial subgroups.*

III.4.j. Proposition. *A non-abelian group of order* 8 *is isomorphic either to the dihedral group* D_8 *or to the quaternion group* Q_8. *In particular, a non-abelian group of the form* $[C_2 \times C_2]C_2$ *is isomorphic to* D_8 *and hence also has the form* $[C_4]C_2$. *There are five isomorphism classes of groups of order* 8, *the three classes of abelian groups having types* (3), (2, 1) *and* (1, 1, 1).

III.4.k. Proposition. *If p is an odd prime, a group of order* p^3 *has one of the following three forms* C_{p^3}, $[C_{p^2}]C_p$, *or* $[C_p \times C_p]C_p$; *there is exactly one non-abelian isomorphism class of groups for each of the latter two forms. Furthermore, a group of the form* $[C_p \times C_p]C_p$ *has exponent p, and hence there are exactly five isomorphism classes of groups of order* p^3, *the three classes of abelian groups having types* (3), (2, 1), *and* (1, 1, 1).

We list three more propositions for the reader to prove, which will be useful in the further classification of groups.

III.4.1. Proposition.   *If p is an odd prime and $n \geq 2$, then any two non-abelian split extensions $[C_{p^n}]C_p$ are isomorphic. There are three non-isomorphic non-abelian split extensions $[C_{2^n}]C_2$ for $n > 2$ (since $\mathfrak{A}(C_{2^n})$ is not cyclic (cf. III.2.m)); one of these has derived group of order 2, and the other two have derived groups of order 2^{n-1}.*

III.4.m. Proposition.   *For any prime p a group of the form $[C_{p^n}]C_p$ has a non-cyclic abelian subgroup, and also has more than one subgroup of order p^m for each integer m with $1 \leq m \leq n$.*

III.4.n. Proposition.   *The automorphism group of Q_8 is isomorphic to S_4 (cf. [Z], p. 148); that of D_8 is isomorphic to D_8.*

We conclude this section with the study of the class of complete groups as defined below; and we show that a complete group is a direct factor of any group containing it as a normal subgroup.

III.4.o. Definition.   A group is **complete** if its center is 1 and all its automorphisms are inner.

III.4.p. Theorem (*Baer*).   *Let G be a group with center 1; then G is complete if and only if G is a direct factor of any group T in which G is a normal subgroup.*

Proof.   We first prove that G is complete under the stated hypothesis.   Let α be an automorphism of G and let H be the holomorph of G with (α).   Then ρ_G is normal in H so that by the hypothesis (since ρ is an isomorphism of G onto ρ_G) $H = \rho_G \times M$ for some M. Now $(\rho_g)^{\alpha^{-1}} = \alpha \rho_g \alpha^{-1} = \rho_{g\alpha^{-1}}$ for each ρ_g in ρ_G; on the other hand, $\alpha^{-1} = m\rho_c$ for some $m \in M$, $\rho_c \in \rho_G$, and $\rho_g^{\alpha^{-1}} = \rho_g^{m\rho_c} = \rho_g^{\rho_c} = \rho_{g^c}$ (since ρ is an isomorphism).   It follows that for each g in G, $g\alpha^{-1} = g^c$, and hence α is inner.   Since this is true for each $\alpha \in \mathfrak{A}(G)$, G is complete.

Conversely, if G is complete, and if G is a normal subgroup of T, then for each $t \in T$ there is a $g \in G$ so that tg^{-1} is in the centralizer C of G in T.   Thus $T = \mathfrak{S}(G, C)$.   Furthermore, $C \lhd T$, and since G has center 1, $G \cap C = 1$.   It follows that $T = G \times C$ and that G is a direct factor of T, as was to be shown.

In view of the above theorem, any split extension of a complete group with any group is in fact a direct product.

III.4.q. Theorem.   *A group G is complete if and only if it has a characteristic subgroup K such that the following two conditions are satisfied.*

  (i) *Every automorphism of K is the restriction of an inner automorphism of G to K.*
 (ii) *The centralizer of K in G is 1.*

Proof.   If G is complete, then G itself is the characteristic subgroup K, satisfying the two conditions.

Conversely, suppose that K is a subgroup satisfying the requirements of the theorem.   To apply Theorem III.4.p, assume that G is a normal subgroup of a group T, so that K, being characteristic in G, is also normal in T.   This means that every element t of T induces an automorphism of K; so, by (i), there is an element g of G inducing the same automorphism of K, giving tg^{-1} in the centralizer C of K in T. Hence, $T = \mathfrak{S}(G, C)$.   Furthermore, as K is normal in T, so is C; and finally, $G \cap C = 1$ by (ii) so that $T = G \times C$.   Thus G is complete.

The following two propositions will be used in proving our last result on complete groups.   The proofs are direct and are left to the reader.

III.4.r. Proposition.   *If G is a cartesian product or direct product of groups, each of which has center 1, then G has center 1.*

III.4.s. Proposition.   *If G is a direct product of non-abelian simple groups, and if $M \lhd G$, then M is the product of some of the simple direct factors of G, and $G = M \times \mathfrak{C}(M)$.*

III.4.t. Theorem.   *If K is a direct product of non-abelian simple groups, then $\mathfrak{A}(K)$ is complete.*

Proof. We shall show that the conditions of Theorem III.4.q are satisfied by $\mathfrak{A}(K)$ and K. Here we are regarding K as a subgroup of $\mathfrak{A}(K)$ (cf. III.2.b and III.2.c). Indeed condition (i) is immediate, and (ii) follows directly from III.2.d. It remains to be shown that K is characteristic in $\mathfrak{A}(K)$ or, equivalently, that for every automorphism α of $\mathfrak{A}(K)$, $K\alpha = K$. Indeed, if $M = K \cap K\alpha$, then, by III.4.s, $K = M \times (\mathfrak{C}(M) \cap K)$, and $K\alpha = M \times (\mathfrak{C}(M) \cap K\alpha)$. Now

$$[\mathfrak{C}(M) \cap K\alpha, M] = 1$$

and

$$[\mathfrak{C}(M) \cap K\alpha, \mathfrak{C}(M) \cap K] \leq \mathfrak{C}(M) \cap K \cap K\alpha = \mathfrak{C}(M) \cap M = 1.$$

Hence $\mathfrak{C}(M) \cap K\alpha$ is in the centralizer of K, and therefore is 1 by III.2.d. It follows that $K\alpha = M$ and hence $K\alpha \leq K$. Similarly $K\alpha^{-1} \leq K$, and therefore $K\alpha = K$. Thus K is characteristic, as was to be shown, and the theorem is proved.

III.4.u. Corollary.   *If K is a simple non-abelian group, then $\mathfrak{A}(K)$ is complete.*

We list two more classes of complete groups.

III.4.v. Proposition.   *The holomorph of a cyclic group of odd order with its full automorphism group is complete.*

III.4.w. Proposition.   *If $n \geq 3$, $n \neq 6$, then the symmetric group S_n is complete.*

The proof of III.4.v is left as an exercise for the reader; the proof of III.4.w may be found in [K], vol. 1, p. 92.

5. The wreath product

A very useful construction based on that of the semi-direct product is that of the wreath product. Let G be a group and B be a group of permutations of a set Y; if $y \in Y$ and $b \in B$, the image of y under b

will be written yb.   The cartesian power G^Y (or $\mathsf{P}_{y \in Y} \, G_y$ with each $G_y \cong G$) of G indexed by Y is the set of functions f on Y with values in G as in Section I.6.   An action of B on G^Y is induced on G^Y as follows: if $f \in G^Y$ and $b \in B$, then f^b is the function defined by the equation $f^b(y) = f(yb^{-1})$ for $y \in Y$.   It is easy to check that, with this definition, B is a group of automorphisms of G^Y (more properly, there is a homomorphism, in fact an isomorphism, ϕ from B into $\mathfrak{A}(G^Y)$). We can now make our definitions as follows.

III.5.a. Definitions.   If G, B, and Y are as before, the semi-direct product of G^Y with B acting as above (i.e., according to the homomorphism ϕ), is the **unrestricted wreath product** of G with B and is denoted by $G \operatorname{Wr} B$.   The subgroup of $G \operatorname{Wr} B$ generated by B and the direct power $\prod_{y \in Y} G_y$ is the **restricted wreath product** of G with B, denoted by $G \operatorname{wr} B$.   In case Y is a group B and B is the group of right multiplications of B, then $G \operatorname{Wr} B$ and $G \operatorname{wr} B$ are the **standard** unrestricted and restricted wreath products, respectively.

In what follows we shall be concerned with the standard wreath products without mentioning the word "standard" explicitly.   We begin with the notion of the diagonal and list some elementary properties.

III.5.b. Definition.   The set of constant functions f (f is a constant if $f(y) = f(z)$ for all y, $z \in Y$) is the **diagonal** of $G \operatorname{Wr} B$.

The following facts follow immediately from the definitions.

(i) $\prod_{y \in Y} G_y$ *is normal in $G \operatorname{wr} B$, and $G \operatorname{wr} B$ is a split extension of $\prod_{y \in Y} G_y$ by B.*

(ii) $G \operatorname{Wr} A = G \operatorname{wr} A$ *if and only if A is finite or G is trivial.*

(iii) *The diagonal of $G \operatorname{Wr} A$ is isomorphic to G.*

(iv) *The diagonal of $G \operatorname{Wr} A$ is in the centralizer of A.*

(v) *(Baumslag).   If A and G are non-trivial groups, the center of $G \operatorname{Wr} A$ coincides with the center of the diagonal and the center of $G \operatorname{wr} A$ is trivial when A is infinite.*

(vi) *If G and A have exponent m and n, respectively, then $G \operatorname{Wr} A$ has exponent dividing mn.*

(vii) *If G and A are p-groups with p a prime, then so also is G wr A;*
G Wr A is a p-group if and only if G has finite exponent.

In view of (v) and (vii) we have the following example due to Baumslag.

III.5.c. Example. C_p wr C_{p^∞} is an infinite p-group with trivial center.

This is in contrast to the situation for finite p-groups, as will be seen in Chapter IV.

III.5.d. Exercise. *Show C_2 Wr $C_2 \cong D_8$ and C_3 Wr $C_2 \cong C_3 \times S_3$.*

The next theorem shows that an arbitrary group may always be embedded in the derived group of a suitable group.

III.5.e. Theorem (*B. H. Neumann and H. Neumann*). *If G is an arbitrary group and if B is a cyclic group, either of infinite order or of order a multiple of the exponent of G, then the derived group of G Wr B contains a subgroup isomorphic to G.*

Proof. To each fixed $g \in G$ consider the element f_g of G^B defined by the equations $f_g(b^k) = g^{-k}$ for all integers k. Then the conjugate $f_g{}^b$ of f_g by b is defined by the equations $f_g{}^b(b^k) = f_g(b^k b^{-1}) = g^{1-k}$ for all k. Finally $[f_g, b]$ is the element of G^B given by the constant function with value g. Hence every element of the diagonal of G Wr B is a commutator and the theorem follows in view of (iii).

We next use the wreath product to embed an arbitrary group in a divisible group. A group is **divisible** if each of its elements is an nth power for each integer n (cf. Section II.7 for the special case of divisible abelian groups). First we give a general lemma.

III.5.f. Lemma. *Let A be an abelian normal subgroup of a group G, let a be an element of A, and let $b \in G$ have finite order n. Then*
$(ba)^n = \prod_{k=0}^{n-1} a^{b^k}$.

Proof. Regardless of the order of b, a direct induction on n (multiplying ba on the right) gives $(ba)^n = b^n \prod_{k=0}^{n-1} a^{b^k}$. The lemma then follows directly.

III.5.g. Proposition (*Baumslag*).   *If G is an arbitrary group and B a cyclic group of order n, then each element of the diagonal of $G \operatorname{Wr} B$ is an nth power.   Thus G is embedded in a group so that each element of G is an nth power.*

Proof. For $g \in G$ let f_g be the element of G^B defined by the equations $f_g(b^i) = g$ if i is zero (or a multiple of n) and let $f_g(b^i) = 1$ otherwise.

Then for $s = 0, 1, \cdots, n-1$, the conjugate $f_g^{b^s}$ of f_g by b^s is defined by the equations $f_g^{b^s}(b^k) = f_g(b^{k-s})$; and hence $f_g^{b^s}(b^k)$ is g when $k - s$ is a multiple of n and is 1 otherwise.   Thus all the conjugates $f_g^{b^s}$ commute in pairs and their product is the element of the diagonal given by the constant function with value g.   On the other hand, by III.5.f this product is the element $(bf)^n$ of $G \operatorname{Wr} B$ and the first statement of the proposition follows.   The second statement follows immediately from (iii).

The preceding result can be used to prove the following theorem of B. H. Neumann.

III.5.h. Theorem.   *Any group may be embedded in a divisible group.*

Proof. Let the group be denoted by G_1 and for each natural number n let G_{n+1} denote $G_n \operatorname{Wr} C_{n+1}$.   Then we have G_n (actually an isomorphic copy of G_n, namely, the diagonal of $G_n \operatorname{Wr} C_{n+1}$) as a subgroup of G_{n+1}.   The ascending union $\bigcup_{n=1}^{\infty} G_n$ is then divisible in view of III.5.g, and the theorem is proved.

Theorem III.5.e can be used to give a simple proof (cf. Ph. Hall [11]) of a theorem (III.5.j) first proved by Higman, Neumann, and Neumann.   It is based on the following lemma.

III.5.i. Lemma.   *If H is a countable group, then there is a two-generator group which contains the derived group H' of H.*

Proof.   Let the elements of H be h_1, h_2, $\cdots$, let K be the cartesian product of a set of copies H_n of H indexed by all the integers n, and let M be the holomorph of K with an element t which acts as a shift operator τ in K; thus if $k \in K$, $(k\tau)(n) = k(n+1)$ or $k^t(n) = k(n+1)$. Let $u \in K$ be defined so that for $r > 0$, $u(2^r) = h_r$ while for n not a power of 2, $u(n) = 1$. We shall show that $\mathfrak{S}(t, u)$ contains H_2'. Indeed $u(2) = h_1$ and if $a = 2^r - 2$, $u^{t^a}(2) = u(2 + a) = h_r$; thus if $b = 2^s - 2$, the element $v_{r,s} = [u^{t^a}, u^{t^b}]$ is the function such that $v_{r,s}(2) = [h_r, h_s]$ and $v_{r,s}(n) = 1$ for $n \neq 2$. This statement is trivial for $r = s$ and can be proven easily for $s > r$, first for $r = 1$ and then for $r > 1$. It follows that the two-generator group $\mathfrak{S}(t, u)$ contains a copy of H' as the lemma asserts.

III.5.j. Theorem.   *Any countable group can be embedded in a group on two generators.*

Proof.   Let G be a countable group, and let B be a cyclic group as in III.5.e so that the derived group of G Wr B contains G. Since G is countable, we can choose a countable subgroup H of G Wr B so that $H' \geq G$. The theorem then follows from III.5.i.

We now give an important theorem of Kaloujnine and Krasner.

III.5.k. Theorem.   *If the group G has a normal subgroup A, then G is isomorphic to a subgroup of A Wr G/A.*

Proof.   Let B denote G/A. We must define an isomorphism from G into A Wr B. To do so we first pick a set of elements of G, one from each coset of A in G (this is known as a "set of representatives" or a **transversal**, cf. IV.3.a). Then we define a map from B into G which will be denoted by [ ]; thus if $b \in B$, $[b]$ is the chosen representative of the coset b. We denote the canonical homomorphism from G onto B by a bar; thus if $g \in G$, $\bar{g}$ is the image of G under the canonical homomorphism. The map [ ] is not a homomorphism; it has the properties that $[\bar{b}] = b$ and that $[\bar{g}^{-1}g]$ is in A.

Our isomorphism θ from G into A Wr B will now be defined so that for $g \in G$, $g\theta = \bar{g}f_g$ with f_g the element of A^B given by the function $f_g(b) = [b\bar{g}^{-1}]g[b]^{-1}$ for $b \in B$. Since $\overline{(g[\bar{b}]^{-1})^{-1}} = (\bar{g}b^{-1})^{-1} = b\bar{g}^{-1}$, $[b\bar{g}^{-1}]g[b]^{-1}$ is in A.

To show that θ is one-one we note that if $g\theta = h\theta$, then $\bar{g} = \bar{h}$ and $f_g = f_h$. Hence g and h are in the same coset of A from which it follows that $b\bar{g}^{-1} = b\bar{h}^{-1}$ and hence $g = h$.

Lastly we must show that θ is a homomorphism. Now $(gh)\theta = g\theta\, h\theta$ if and only if $\overline{gh}f_{gh} = \bar{g}f_g\bar{h}f_h$ which is the case if and only if $f_{gh} = f_g^{\,h}f_h$ since $\overline{gh} = \bar{g}\bar{h}$. Thus we must show that $f_{gh} = f_g^{\,h}f_h$. But for $b \in B$,

$$f_g^{\,h}(b)f_h(b) = [b\bar{h}^{-1}\bar{g}^{-1}]g[b\bar{h}^{-1}]^{-1}[b\bar{h}^{-1}]h[b]^{-1} = f_{gh}(b)$$

and the proof is complete.

A portion of the above theorem may be conveniently reformulated in terms of the following definition (cf. [Z], p. 133).

III.5.1. Definition. Let the group G have a normal subgroup A, and let G/A be denoted by B. A semi-direct product $\bar{G} = [\bar{A}]B$ is a **splitting group of G over A** if $\bar{G} \geq G$ and $\bar{A} \cap G = A$.

III.5.m. Theorem. *An extension G of a group A (with factor group B) has a splitting group $\bar{G} = [\bar{A}]B$ over A with $\bar{A}$ in the variety generated by A.*

As a last application of the wreath product we exhibit certain important subgroups (the Sylow p-subgroups of Chapter IV) of the symmetric groups S_n. It may be a little easier for the reader to read Section III.7 first in order to get more familiarity with the symmetric groups.

If n is a natural number and p a prime, we shall use the term **p-share of n** to denote the highest power of p dividing n. The following two lemmas on p-shares will now be needed.

III.5.n. Lemma. *If n is a natural number and p^k is the largest power of the prime p not greater than n, then the p-share of $n!$ is equal to the p-share of $p^k!$ times the p-share of $(n - p^k)!$.*

Proof. If r is an integer with $p^k < r \le n$, then the p-share of r is equal to that of $r - p^k$ and the lemma follows.

III.5.o. Lemma. *If p is a prime and k a natural number, the p-share of $p^k!$ is equal to p times the pth power of the p-share of $p^{k-1}!$.*

Proof. Let j index the natural numbers with $1 \le j \le p^{k-1}$ and for $i = 0, 1, \cdots, p-1$, let $a_{ij} = ip^{k-1} + j$. Then the p-shares of a_{ij} and a_{hj} are equal except when $h = p-1$, $j = p^{k-1}$, and $i < h$, in which case the p-share of a_{hj} is p times the p-share of a_{ij}. It follows that for each $i < p-1$ the p-share of $\prod_{j=1}^{p^{k-1}} a_{ij}$ is equal to that of $p^{k-1}!$, and for $i = p-1$ it is equal to p times the p-share of $p^{k-1}!$. The lemma then follows immediately from this fact.

III.5.p. Theorem. *Let n be a natural number, let p be a prime, and let m be the p-share of $n!$; then the symmetric group S_n has a p-subgroup P_n of order m (this is a Sylow p-subgroup of S_n (cf. IV.1.h)). If there is an integer k so that $n = p^k$, the Sylow p-subgroup P_n of S_n is the wreath product of $P_{p^{k-1}}$ with C_p.*

Proof. The theorem follows trivially if $n = 1$ and we proceed by induction on n. Let p^k be the largest power of p not greater than n and let s denote $n - p^k$. If $s > 0$, then by the induction assumption there is a p-subgroup P_{p^k} of order equal to the p-share of $p^k!$ and involving only the symbols $1, 2, \cdots, p^k$. Similarly there is a p-subgroup P_s of order equal to the p-share of $s!$ involving the s symbols given by the integers $p^k + 1, \cdots, n$. Since the above two sets of integers are disjoint, each element of P_{p^k} commutes with each element of P_s and therefore $\mathfrak{S}(P_{p^k}, P_s) = P_{p^k} \times P_s$. This latter is a p-subgroup of order m by III.5.n, as we wished to show.

If $n = p^k$ for some integer k, then, by the induction assumption, S_n has a p-subgroup R (isomorphic to $P_{p^{k-1}}$) of order equal to the p-share of $p^{k-1}!$ which moves only the first p^{k-1} natural numbers. Now the first p^k natural numbers may be partitioned into p disjoint sets $A_{ij} = \{a_{ij}, j = 1, 2, \cdots, p^{k-1}\}$ (notation as in III.5.o) of p^{k-1} integers each, for $i = 0, 1, \cdots, p-1$ (Thus R moves only the symbols of A_{0j}.) Let b denote the product of the p^{k-1} disjoint and hence commuting

p-cycles $(jp^{k-1}+j2p^{k-1}+j\cdots(p-1)p^{k-1}+j)$ with j ranging as before so that b has order p. Then it is easy to check that if r is in R, r^{b^i} moves only the symbols of A_{ij}. Hence, if $0 \le i$, $k \le p-1$, R^{b^i} commutes with R^{b^h} when $h \ne i$, and the subgroup generated by all the R^{b^i} is their direct product. Finally, the subgroup generated by R and b is isomorphic to the wreath product of R with a cyclic group of order p and has order equal to the p-share of $p^k!$ by III.5.o. This completes the proof of the theorem.

6. The normal structure of groups

The object of this section is an introduction to the study of the normal structure of groups. We consider chains of subgroups in which each member subgroup is normal in its successor and we prove generalizations of the Jordan-Hölder theorem and the Schreier theorem. We also give the theorem that a group is locally finite if all the factors of a normal series are locally finite. Finally, we conclude with an introduction to the study of serial and subinvariant subgroups.

We begin with the notion of completeness which is basic in the study of the real numbers and which has a similar importance in certain branches of group theory.

III.6.a. Definitions. A chain of subsets of a set ordered by inclusion is **complete** if it contains the union and intersection of the elements of each of its subchains. A chain is an **ascending chain** if the ordering is a well-ordering, that is, if each of its non-empty subchains has a least element; it is a **descending chain** if the reverse ordering is a well-ordering, that is, if each of its non-empty subchains has a greatest element. The **completion** of a chain is the set of subsets consisting of all possible unions and intersections of the elements of the chain.

III.6.b. Examples. Let p be a prime; for each integer n let G_n be the subgroup of the additive rationals consisting of all integral multiples of p^n and let $G = \bigcup_{n=-\infty}^{\infty} G_n$. Let $\mathscr{F}$ be the family of subgroups consisting of 0, G, and all the G_n, let $\mathscr{F}_+$ be the family consisting of

0, G, and all the G_n with n positive, and let $\mathscr{F}_-$ be the family consisting of 0, G, and all the G_n with n negative. Then $\mathscr{F}$ is a complete chain but neither an ascending nor a descending chain; $\mathscr{F}_-$ is an ascending but not a descending chain, $\mathscr{F}_+$ is a descending but not an ascending chain. Both $\mathscr{F}_+$ and $\mathscr{F}_-$ are complete, but if G is not in $\mathscr{F}_-$ or 0 not in $\mathscr{F}_+$, then the resulting chains are no longer complete.

Any finite chain is obviously both an ascending and a descending chain, and, conversely, a chain which is both ascending and descending is finite.

In view of the following easily verified proposition, each chain is part of a complete chain.

III.6.c. Proposition.   *The completion of a chain is a complete chain.*

The above proposition may be used to construct the real field from the rational field as follows.

III.6.d. Construction.   Let R be the set of rational numbers and let ϕ be a map from R onto a set $\mathscr{S}$ of subsets of R so that if r is in R, $r\phi = s_r$, where s_r is the set of all rationals less than r. Then $\mathscr{S}$ is a chain and addition and multiplication may be defined in $\mathscr{S}$ so that ϕ is an isomorphism of both the additive and multiplicative groups of R onto those of $\mathscr{S}$; thus $r\phi + q\phi$ is defined to be $(r+q)\phi$ and $r\phi q\phi$ is defined to be $(rq)\phi$. It is easy to check that each element of the completion $\mathscr{T}$ of $\mathscr{S}$ is a union of elements of $\mathscr{S}$ and that $\mathscr{T}$ may be turned into a field as follows: If $\bar{s}$ and $\bar{t}$ are in $\mathscr{T}$, then $\bar{s}+\bar{t}$ is defined to be the union of all $(s+t)\phi$ with s in $\bar{s}$, t in $\bar{t}$; and $\bar{s}\bar{t}$ is defined to be the intersection of all $(st)\phi$. Then $\mathscr{T}$ is the real number field.

III.6.e. Definitions.   A pair of elements $H < J$ of a chain of subgroups of a group is a **jump** if there is no element K of the chain so that $H < K < J$: in such a case J is the **successor** of H, denoted by $S(H)$. If $H \lhd S(H)$, the jump is **normal** and the factor group is the **factor** of the jump.

Two facts are immediately obvious.

(i) *Every element except the largest (if there is such) of an ascending chain has a successor, namely the least of the elements of the chain properly containing the given element.*

(ii) *If $\mathscr{S}$ is a complete chain of subsets of a given set X, then each $x \in X$ determines a jump in $\mathscr{S}$, given by the union of all elements of $\mathscr{S}$ not containing x and the intersection of all elements of $\mathscr{S}$ containing x.*

III.6.f. Definitions. A complete chain of subgroups of a group G is a **normal system** if each jump is normal. If a normal system has a least member H and greatest member K, it is a **normal system between H and K**; if $H = 1$ and $K = G$, it is a **normal system of G**. In case the chain of a normal system is an ascending chain, the normal system is an **ascending normal series**. The **length** of a series or chain is the cardinality of the set of its members properly containing the least member.

We shall usually index the members of an ascending chain by the ordinals.

III.6.g. Definitions. One chain is a **refinement** of a second if every member of the second is a member of the first. The refinement is **proper** if the first chain contains the second one properly. A **refinement** of a normal system or ascending normal series is defined analogously.

III.6.h. Definitions. A normal system with no proper refinement is a **composition system**; an ascending normal system with no proper refinement is an **ascending composition series**.

III.6.i. Examples. For each prime p the chain of subgroups $1 < \cdots < (x^{p^n}) < \cdots < (x^{p^2}) < (x^p) < (x)$ of the infinite cyclic group (x) is a composition system. The chain of all subgroups of a p-quasicyclic group is also a composition system; in fact, it is an ascending composition series.

III.6.j. Exercise.   *If p, q, and r are any primes, exhibit all composition series of the groups of order pq (cf. III.4.g), and also of the abelian groups of order pqr.*

That every group has a composition system is a consequence of the following.

III.6.k. Proposition.   *Any normal system of a group may be refined to a composition system.*

The reader may consult [K], vol. 2, p. 172, for a proof, or he may supply a proof by showing first that the completion of the limit of a towered system of refinements of a normal system has normal jumps, and then applying Zorn's lemma with "refinement" as the partial ordering.   Here a system of refinements of a chain of subsets is defined to be a **towered system** of refinements of the chain if, for any two refinements of the system, one is a refinement of the other. The **limit** of the towered system is the chain consisting of all the subsets of all of the chains of the system.

Occasionally we are interested in a normal system of a group G, each of whose members is normal in G; such a system is an **invariant system**.   An invariant system with no proper refinement is a **principal system**.   An invariant system which is well-ordered under inclusion is an **ascending invariant series**; if further it has no proper refinement, it is an **invariant principal series**.

The next notion to be introduced is that of isomorphism of normal systems.   We then give the important theorem that any two ascending composition series of a group are isomorphic.

III.6.l. Definition.   Two normal systems of a group are **isomorphic** if there is a one-one correspondence between the jumps of the two systems so that the corresponding factors at the jumps are isomorphic.

The following fact is immediately obvious.

(iii) *Isomorphic normal series have the same length.*

That two composition systems of a group need not in general be isomorphic follows from the fact that the infinite cyclic group has non-isomorphic composition systems, namely, the composition systems of III.6.i for primes p and q, $p \neq q$.

Two lemmas are needed now for the proof of the main theorem on isomorphism of ascending composition series.   The proof of the first lemma will be left as an exercise for the reader.

III.6.m. Lemma.   *If $\mathscr{A}$ and $\mathscr{B}$ are ascending complete chains of a group, let*

$$\bar{\mathscr{A}} = \{G_{AB} \mid G_{AB} = \mathfrak{S}(A, (S(A) \cap B)),\ A \in \mathscr{A}, B \in \mathscr{B}\}$$

and let

$$\bar{\mathscr{B}} = \{G_{BA} \mid G_{BA} = \mathfrak{S}(B, S(B) \cap A)),\ A \in \mathscr{A}, B \in \mathscr{B}\}.$$

Then $\bar{\mathscr{A}}$ and $\bar{\mathscr{B}}$ are also ascending complete chains.

III.6.n. Lemma (*Zassenhaus*).   *If A, A_1, B, B_1, are subgroups of a group G, with A_1 normal in A, B_1 normal in B, then $A_1(A \cap B_1)$ is normal in $A_1(A \cap B)$, $B_1(A_1 \cap B)$ is normal in $B_1(A \cap B)$, and $A_1(A \cap B)/A_1(A \cap B_1) \cong B_1(A \cap B)/B_1(A_1 \cap B)$.*

Proof. A_1 is normal in the subgroups $A_1(A \cap B_1)$ and $A_1(A \cap B)$ of A.   Then if C denotes $A \cap B$, the elements of $A_1 C$ are of the form $a_1 c$, $a_1 \in A_1$, $c \in C$.   It follows that

$$a_1 c A_1(A \cap B_1) = A_1 a_1 c(A \cap B_1) = A_1 c(A \cap B_1) = A_1(A \cap B_1)c$$
$$= (A \cap B_1)A_1 c = (A \cap B_1)A_1 a_1 c = A_1(A \cap B_1)a_1 c.$$

Hence $A_1(A \cap B_1) \lhd A_1(A \cap B)$, and the elements of

$$A_1(A \cap B)/A_1(A \cap B_1)$$

are given by the cosets $c A_1(A \cap B_1)$, $c \in C$.

Similarly, $B_1(A_1 \cap B) \lhd B_1(A \cap B)$,   and   the   elements   of $B_1(A \cap B)/B_1(A_1 \cap B)$ are given by the cosets $c B_1(A_1 \cap B)$, $c \in C$.

Now it is easy to check that $B \cap A_1(A \cap B_1) = (B \cap A_1)(A \cap B_1) = A \cap B_1(A_1 \cap B)$.   But then if ϕ is defined by the equation $c A_1(A \cap B_1)\phi = c B_1(A_1 \cap B)$, ϕ is a one-one map from

$$A_1(A \cap B)/A_1(A \cap B_1)$$

onto $B_1(A \cap B)/B_1(A_1 \cap B)$, since $cB_1(A_1 \cap B) = dB_1(A_1 \cap B)$ if and only if $cd^{-1} \in B \cap B_1(A_1 \cap B)$, which is precisely the criterion that $cA_1(A \cap B_1) = dA_1(A \cap B_1)$ in view of the above equations. A direct check shows that ϕ is in fact an isomorphism. This proves the lemma.

III.6.o. Theorem. *Any two ascending normal series have isomorphic refinements* (*cf.* [*K*], *vol. 2*).

Proof. If $\mathscr{A}$ and $\mathscr{B}$ are the two ascending normal series, let $\bar{\mathscr{A}}$ and $\bar{\mathscr{B}}$ be defined as in Lemma III.6.m. If the pair $G_{AB} < S(G_{AB})$ is a jump in $\bar{\mathscr{A}}$, let $\bar{B}$ be chosen as large as possible so that $G_{AB} = G_{A\bar{B}}$ and hence $S(G_{A\bar{B}}) = G_{AS(\bar{B})}$. Then by Lemma III.6.n, $G_{AS(\bar{B})}/G_{AB}$ $\cong G_{\bar{B}S(A)}/G_{\bar{B}A}$. Accordingly the pair $G_{\bar{B}A}$ $G_{\bar{B}S(A)}$, is a jump of $\bar{\mathscr{B}}$ and we let it correspond to the given jump of $\bar{\mathscr{A}}$. Since $G_{\bar{B}A} < G_{\bar{B}S(A)}$ the same rule applied to this jump of $\bar{\mathscr{B}}$ makes the given jump of $\bar{\mathscr{A}}$ correspond to it, the correspondence is one-one, the corresponding jumps have isomorphic factors and the theorem is proved.

III.6.p. Corollary. *Any two ascending composition series of a group are isomorphic.*

For the case of finite series, Theorem III.6.o is due to Schreier and Corollary III.6.p is the Jordan-Hölder theorem.

From time to time we shall be interested in properties which a group shares with each factor of any of its normal series. Here we shall prove that local finiteness is one of these properties. It should be recalled that a group is **locally finite** if each of its finitely generated subgroups is finite (*cf.* II.2.a).

III.6.q. Theorem (*O. Yu. Schmidt*). *Let A be a normal subgroup of the group G and suppose that both A and G/A are locally finite; then G is locally finite.*

Proof. If M is a finite set of elements of G, then by the hypothesis in G/A, the subgroup $\mathfrak{S}(mA, m \in M)$ of G/A is a finite group; if R

is its complete inverse image in G, A has finite index in R.   We choose a finite subset $N = \{x_1, \cdots, x_t\}$ of G containing M and M^{-1} and such that N has at least one element in each coset of A in R.   Then for each pair i, j, $1 \leq i, j \leq t$, there is an element $x_k \in N$ and an element $a_{ij} \in A$ so that $x_i x_j = x_k a_{ij}$.   Let B denote the finite set of a_{ij} chosen; if $C = \mathfrak{S}(B)$, then C is finite by the hypothesis on A.   Then the elements of the semigroup generated by the elements of N can be written in the form nc with $n \in N$, $c \in C$, and hence there are only a finite number of such elements.   Since this semigroup contains $\mathfrak{S}(M)$, $\mathfrak{S}(M)$ is finite and G is locally finite as the theorem asserts.

III.6.r. Corollary.   *A group is locally finite if it has a normal series each of whose factors is locally finite.*

III.6.s. Corollary.   *A group is locally finite if it has a normal series each of whose factors is periodic and abelian.*

In connection with questions of finiteness the following fact is of interest.

III.6.t. Proposition (*Dietzmann*).   *If a normal subset of periodic elements of a group is finite, then it generates a finite subgroup.*

Proof.   For $i = 1, \cdots, k$, let the given normal subset M be a union of conjugate classes C_i of elements of order m_i and let $D_i = \bigcup_{j=1}^{m_i} C_i^j$. Then if S_k denotes the set of all permutations of the integers $1, 2, \cdots, k$, and if D denotes $\bigcup_{\sigma \in S_k} D_{1\sigma} D_{2\sigma} \cdots D_{k\sigma}$, D is finite and we leave it to the reader to check that for $m \in M$, $Dm = D$.

The concluding topic for this section is concerned with serial and subinvariant subgroups.

III.6.u. Definitions.   A member of an ascending normal series of a group G is a **serial** subgroup.   A member H of a normal series of G is **subinvariant**; we shall write $H \lhd \lhd G$ to denote that H is subinvariant in G.

Some elementary facts are listed below.

(iv) *If H and K are serial subgroups of a group G, then so also is $H \cap K$; if H and K are subinvariant, then so is $H \cap K$.*

(v) *If H is serial in the group G and K is serial in H, then K is serial in G. Similarly, $K \lhd \lhd G$ if $K \lhd \lhd H$ and $H \lhd \lhd G$.*

(vi) *If K is a subgroup of a group G and H is serial (or subinvariant) in G, then $H \cap K$ is serial (or subinvariant) in K.*

(vii) *If ϕ is a homomorphism of a group G and H is serial (or subinvariant) in G, then $H\phi$ is serial (or subinvariant) in $G\phi$.*

(viii) *If $H \lhd G$ and K is serial (or subinvariant) in G, then HK is serial (or subinvariant) in G.*

(ix) *If H is a simple group and is subinvariant in G, then the normal closure of H in G is isomorphic to a direct product of isomorphic copies of H.*

III.6.v. Theorem (*Wielandt*). *Let G be a group and for $i = 1, 2$ let H_i be a subinvariant subgroup of G; if there is a bound b_i on the lengths of the normal series between H_i and G, then $\mathfrak{S}(H_1, H_2)$ is subinvariant in G.*

Proof. Let $b_1 \le b_2$ and let m be chosen as small as possible so that there are subgroups $K_1, \cdots, K_m$ such that $H_1 = K_1 \lhd K_2 \lhd \cdots \lhd K_m \lhd G$. We can suppose that $b_1 \ge 2$ since otherwise the theorem follows from (viii) above. We then proceed by induction on $b_1 + b_2$; without loss of generality we may assume that $G = H_2 K_m$.

Suppose first that H_2 is in the normalizer of H_1. Since each g in G has the form hk, $h \in H_2$, $k \in K_m$, it follows that $H_1{}^g = H_1{}^{hk} = H_1{}^k \le K_{m-1}$ and hence that $H_1{}^G \le K_{m-1}$. Then if R is the normal subgroup generated by H_1, $R \le K_{m-1}$, and $H_1 = K_1 \lhd K_2 \cap R \lhd \cdots \lhd K_{m-1} \cap R \lhd G$ contrary to the minimality of m. We conclude that H_2 is not in the normalizer of H_1.

It follows from the above that there is an $h \in H_2$ so that $H_1{}^h \ne H_1$. Let $H_3 = \mathfrak{S}(H_1, H_1{}^h)$; then $H_3 > H_1$ and the induction assumption gives that $H_3 \lhd \lhd K_m$ and consequently that $H_3 \lhd \lhd G$. Then again by the induction assumption (since $H_3 > H_1$), $\mathfrak{S}(H_2, H_3) \lhd \lhd G$. But $\mathfrak{S}(H_2, H_3) = \mathfrak{S}(H_1, H_3)$ and the theorem follows.

As an immediate consequence of (v) and (iv), we have the following.

III.6.w. Theorem (*Wielandt*).   *The set of subinvariant subgroups of a finite group is a lattice, with the join of two subgroups the subgroup they generate.*

7. The symmetric and alternating groups

The object of this section is an introduction to the study of the symmetric and alternating groups, and so show that the alternating groups on five or more symbols are simple non-abelian groups.

III.7.a. Definitions.   The group of all permutations of a set M (cf. I.1.f) is the **symmetric group on M**; the elements of M are called **symbols** to avoid confusion with the group elements.

The following fact is immediately obvious.

(i) *The symmetric group on M is determined up to isomorphism by $|M|$, the cardinality of M.*

III.7.b. Definitions.   Two symbols r and s of M are **related** by an element σ of the symmetric group on M if $r = s\sigma^k$ for some integer k. This is clearly an equivalence relation on M, the equivalence classes are called the **orbits** of σ.   An orbit is **trivial** if it has only one symbol.

III.7.c. Definitions.   A permutation which has exactly one non-trivial orbit is a **cycle**; if the non-trivial orbit has **a finite number k of symbols, the permutation is a k-cycle.**   A 2-cycle is also called a **transposition**.   Two cycles are **disjoint** if their non-trivial orbits are disjoint.

There is a particularly convenient description of the cycle in terms of its non-trivial orbits (cf. I.1.g).   Firstly, if the orbit is infinite, write its elements in a row with $r\sigma$ immediately to the right of r, thus: $(\cdots r\sigma^{-1} r\, r\sigma \cdots)$.   If, on the other hand, there are just l elements in the orbit, they are $r, r\sigma, \cdots, r\sigma^{h-1}$ for some r and the cycle can be represented by $(r\, r\sigma \cdots r\sigma^{k-1})$.   The inverse of a cycle is the cycle with the symbols written in reverse order.

We note the following facts.

(ii) *The order of a k-cycle is k; in particular a 2-cycle is its own inverse.*

(iii) *A permutation with only a finite number of non-trivial orbits is a product of disjoint cycles which are pair-wise commutative: furthermore each of the above cycles involves only the symbols of one of the non-trivial orbits.*

III.7.d. Definition.   The subgroup of the symmetric group on a set M, generated by the cycles of finite order, is the **restricted symmetric group** on M.   This will often be denoted by S_M.   In view of (i), each finite restricted symmetric group will be denoted by S_n for an appropriate natural number n and will be represented as a group of permutations on the first n natural numbers (cf. I.1.g).

(iv) *The restricted symmetric group on a set M is the full symmetric group on M if and only if M is finite.*

(v) *The order of the finite symmetric group S_n is $n!$.*

(vi) *The restricted symmetric group on a set M is the subset of permutations, each having only a finite number of finite non-trivial orbits and no infinite orbits.*

(vii) *The restricted symmetric group on a set M is normal in the symmetric group on M.*

It will be very instructive to the reader to work out the details of the proof of the following proposition.

III.7.e. Proposition.   *The symmetric group S_4 has the following five conjugate classes: (1) the identity, (2) three products, each of two disjoint 2-cycles, (3) eight 3-cycles, (4) six 2-cycles, and (5) six 4-cycles.   The proper non-trivial normal subgroups of S_4 are the alternating group A_4 (see below) containing classes (1), (2), and (3), and the subgroup K_4 which contains classes (1) and (2) and is isomorphic to the Klein four-group of I.6.b.   Any other proper non-trivial subgroup of S_4 is isomorphic to one of C_2, C_3, C_4, S_3, or D_8, and each of these types of subgroups occurs in S_4.   Finally S_4 is a split extension of the form $[K_4]S_3$ and also of the form $[A_4]C_2$, while A_4 is a split extension of the form $[K_4]C_3$.*

We now give an important proposition which leads to the definition of the alternating groups.

III.7.f. Proposition.   *If n is a natural number, $n > 1$, there is a homomorphism from the symmetric group S_n onto the integers mod 2.*

Proof.   For $\sigma \in S_n$ define θ by the equation
$$\sigma\theta = \prod_{1 \leq i < j \leq n} (j\sigma - i\sigma)/|j\sigma - i\sigma|.$$
To show that θ is a homomorphism we must show that
$$(\sigma\tau)\theta = \sigma\theta\,\tau\theta \text{ for } \tau \in S_n.$$
Now $(\sigma\tau)\theta = \prod_{1 \leq i < j \leq n} (j\sigma\tau - i\sigma\tau)/|j\sigma\tau - i\sigma\tau|$.   We multiply both sides of the equation by $\sigma\theta$, remembering that $\sigma\theta$ is $(-1)^k$ with k the number of pairs $i < j$ for which $j\sigma < i\sigma$, and obtain
$$\sigma\theta(\sigma\tau)\theta = \prod_{1 \leq i\sigma < j\sigma \leq n} (j\sigma\tau - i\sigma\tau)/|j\sigma\tau - i\sigma\tau|.$$
But this latter expression is $\tau\theta$ since σ is a one-one map of the set $\{1, 2, \cdots, n\}$ onto itself.   Thus $\sigma\theta(\sigma\tau)\theta = \tau\theta$.   Multiplying both sides of the above by $\sigma\theta$ we get $(\sigma\theta)^2(\sigma\tau)\theta = \sigma\theta\,\tau\theta$; but $\sigma\theta$ is ± 1 and hence $(\sigma\theta)^2 = 1$ and therefore θ is a homomorphism as was to be shown.   It is clear that $(12)\theta = -1$ and hence that θ maps S_n onto the integers mod 2.

In view of the above proposition we say that an element of S_n is *even* or *odd* according as it maps under θ onto 1 or -1.   Now any two 2-cycles of S_n are conjugate in S_n, since $(13)(24)(12)(13)(24) = (34)$ and $(123)(12)(321) = (13)$.   Then, since $(12)\theta = -1$, it follows that every 2-cycle maps onto -1 under θ.   Hence an element of S_n is even or odd according as it is a product of an even or an odd number of 2-cycles.   Furthermore, if an element is a product of an even (or odd) number of 2-cycles, then every representation of it as a product of 2-cycles involves an even (or odd) number of them.   For each integer $k \leq n$, $(12 \cdots k) = (12)(13) \cdots (1k)$, and hence, since every element of S_n is in fact a product of disjoint cycles, it may be written as a product of 2-cycles.

We can now make the following definitions.

III.7.g. Definitions.   An element of the restricted symmetric group on a set M is **even** or **odd** according as it can be written as a product of an even or an odd number of 2-cycles.   The **alternating subgroup on M** is the subset of even elements of the restricted symmetric group;

or equivalently, it is the kernel of the homomorphism of III.7.f.   The finite alternating group on n symbols is denoted by A_n.

The following basic fact is now immediate.

III.7.h. Theorem.   *The alternating group on a set M is a normal subgroup of index 2 in the symmetric group on M.*

III.7.i. Exercise.   *Show that a k-cycle is even or odd according as k is odd or even; and that an element of a restricted symmetric group is even or odd according as the number of its non-trivial orbits having an even number of elements is even or odd.*

As a familiarity with the alternating groups is of great value, we leave the proof of the following proposition to the reader.

III.7.j. Proposition.   *The alternating group A_5 has the following five conjugate classes: (1) the identity, (2) twenty 3-cycles, (3) fifteen products each of two disjoint 2-cycles, (4) and (5) two classes, each of twelve 5-cycles. It follows (since a normal subgroup is a set union of conjugate classes) that A_5 is a simple group and is generated by the 3-cycles.   Furthermore, any two 3-cycles are conjugate in A_5 (since the centralizer of a 3-cycle is the subgroup it generates).   Finally a subgroup of A_5 is isomorphic either to a subgroup of A_4 or to C_5 or to D_{10}.*

III.7.k. Proposition.   *Each alternating group is generated by its 3-cycles.   Any two 3-cycles of an alternating group A_n, for n a natural number not 4, are conjugate in A_n.*

Proof.   An even element is a product of an even number of 2-cycles. Since $(12)(34) = (143)(142)$ and $(12)(13) = (123)$, it follows that an even element is a product of 3-cycles and the first statement of the proposition follows.   The second statement of the proposition for $n = 5$ was given in III.7.j.   For $n = 3$ it is easy to check.   For $n > 5$ it follows from the fact that (123) is conjugate to (145) in an appropriate A_5 (the subgroup of A_n fixing all but five symbols) and (145) is similarly conjugate to (456).

We now come to the main result of this section.

III.7.1. Theorem.   *If $|M| > 4$, the alternating group on M is simple.*

Proof.   We first prove that A_n is simple for n a natural number greater than 4.   For $n = 5$, this was shown in III.7.j and we proceed by induction on n.   Suppose then that C is a normal non-trivial subgroup of A_n.   We shall first show that C contains a non-trivial element of some A_{n-1} (the subgroup of A_n fixing one symbol is isomorphic to A_{n-1} and that is what we mean here), and hence that C contains all 3-cycles.   To do this we begin with any element $g \neq 1$ of C and express g as a product $c_1 c_2 \cdots c_k$ of pairwise commutative disjoint cycles c_i with $i = 1, 2, \cdots, k$ as in (iii).   If each c_i is a 2-cycle and if $k = 2$, then g itself is the desired element.   If each c_i is a 2-cycle with $k > 2$, let $c_1 = (12)$, $c_2 = (34)$, $c_3 = (56)$; then $[(12)(35), g]$ is the desired element since it leaves fixed the symbols 1 and 2 but not 3.

If $c_1 = (123)$ and $c_2 = (45)$ or (456), then $[(134), g]$ is the desired element since it leaves 6 fixed but not 2.   Finally, if $c_1 = (1234)$ or $(1234\cdots)$, then the element $[(321), g^{-1}]$ leaves 1 fixed but not 2, and hence is the desired element.   Thus in any event C contains a non-trivial element of some A_{n-1} and hence all of that A_{n-1}, since A_{n-1} is simple by the induction assumption.   In particular, C contains all the 3-cycles by III.7.k and hence is A_n itself.   Thus A_n is simple as was to be shown.

Now if M is arbitrary, a non-trivial normal subgroup of the alternating group on M must contain an A_n for some $n > 4$.   It follows that it must contain a 3-cycle and hence all 3-cycles by III.7.k.   Thus the alternating group on M with $|M| > 4$ is simple and the theorem is proved.

We conclude this section by showing that each symmetric group S_n is generated by two elements.

III.7.m. Proposition.   *If n is a natural number greater than 1, the symmetric group S_n is generated by its elements $(12\cdots n)$ and (12).*

Proof.   Let σ denote $(12\cdots n)$ and τ denote (12).   Then for $1 \leq k \leq n$, the conjugate of $(k, k\sigma)$ by σ is $(k\sigma, k\sigma^2)$ and the conjugate of $(k, k\sigma^m)$ by $(k\sigma^m, k\sigma^{m+1})$ is $(k, k\sigma^{m+1})$.   Thus all transpositions and hence S_n itself are in the subgroup generated by σ and τ.

In view of the above proposition and Cayley's theorem we have the following special case of Theorem III.5.j.

III.7.n. Corollary. *Any finite group may be embedded in a finite group on two generators.*

Proof.   If G is a finite group, then it is isomorphic to a subgroup of the symmetric group on $|G|$ symbols by I.3.c.   The statement of the corollary then follows from III.7.m.

8. Linear groups

The object of this section is to introduce the reader to some linear groups and in particular to show that the projective unimodular groups are (with a few exceptions) simple.

III.8.a. Definitions.   If V is an n-dimensional vector space over a field K (cf. [A] for the more general case where K is a division ring), the multiplicative group of non-singular linear transformations of V is the **full linear** group; it will be denoted here by $L(K, n)$.   The subset of $L(K, n)$ consisting of the linear transformations of determinant 1 is the **special linear group**, denoted here by $S(K, n)$.   If Z is the intersection of the center of $L(K, n)$ with $S(K, n)$, then $S(K, n)/Z$ is the **projective unimodular group**, denoted here by $P(K, n)$.

The reader should either prove the following facts or consult a book on linear algebra for the proofs.

(i) *Relative to any fixed basis of V, the elements of $L(K, n)$ are described by the non-singular n by n matrices; the elements of $S(K, n)$ are described by the n by n matrices of determinant 1. Thus the notations $L(K, n)$ and $S(K, n)$ will also be used to denote these matrix groups once a basis is fixed.*

(ii) *The set of all matrices (as the basis of the vector space is varied) which describe a non-singular linear transformation is the conjugate class in the matrix group $L(K, n)$ of each matrix of the set.*

(iii) *To each linear transformation T, there is a decomposition of the vector space V as a direct sum of subspaces V_i, $i = 1, 2, \cdots, k$ of dimension n_i, and for each i there is a linear transformation T_i of V so that T_i acts as the identity transformation on V_j for $j \neq i$ and so that T and T_i are the same when restricted to V_i. Furthermore, for $i \neq j$, $T_i T_j = T_j T_i$ and $T = T_1 T_2 \cdots T_k$. Finally there is a basis of V_i so that the matrix of T_i restricted to V_i is either a scalar matrix or has the form*

$$\begin{pmatrix} 0 & 1 & 0 & \cdots & 0 \\ 0 & 0 & 1 & \cdots & 0 \\ \vdots & & & & \vdots \\ a_1 & a_2 & a_3 & \cdots & a_{n_i} \end{pmatrix} ;$$

and unless T itself is a scalar matrix, there is a decomposition of V with at least one T_i having the latter form (with $n_i \geq 2$). In particular, a non-central element of $S(K, 2)$ may be given the form $\begin{pmatrix} 0 & 1 \\ -1 & s \end{pmatrix}$ by an appropriate choice of basis of V.

(iv) *$S(K, n)$ is normal in $L(K, n)$.*

(v) *When p is a prime power and K is the field of p elements, then the order of $L(K, n)$ is $p^{n(n-1)/2} \prod_{i=1}^{n} (p^i - 1)$, the order of $S(K, n)$ is $p^{n(n-1)/2} \prod_{i=2}^{n} (p^i - 1)$ (cf. III.3.n), and the order of $P(K, n)$ is $(1/d) p^{n(n-1)/2} \prod_{i=2}^{n} (p^i - 1)$, where d is the greatest common divisor of n and p (cf. [A]).*

Of particular importance in the study of the linear groups are the transvections defined as follows.

III.8.b. Definition.   A non-trivial element T of $L(K, n)$ is a **transvection** if there is an $(n-1)$-dimensional subspace W of V so that $wT = w$ for $w \in W$ and $vT - v \in W$ for all $v \in V$.

The following facts are then easy to deduce.

(vi) *Each transvection has the form* $I_n + \begin{pmatrix} 0 & \cdots & 0 & 1 \\ \vdots & & & \vdots \\ 0 & \cdots & & 0 \end{pmatrix}$ *relative*

to a suitable basis (here I_n is the n by n identity matrix).

(vii) *If the characteristic of the field is p, the transvections have order p.*

(viii) *Each transvection is in $S(K, n)$.*

(ix) *Any two transvections of $L(K, n)$ are conjugate in $L(K, n)$, and in fact are conjugate in $S(K, n)$ when $n > 2$.*

The importance of the transvections is apparent from the following theorem.

III.8.c. Theorem.   *For $n > 1$, the transvections generate $S(K, n)$.*

Proof.   For $i \neq j$ let $B_{ij}(t)$ denote the matrix obtained from the unit matrix by replacing the zero entry in the i, j position by t.   Then $B_{ij}(t)$ is a transvection and premultiplication of a matrix $A = (a_{ij})$ by $B_{ij}(t)$ amounts to adding t times the jth row of A to the ith row. We shall show how premultiplication of an arbitrary matrix A of $S(K, n)$ by a sequence of transvections $B_{ij}(t)$ leads to the identity matrix.

If the entry a_{21} of A is zero, there is an $i \neq 2$ so that $a_{i1} \neq 0$, since A is non-singular; then premultiplication of A by $B_{2i}(1)$ gives a matrix with non-zero entry in the 2, 1 position.   If $a_{21} \neq 0$, premultiplication of A by $B_{12}((1 - a_{11})a_{21}{}^{-1})$ gives a matrix with entry in the 1, 1 position equal to 1.   By now subtracting suitable multiples of the first row (i.e., by premultiplying by suitable transvections), we can obtain a matrix with 1 in the first entry and zeros elsewhere in the first column.   The minor of the 1, 1 entry of the resulting matrix is in $S(K, n-1)$, and the above procedure can be repeated until we obtain a matrix with 1's down the main diagonal and zeros beneath it.   A similar procedure then allows us to replace each entry above the diagonal by a zero and the task is completed.   It follows that the product of the above transvections is A^{-1} and the theorem is proved since A^{-1} is arbitrary in $S(K, n)$.

Before proceeding to the main theorem of this section, a study of the exceptional cases will be instructive.   When K is the field of three elements, a direct computation reveals that in $L(K, 2)$, $-I_2$ has six square roots which generate a subgroup of order 8.   It follows that this subgroup must be isomorphic to the quaternion group Q_8, and must be normal in $L(K, 2)$, since $-I_2$ is central in $L(K, 2)$.   Given this information, the details of the proof of the following proposition are fairly easy and will be left to the reader.

III.8.d. Proposition.   *If K is the field of 2 elements, $L(K, 2)$ coincides with $S(K, 2)$ and is isomorphic to the symmetric group S_3.   If K is the field of three elements, the center Z of $L(K, 2)$ consists of the elements $\pm I_2$; $L(K, 2)$ is a split extension of the form $[Q_8]S_3$, $L(K, 2)/Z$ is isomorphic to the symmetric group S_4, $S(K, 2)$ has the form $[Q_8]C_3$, and $P(K, 2)$ is isomorphic to the alternating group A_4.*

The main theorem is as follows.

III.8.e. Theorem.   *Let H be a non-central normal subgroup of $S(K, n)$; if either $n > 2$, or $n = 2$ with $|K| > 3$, then $H = S(K, n)$.*

Proof for the case $n = 2$, $|K| > 3$.   Since H contains a non-central element A, a basis may be chosen for the vector space V in which $L(K, n)$ acts, so that relative to this basis A is described by the matrix $\begin{pmatrix} 0 & 1 \\ -1 & m \end{pmatrix}$.   This basis will be fixed for the rest of the proof and we write $A = \begin{pmatrix} 0 & 1 \\ -1 & m \end{pmatrix}$.   Then for each non-zero $a \in K$, H also contains the commutator

$$\left[\begin{pmatrix} 0 & 1 \\ -1 & m \end{pmatrix}^{-1}, \begin{pmatrix} 1 & -a \\ 0 & 1 \end{pmatrix} \right] = \begin{pmatrix} 1 & -a \\ -a & 1+a^2 \end{pmatrix}.$$

It follows that H contains the conjugate of $\begin{pmatrix} 1 & -a^2 \\ -a^2 & 1+a^4 \end{pmatrix}$ by $\begin{pmatrix} a^{-1} & -a^{-1} \\ 0 & a \end{pmatrix}$ which is $\begin{pmatrix} 0 & 1 \\ -1 & 2+a^4 \end{pmatrix}$.   Finally for $h \neq 0$, $h \in K$, H contains

$$\begin{pmatrix} 1 & a^4-b^4 \\ 0 & 1 \end{pmatrix} = \begin{pmatrix} 0 & 1 \\ -1 & 2+a^4 \end{pmatrix}^{-1} \begin{pmatrix} 0 & 1 \\ -1 & 2+b^4 \end{pmatrix}.$$

Now K has two distinct non-zero fourth powers $a^4 \neq b^4$ except when $|K| = 5$. When $|K| = 5$, H contains $\begin{pmatrix} 0 & 1 \\ -1 & 3 \end{pmatrix}$ since $3 = 2 + 1^4$, and also $\begin{pmatrix} 0 & 1 \\ -1 & 1 \end{pmatrix}$ which is the conjugate of $\left[\begin{pmatrix} 0 & 1 \\ -1 & m \end{pmatrix}^{-1}, \begin{pmatrix} 1 & -2 \\ 0 & 1 \end{pmatrix} \right]$ by $\begin{pmatrix} 2 & -1 \\ -2 & -1 \end{pmatrix}$. Thus in this case H contains

$$\begin{pmatrix} 1 & 2 \\ 0 & 1 \end{pmatrix} = \begin{pmatrix} 0 & 1 \\ -1 & 3 \end{pmatrix}^{-1} \begin{pmatrix} 0 & 1 \\ -1 & 1 \end{pmatrix}.$$

In either case we see that H contains a transvection $\begin{pmatrix} 1 & q \\ 0 & 1 \end{pmatrix}$ with $q \neq 0$. It follows from (ix) and III.8.c that the normal closure of H in $L(K, 2)$ is $S(K, 2)$.

We shall now show that $H = S(K, 2)$. We already have seen that H contains a transvection $\begin{pmatrix} 1 & q \\ 0 & 1 \end{pmatrix}$ for some $q \neq 0$. Then H contains $\begin{pmatrix} 1 & qk^2 \\ 0 & 1 \end{pmatrix}$ for each $k \in K$ since $\begin{pmatrix} 1 & qk^2 \\ 0 & 1 \end{pmatrix}$ is the conjugate of $\begin{pmatrix} 1 & q \\ 0 & 1 \end{pmatrix}$ by $\begin{pmatrix} k^{-1} & 0 \\ 0 & k \end{pmatrix}$. It follows that H also contains

$$\begin{pmatrix} 1 & q(k^2 - t^2) \\ 0 & 1 \end{pmatrix} = \begin{pmatrix} 1 & qk^2 \\ 0 & 1 \end{pmatrix} \begin{pmatrix} 1 & qt^2 \\ 0 & 1 \end{pmatrix}^{-1}$$

for all $k, t \in K$.

If $x \in K$ and the characteristic of K is not 2, let $k = (q^{-1}x + 1)/2$ and let $t = (q^{-1}x - 1)/2$; since $x = q(k^2 - t^2)$, it follows from the above that H contains $\begin{pmatrix} 1 & x \\ 0 & 1 \end{pmatrix}$. If the characteristic of K is 2, choose $t \in K$, $t \neq 0, 1$ and let $v = q(q^{-2} + q^{-2}t^{-2})$ and $w = qt^2$; then v and w are not zero and $qvw = q + w$. Since H contains $\begin{pmatrix} 1 & q(k^2 - t^2) \\ 0 & 1 \end{pmatrix}$ for all $k, t \in K$, it follows that H contains $\begin{pmatrix} 1 & v \\ 0 & 1 \end{pmatrix}$ and $\begin{pmatrix} 1 & w \\ 0 & 1 \end{pmatrix}$. Since the conjugate of $\begin{pmatrix} 1 & x \\ 0 & 1 \end{pmatrix}$ by $\begin{pmatrix} 0 & 1 \\ -1 & 0 \end{pmatrix}$ is $\begin{pmatrix} 1 & 0 \\ -x & 1 \end{pmatrix}$, it follows that H contains $\begin{pmatrix} 1 & 0 \\ -q & 1 \end{pmatrix}$, $\begin{pmatrix} 1 & v \\ 0 & 1 \end{pmatrix}$, $\begin{pmatrix} 1 & 0 \\ -w & 1 \end{pmatrix}$ and their product written in order, which is $\begin{pmatrix} 1 - vw & v \\ 0 & 1 - vq \end{pmatrix}$ (for $qvw - q - w = 0$). Finally, for all $y \in K$, H

contains

$$\left[\begin{pmatrix} 1-vq & v \\ 0 & 1-vw \end{pmatrix}, \begin{pmatrix} 1 & -y \\ 0 & 1 \end{pmatrix}\right]$$

which is $\begin{pmatrix} 1 & ((1-vw)^2-1)y \\ 0 & 1 \end{pmatrix}$.   Since $(1-vw)^2-1 \neq 0$, $((1-vw)^2-1)y$ ranges over K as y does.   Hence, also when the characteristic of K is 2, H contains all $\begin{pmatrix} 1 & x \\ 0 & 1 \end{pmatrix}$ with $x \in K$.

Since the determinant is a multiplicative function, each $X \in L(K, 2)$ has the form DS with $S \in S(K, 2)$ and $D = \begin{pmatrix} d & 0 \\ 0 & 1 \end{pmatrix}$.   Since

$$\begin{pmatrix} d & 0 \\ 0 & 1 \end{pmatrix}\begin{pmatrix} 1 & q \\ 0 & 1 \end{pmatrix}\begin{pmatrix} d^{-1} & 0 \\ 0 & 1 \end{pmatrix} = \begin{pmatrix} 1 & dq \\ 0 & 1 \end{pmatrix},$$

it follows that H contains all the conjugates of $\begin{pmatrix} 1 & q \\ 0 & 1 \end{pmatrix}$ in $L(K, 2)$.

Hence H contains the normal closure in $L(K, 2)$ of $\begin{pmatrix} 1 & q \\ 0 & 1 \end{pmatrix}$; but this normal closure is normal in $L(K, 2)$ and hence is all of $S(K, 2)$ by the first part of the proof.   This completes the proof of the theorem when $n = 2$.

Proof for the case $n > 2$.   In view of (ix) and III.8.c, it is only necessary to show that H contains a transvection, not the identity. Now H has a non-central element T; by (iii), V is a direct sum of subspaces U (of dimension r) and W so that for appropriate choice of basis of U, the matrix T_r of T restricted to U has bottom row $a, b \cdots r$ with $a \neq 0$, and has 1's directly above the diagonal.   Then the inverse of T_r has top row $-ba^{-1} - ca^{-1} \cdots - ra^{-1}a^{-1}$ and has 1's directly below the diagonal.   A direct verification then shows that if $r > 2$,

the commutator $[T_r, B_{r1}(-1)]$ is $\begin{pmatrix} 1 & a^{-1} & 0 & \cdots & 0 & 0 \\ 0 & 1 & 0 & \cdots & 0 & 0 \\ \vdots & \vdots & & & \vdots & \vdots \\ -1 & 0 & 0 & \cdots & 0 & 1 \end{pmatrix}$ and that

$[[B_{r1}(-1), T_r], B_{r1}(-1)] = B_{r2}(a^{-1})$ is a transvection of H.

If $r = 2$ there is an element of $S(K, 2)$ acting on U which does not commute with T_r.   The commutator of this element with T_r is therefore a non-identity element of H (if it is $-I_2$, then the commutator

of $\begin{pmatrix} -1 & 0 & 0 \\ 0 & 1 & 0 \\ 0 & 0 & -1 \end{pmatrix}$ with $\begin{pmatrix} 1 & 1 & 0 \\ 0 & 1 & 0 \\ 0 & 0 & 1 \end{pmatrix}$ is already a transvection) whose restriction to U (with the above exception) has the form $\begin{pmatrix} 0 & 1 \\ -1 & b \end{pmatrix}$ for appropriate choice of basis of U and whose restriction to W is the identity. Then let B^{-1} denote the matrix whose upper left corner is $\begin{pmatrix} 0 & 1 \\ -1 & b \end{pmatrix}$ and whose only other non-zero entries are 1's down the diagonal. A direct verification shows that $[[B_{13}(-1), B], B_{12}(-1)] = B_{13}(1)$ is a non-identity transvection of H. This proves the theorem for $n > 2$.

III.8.f. Corollary. *If either $n > 2$ or $n = 2$ with $|K| > 3$, the projective unimodular group $P(K, n)$ is simple.*

We conclude this section by pointing out that each transvection belongs to a stability group of automorphisms of a group. The notion of stability group is defined as follows.

III.8.g. Definition. Let H be a normal subgroup of a group G, and let S be the set of automorphisms σ of G so that $g\sigma g^{-1}$ is in H for $g \in G$ and $g\sigma = g$ for $g \in H$. It is easy to check that S is a group; it is called the **stability group** of G with respect to H.

III.8.h. Example. To each transvection T acting in an n-dimensional space V there is an $(n-1)$-dimensional subspace W so that $vT - v$ is in W for $v \in V$ and is 0 for $v \in W$; thus T is in the stability group of V with respect to W.

We leave the main topic of this section and give a theorem on stability groups which is of interest.

III.8.i. Theorem. *Every stability group is abelian.*

Proof. Let S be the stability group of a group G with respect to a normal subgroup H, and let σ, τ be in S. We first show that if $g \in G$ and $g\sigma = hg$, then h is in the center of H. Indeed, if $k \in H$, then $[k, g]\sigma = [k, g]$ since $[k, g] \in H$; on the other hand, $[k, g]\sigma = (k^{-1}g^{-1}kg)\sigma$

$= k^{-1}(hg)^{-1}k(hg) = [k, hg]$. By an elementary formula on commutators (see VI.1.k below), $[k, hg] = [k, g][k, h]^g$. Comparison of the two expressions for $[k, g]\sigma$ shows $[k, h]^g$ and hence $[k, h]$ is 1; since k was arbitrary in H, it follows that h is in the center of H as was to be shown.

Now suppose that $g\tau = fg$ with f in the center of H; then $g(\sigma\tau) = (hg)\tau$ $= hfg$ and $g(\tau\sigma) = fhg$. Thus $g\sigma\tau = g\tau\sigma$ and hence $\sigma\tau = \tau\sigma$ so that S is abelian, as was to be shown.

Chapter IV

SYLOW THEOREMS AND
GENERALIZATIONS

In this chapter, order and index play the significant role. The Norwegian mathematician Sylow first pointed out the following basic facts for finite groups: If p^n is the highest power of a prime p dividing the order of a finite group G, then

(1) *G has a subgroup of order p^m for each $m \leq n$.*

(2) *Any two subgroups of G of order p^n are conjugate in G.*

(3) *Any p-subgroup of G is contained in a subgroup of order p^n.*

(4) *The number of subgroups of order p^n is 1 mod p.*

These theorems and their generalizations to certain classes of infinite groups are given here.

The transfer is introduced and is used in proving theorems of Burnside, Grün, and Frobenius. These theorems give conditions that imply the existence of normal subgroups, and consequently imply the non-existence of simple groups of certain orders. Finally some conditions are given under which the existence of a normal subgroup implies that the group is a split extension. Included here are theorems of Schur and Gaschütz and also the theorem of complete reducibility of Maschke.

1. Sylow theory

IV.1.a. Definitions. Let Π be a non-empty set of primes. A *Π-number* is a natural number each of whose prime factors is in Π.

124

A **Π-element** of a group is an element whose order is a Π-number. A **Π-subgroup** of a group is a subgroup, each of whose elements is a Π-element, and a **Π-group** is a group which is a Π-subgroup of itself. The **Π-share** of a natural number n is the largest Π-number dividing n.

The set consisting of the single prime p will also be denoted by p in expressions such as p-number, p-element, p-subgroup, p-group (cf. Definition II.1.c). The term p-share was already used in Section III.5.

For any set of primes Π, the number 1 is a Π-number, the element 1 is a Π-element, and the subgroup 1 is a Π-subgroup.

The set of all the primes not in Π will be denoted by Π'; in particular, p' will denote the set of all primes other than p in expressions such as p'-element, p'-subgroup, p'-group.

IV.1.b. Definition. If Π is a set of primes, a **Sylow Π-subgroup** of a group G is a Π-subgroup of G not properly contained in any Π-subgroup of G.

The following are easy consequences of the definition.

(i) *If G contains no Π-element other than 1, then 1 is the only Sylow Π-subgroup of G.*

(ii) *Any conjugate of a Sylow Π-subgroup is a Sylow Π-subgroup.*

(iii) *For a fixed set of primes Π, subgroups, homomorphic images, and ascending unions of Π-subgroups are Π-subgroups; hence any Π-subgroup of a group is contained in a Sylow Π-subgroup.*

(iv) *The cardinality of the set of Sylow Π-subgroups of a subgroup H of a group G is bounded by the cardinality of the set of Sylow Π-subgroups of G.*

(v) *If K is a normal subgroup of a group G and if both K and G/K are Π-groups for some set of primes Π, then G is also a Π-group.*

As a consequence of (v) we have the following proposition.

IV.1.c. Proposition. *If Π is a set of primes, a normal Π-subgroup of a group G is in every Sylow Π-subgroup of G; if G has a normal Sylow Π-subgroup P, then P contains every Π-element and every Π-subgroup of G and is the only Sylow Π-subgroup of G.*

From IV.1.c we can readily deduce the following.

IV.1.d. Proposition. *A Sylow Π-subgroup is weakly closed in its normalizer. The normalizer of a Sylow Π-subgroup is its own normalizer.*

We have already seen in (iii) that any Π-subgroup of a group is contained in a Sylow Π-subgroup. We now give a theorem from which we get the order of some of the Sylow p-subgroups of a finite group.

IV.1.e. Theorem (Sylow). *If p is a prime and p^m is the p-share of the order of a finite group G, then G has a subgroup of order p^m.*

Proof. For $|G| = 1$ or for $m = 0$, the theorem is trivially true. We proceed by induction on $|G|$, assuming that $m > 0$ and that the theorem is true for all groups whose orders are less than $|G|$. Then, if G has a proper subgroup of index prime to p, this subgroup has, by the induction hypothesis, a subgroup of order p^m. On the other hand, if p divides the index in G of each proper subgroup, then by the class equation of III.1.q, p divides $|\mathfrak{Z}(G)|$. It follows that $\mathfrak{Z}(G)$ contains an element b of order p. But b is central in G. By the induction assumption, $G/(b)$ has a subgroup of order p^{m-1} whose complete inverse image has order p^m, and the theorem is proved.

Since the order of a subgroup divides the order of the group and a group of order p^m, $m > 0$, has an element of order p, we have the following corollaries of IV.1.e.

IV.1.f. Corollary *(Cauchy).* *A finite group has a non-trivial p-element for every prime p dividing the group order.*

IV.1.g. Corollary. *The order of a finite group is a p-number (Π-number) if and only if the group is a p-group (Π-group).*

IV.1.h. Corollary. *If p is a prime and p^m the p-share of the order of a finite group G, then a subgroup of order p^m is a Sylow p-subgroup of G.*

We shall now give a generalization of a theorem of Sylow from which we see immediately that each Sylow p-subgroup of a finite group has order equal to the p-share of the order of the group.   This theorem does not require the hypothesis that the group be finite but merely that the normalizer of a Sylow p-subgroup has finite index or equivalently (in view of III.1.p) that the group has a finite class of Sylow p-subgroups.

IV.1.i. Theorem. *Let p be a prime and P a Sylow p-subgroup whose normalizer has finite index k in the group G.   Then k is of the form $mp + 1$ for some integer m and the k conjugates of P are all the Sylow p-subgroups of G.*

Proof. Let R denote any Sylow p-subgroup of G and let N denote the normalizer of P.   For $x \in G$ the number of right cosets of N in G which are contained in the double coset NxR is equal to

$$|R:(x^{-1}Nx \cap R)|$$

by III.1.z.   If R is P, this number is a positive power of p (cf. IV.1.d and III.1.z) except when x is in N, in which case the double coset is N itself.   Since G is the disjoint union of the double cosets of N and P, it follows that k has the form $mp + 1$ as was asserted in the theorem. If R is not P, then $|R:x^{-1}Nx \cap R|$ is a positive power of p for all x unless $R \le x^{-1}Nx$ (which means, since R is a Sylow p-subgroup, R is a conjugate of P (cf. IV.1.c and (ii))).   Thus if R is not a conjugate of P, the number k of right cosets of N in G (since G is the disjoint union of the double cosets of N with R) is a positive power of p. But this is contrary to what was just shown.   We conclude that each Sylow p-subgroup of G is a conjugate of P and the theorem is proved.

At this point we see that we have the four facts discovered by Sylow for finite groups mentioned in the introduction about existence, conjugacy, imbedding, and counting.   In view of our definition, the existence of Sylow Π-subgroups and the embedding of a given Π-subgroup in a Sylow Π-subgroup for any set of primes Π are immediate from (iii).   The facts that the Sylow p-subgroups of a finite group G all have orders equal to the p-share of $|G|$, and that they comprise one conjugate class, are the more difficult to prove.   Similar facts will be proved in Chapter VII for finite solvable groups for arbitrary sets of primes.

2. Applications of Sylow theory

We return to Theorem IV.1.i and deduce some important consequences from it.

IV.2.a. Proposition. *Let G be a group with a finite number of Sylow p-subgroups.   If N is the normalizer of one of these Sylow subgroups S, and if M is a subgroup containing N, then $M = \mathfrak{N}(M)$.*

Proof. If $n \in \mathfrak{N}(M)$, then $n^{-1}Sn \le M$, and since all Sylow p-subgroups are conjugate in M, $n^{-1}Sn = m^{-1}Sm$ for some $m \in M$.   Consequently, $mn^{-1} \in N \le M$, and therefore $n \in M$, and $\mathfrak{N}(M) = M$, as was to be shown.

In the sequel it will often be convenient to speak of a subgroup M as **self-normalizing** if $M = \mathfrak{N}(M)$.

IV.2.b. Theorem (*Wielandt*). *If G is a finite group with $\Phi(G) \ge G'$ then G has exactly one Sylow p-subgroup for each prime p and G is the direct product of its non-trivial Sylow p-subgroups.*

Proof. Let P be a Sylow p-subgroup for some prime p.   If $\mathfrak{N}(P) \ne G$, let M be a maximal subgroup of G containing $\mathfrak{N}(P)$.   Then $M \ge \Phi(G) \ge G'$, and hence M is normal in G by III.1.e.   But this is a contradiction since $M = \mathfrak{N}(M)$ by IV.2.a.   We conclude that $\mathfrak{N}(P) = G$, and hence that G has exactly one Sylow p-subgroup by IV.1.c.   Since this is true for each prime p, it follows readily that G is the direct product of its non-trivial Sylow p-subgroups, as the theorem asserts.

The notion of intravariance will be convenient before the next theorem.

IV.2.c. Definition. A subgroup H of a group G is **intravariant in G** if each automorphism of G maps H onto a conjugate of H.

IV.2.d. Example. If p is a prime and G a finite group, then by IV.1.i each Sylow p-subgroup of G is intravariant in G.

The following proposition is an easy consequence of the definition.

IV.2.e. Proposition. *If M is a normal subgroup of a group G and H is intravariant in M, then $G = M\mathfrak{N}(H)$.*

Proof. If $g \in G$, then for appropriate $m \in M$, $H^g = H^m$. It follows that $gm^{-1} \in \mathfrak{N}(H)$ and hence that $g \in M\mathfrak{N}(H)$. Thus $G = M\mathfrak{N}(H)$ and the proof is complete.

The following proposition follows immediately from IV.1.i and IV.2.e.

IV.2.f. Proposition. *Let G be a group with a normal subgroup K which has only finitely many Sylow p-subgroups for some prime p. Then $G = K\mathfrak{N}(P)$ for any Sylow p-subgroup P of K.*

IV.2.g. Theorem (*Frattini*). *Each Sylow p-subgroup of the Frattini subgroup $\Phi(G)$ of a finite group G is normal in G, and hence $\Phi(G)$ is the direct product of its non-trivial Sylow p-subgroups.*

Proof. Let P be a Sylow p-subgroup of $\Phi(G)$ for some prime p. Then by IV.2.f, $G = \Phi(G)\mathfrak{N}(P)$, and hence, by the definition of $\Phi(G)$, $G = \mathfrak{N}(P)$. Thus $P \lhd G$ and the theorem follows.

We have seen that the index of a Sylow p-subgroup of a finite group is prime to its order. We single out this property to give another definition.

IV.2.h. Definition. If Π is a set of primes, a **Hall Π-subgroup** of a group G (after Philip Hall) is a Sylow Π-subgroup whose index in G is a Π'-number.

IV.2.i. Example. The Sylow p-subgroups of a finite group are Hall p-subgroups.

The proof of the following proposition is direct and is left for the reader.

IV.2.j. Proposition. *Let Π be a set of primes and let K be a normal Π-subgroup of a group G; then G has a Hall Π-subgroup if and only if G/K has.*

We now give some general facts which will be needed in connection with the further study of Hall Π-subgroups.

IV.2.k. Proposition. *If H and K are subgroups of a group G with $H < K$, then $|G:H| = |G:K|\,|K:H|$.*

The proof is direct and is left to the reader.

IV.2.l. Proposition. *If H and K are subgroups of a group G of index h and k, respectively, with h and k relatively prime, then the index of $H \cap K$ in G is hk.*

Proof. It was seen in the argument leading to I.2.k that a right coset of $H \cap K$ is the intersection of a right coset of H with a right coset of K. Thus the index of $H \cap K$ in G is not greater than hk. On the other hand, both h and k divide $|G:H \cap K|$ by IV.2.k, and hence, since h and k are relatively prime, the index of $H \cap K$ in G is hk as was to be shown.

IV.2.m. Proposition. *If H is a subgroup of finite index h in the Π-group G, then h is a Π-number.*

Proof. In view of III.1.u, G has a normal subgroup K which is contained in H and of finite index in G. By (iii), G/K is a finite Π-group; hence $|G:H|$ which is $|G/K:H/K|$ is a Π-number by IV.1.g.

The proof of the next proposition is similar to that of IV.2.m and is left for an exercise.

IV.2.n. Proposition. *If for some prime p a group has a Sylow p-subgroup of finite index n, then n is prime to p.*

IV.2.o. Proposition. *Let G be a periodic group with no elements other than 1 of order less than the fixed prime p, and let H be a subgroup of index p in G. Then H contains all the p'-elements of G and is normal in G.*

Proof. It is clear that H contains all the p'-elements of G; for a p'-element is both of order p' and of order p (mod H) since $|G:H| = p$. Then by III.l.u, G has a normal subgroup K contained in H and of finite index in G. Without loss of generality we may assume that K also contains all the p'-elements of G. Hence, G/K is a finite p-group so that H/K is normal in G/K by the normalizer condition in G/K. Then H is normal in G and the proposition is proved.

The proofs of the following are obvious.

IV.2.p. Proposition. *A group is periodic if it has a periodic subgroup of finite index.*

IV.2.q. Proposition. *For some prime p let P be a Sylow p-subgroup of a group G which has only one conjugate class of Sylow p-subgroups. If Q is the subgroup of G generated by the p'-elements, then $G = QP$.*

IV.2.r. Exercise. *Let p be a prime and let H be a subgroup of the group G containing a Sylow p-subgroup of G; then all the Sylow p-subgroups of H are Sylow p-subgroups of G provided that either H or G has only one conjugate class of Sylow p-subgroups.*

In order to simplify the writing later on we introduce the following terminology.

IV.2.s. Definition. If Π is a set of primes, a group **satisfies the Sylow Π-theorem** if it has only one conjugate class of Sylow Π-subgroups and these are Hall Π-subgroups.

The content of Theorems IV.1.e and IV.1.i can then be expressed as follows.

IV.2.t. Theorem. *If p is a prime and P a Sylow p-subgroup whose normalizer has finite index n in the group G, then G satisfies the Sylow p-theorem and $n \equiv 1 \bmod p$.*

The following facts are easy consequences of Definition IV.2.s.

(i) *A group G satisfies the Sylow Π-theorem if and only if it has a Hall Π-subgroup which contains some conjugate of each Π-subgroup of G.*

(ii) *If K is a normal Π-subgroup of a group G, then G/K satisfies the Sylow Π-theorem if and only if G does.*

We conclude this section on Sylow theory with a theorem which has many applications in the sequel. It is essentially a reformulation of a theorem of Burnside.

IV.2.u. Theorem. *If for some prime p, a p-subgroup A of a finite group G is in two Sylow p-subgroups P and R of G, A normal in P but not normal in R, then G has a p-subgroup H contained in P and containing A such that $\mathfrak{N}(H)$ has a p'-element which does not centralize H and a Sylow p-subgroup in which A is normal. Furthermore, if H_1 is any subgroup of P so that $|H_1| > |H|$, and K is any p-subgroup of G containing H_1, then A is normal in K.*

Proof. Let H be of maximal order under the condition that it is the intersection of $\mathfrak{N}(A)$ with a Sylow p-subgroup S of G in which A is not normal. Since $P \leq \mathfrak{N}(A)$, the Sylow p-subgroups of $\mathfrak{N}(A)$ are Sylow in G, and hence H is contained in a Sylow p-subgroup of G in which A is normal, which without loss of generality (i.e., by taking a conjugate of H in $\mathfrak{N}(A)$) may be taken to be P.

If M denotes $\mathfrak{N}(H)$, we shall first show that M (in place of G) and A satisfy the hypothesis of the theorem. Indeed, by the normalizer condition in P, $H < M \cap P \le \mathfrak{N}(A)$; and by the maximality of H it follows that A is normal in every Sylow p-subgroup of G and hence of M which contains $M \cap P$.

Furthermore, by the normalizer condition in S, $H < M \cap S$; and by the maximality of H, $M \cap S \nleq \mathfrak{N}(A)$, so that there is a Sylow p-subgroup of M containing H in which A is not normal.

Now if K is the subgroup generated by the p'-elements of M, $M = KP_1$, where P_1 is a Sylow p-subgroup of M in which A is normal. But if all the p'-elements of M centralize H, they centralize A, and A would be normal in $M = KP_1$ contrary to what was just shown. Thus $M = \mathfrak{N}(H)$ must have a p'-element which does not centralize A, as the theorem asserts.

To prove the last statement of the theorem, we suppose that A is not normal in K, so that A is not normal in a Sylow p-subgroup T of G. Then $T \cap P \ge H_1$ with $|H_1| > |H|$ and we have a contradiction to the maximality in the choice of H.

The reader will find it instructive to extend the first statement of IV.2.u to the case of an infinite periodic group with a finite number of Sylow p-subgroups each satisfying the normalizer condition.

3. The transfer

The object of this section is to give a routine procedure for getting an abelian homomorphic image (possibly trivial) of a group. We introduce a map, the transfer, from the group onto an abelian homomorphic image of a given subgroup; this map is a homomorphism and has proved to be of special interest when the subgroup is a Hall p-subgroup.

We begin with the definition of transversal, a notion already encountered in the proof of III.5.k.

IV.3.a. Definition.   If H is a subgroup of a group G, a **right transversal** of H in G is a set of elements, one from each right coset of H in G and a **left transversal** is a set of elements, one from each left coset of H in G.

We list some easy consequences of the definition.

(i) *If T is a right transversal of a subgroup H of a group G, then each $g \in G$ has a unique expression of the form ht with $h \in H$, $t \in T$; thus $G = HT$, and $|H \cap T| = 1$.*

(ii) *T is a right transversal of H in G if and only if for each $g \in G$, Tg is also a right transversal of H in G.*

(iii) *Let T be a right transversal of a subgroup H of a group G, and suppose that T is a subsemigroup; then T is a subgroup.   If further H is normal in G, then G is a split extension $[H]T$.*

(iv) *If G is a split extension $[H]S$, then S is a right transversal of H in G.*

IV.3.b. Definitions.   If T is a right transversal of a subgroup H of a group G, the **representative map** τ from G onto T and the **projection map** η from G onto H are defined by the equation $g = (g\eta)(g\tau)$ for $g \in G$, with $g\eta \in H$, $g\tau \in T$.

(v) *The map τ has the property that $(hg)\tau = g\tau$ for $h \in H$, $g \in G$.*

(vi) *The map η has the property that $(hg)\eta = h(g\eta)$ for $h \in H$, $g \in G$.*

Definitions IV.3.b and the statements of (i) through (vi) have obvious analogues when T is a left transversal.

IV.3.c. Definition.   Let $T = \{t_1, \cdots, t_n\}$ be a right transversal of a subgroup H of finite index n in a group G, let η be the projection map defined by H and T, and let $\bar{H}$ be a subgroup of H containing the derived group H'; then the **transfer ϕ of G into $H/\bar{H}$** is the map from G into $H/\bar{H}$ defined by the equation $g\phi = \prod_{i=1}^{n} (t_i g)\eta \, \bar{H}$ for $g \in G$. If $\bar{H} = 1$, we say that ϕ is the transfer of G into H.

The importance of the transfer stems from the following theorem.

IV.3.d. Theorem.   *If H is a subgroup of finite index n in the group G and $\bar{H}$ is a subgroup of H containing H', then the transfer ϕ from G into $H/\bar{H}$ is a homomorphism which is independent of the right transversal T of H in G.*

Proof.   We let T and T^* be right transversals of H in G, consisting of elements t_i and t_i^*, respectively, $i = 1, 2, \cdots, n$, and let τ, τ^* and η, η^* be the corresponding representation and projection maps.   Then to show that ϕ is a homomorphism we observe first that for fixed g, $k \in G$, $t_i g k = (t_i g)\eta (t_i g)\tau k = (t_i g)\eta \, t_{i,g} k$ with $t_{i,g} = (t_i g)\tau$.   Then $(t_i g k)\eta = (t_i g)\eta (t_{i,g} k)\eta$.   But Tg is a transversal of H in G and hence the set of $t_{i,g}$ is T.   Then since $H/\bar{H}$ is abelian,

$$\prod_{i=1}^{n} (t_i g k)\eta \, \bar{H} = \prod_{i=1}^{n} (t_i g)\eta (t_{i,g} k)\eta \, \bar{H} = \left(\prod_{i=1}^{n} (t_i g)\eta \, \bar{H}\right) \left(\prod_{i=1}^{n} (t_i k)\eta \bar{H}\right),$$

and hence ϕ is a homomorphism.

To show that ϕ is independent of T we define $h_i \in H$ for $i = 1, 2, \cdots, n$ by the equations $t_i^* = h_i t_i$.   Then $t_i g = h_i^{-1} t_i^* g$ and $(t_i g)\tau = (t_i^*)\tau = h_{i(g)}^{-1}(t_i^* g)\tau^*$ with $i(g)$ defined by the relation $t_{i(g)} = (t_i^* g)\tau$.   It follows that $(t_i g)\eta = (h_i^{-1} t_i^* g)((t_i^* g)\tau^*)^{-1} h_{i(g)} = h_i^{-1}(t_i^* g)\eta^* h_{i(g)}$;   and then

$$\prod_{i=1}^{n} (t_i g)\eta \, \bar{H} = \prod_{i=1}^{n} h_i^{-1}(t_i^* g)\eta^* h_{i(g)} \bar{H}$$
$$= \left(\prod_{i=1}^{n} (t_i^* g)\eta^* \bar{H}\right)\left(\prod_{i=1}^{n} h_i^{-1} h_{i(g)} \bar{H}\right).$$

But the set of $t_{i(g)}$ is the set of t_i so that the set of $h_{i(g)}$ is the set of h_i and hence the second parenthesis on the right of the last equation is 1. Thus the transfer is the same whether defined by T or by T^*.   This proves the theorem.

To compute $g\phi$ for a particular g, it is convenient to choose a right transversal as follows.   Let γ_g be the map defined on the right cosets of H by the equation $(Hx)\gamma_g = Hxg$.   Then γ_g is a permutation on this set of cosets.   From each orbit C_i, $i = 1, \cdots, j$, we pick any coset Hx_i, and if m_i is the number of cosets in C_i, let $x_i, x_i g, \cdots, x_i g^{m_i - 1}$, $i = 1, \cdots, j$ be the elements of T.   Then $(x_i g^r)\eta = 1$ if $r < m_i$ and $(x_i g^{m_i})\eta = (g^{m_i})^{x_i - 1}$ so that we have the following.

(vii) $g\phi = \prod_{i=1}^{j} (g^{m_i})^{x_i - 1} \bar{H}$.

Thus $g\phi$ is the product of conjugates of powers of g, which are in H. Furthermore, each exponent m_i is a divisor of the order of g since m_i is the smallest r such that $(g^{mr})^{x_i - 1}$ is in H.

Since $G\phi$ is abelian, the kernel of ϕ contains G'; hence a group has non-trivial transfers only if $G \neq G'$ and, in particular, only if, when G has composite order, G is not simple.

The proof of the following proposition by means of (vii) is an instructive exercise for the reader.

IV.3.e. Proposition. *Let H be a subgroup of finite index n in the abelian group G, let ϕ be the transfer of G into H, and let μ_n be the endomorphism defined by the equation $g\mu_n = g^n$ for $g \in G$; then $\phi = \mu_n$.*

4. Two theorems on transfer

We devote this section to two important theorems on transfer in the case where H is a Hall p-subgroup and to some of their consequences.

IV.4.a. Theorem. *Let p be a prime and P a Hall p-subgroup of index n in the group G; let Q be the subgroup of G generated by the p'-elements, let $\bar{P} = P \cap G'$, and let ϕ be the transfer from G into $P/\bar{P}$. Then the kernel K of ϕ is $Q\bar{P}$, and $G\phi = P\phi = P/\bar{P}$. Moreover, the restriction of ϕ to P can be expressed as the product $\pi\mu_n$, where π is the canonic homomorphism of P onto $P/\bar{P}$ and μ_n the automorphism of $P/\bar{P}$ defined by the equation $(g\bar{P})\mu_n = g^n\bar{P}$.*

Proof. The image of G under ϕ is an abelian p-group so that its kernel K contains Q, G', and hence $\bar{P}$. By IV.2.q, $G = QP$ so that straightaway we have $G\phi = P\phi$. Using the notation of (vii) of Section IV.3, we find for arbitrary g in G that $g\phi = \prod_{i=1}^{j} (g^{m_i})^{x_i^{-1}}\bar{P}$, with $(g^{m_i})^{x_i^{-1}} \in P$. If in addition $g \in P$, then $[g^{m_i}, x_i^{-1}] \in G' \cap P = \bar{P}$. Hence (since $g^{m_i}[g^{m_i}, x_i^{-1}] = (g^{m_i})^{x_i^{-1}}$) for g in P, the transfer is $g\phi = \prod_{i=1}^{j} g^{m_i}\bar{P} = g^n\bar{P}$. It follows at once that ϕ restricted to P is $\pi\mu_n$; for $g\pi\mu_n = (g\bar{P})\mu_n = g^n\bar{P}$. Since n is prime to p, $(P/\bar{P})\mu_n = P/\bar{P}$ and $P\phi = P/\bar{P}$.

To compute the kernel of ϕ, we proceed as follows. If $g \in K$, then $g = g_1 g_2$ for $g_1 \in Q$, $g_2 \in P$ so that $g\phi = g_2\phi = g_2^n\bar{P}$. But n is prime to p and $P/\bar{P}$ is a p-group, so the equality $g_2\phi = 1$ gives $g_2 \in \bar{P}$. Hence $g \in Q\bar{P}$, $K \le Q\bar{P}$ and hence $K = Q\bar{P}$, as required. This completes the proof of the theorem.

Using the notation of IV.4.a, we see that if θ is a homomorphism of G onto an abelian p-group, then θ is factored by ϕ; that is, there is a homomorphism ψ so that $\theta = \phi\psi$. This follows from the fact that the kernel of θ must contain Q, $\bar{P}$ and hence K. Thus $P\phi$ is the maximal abelian p-factor group of G.

IV.4.b. Theorem. *Let P be a Hall p-subgroup of the group G for some prime p; if Q is a central subgroup of P which is weakly closed in P, and if N is the normalizer of Q, then $G' \cap P = N' \cap P$.*

Proof. Since $G' \cap P \geq N' \cap P$, we need only show that $N' \cap P \geq G' \cap P$. Accordingly, we assume to the contrary that there is an element g of minimal order in $G' \cap P$, $g \notin N' \cap P$; thus if the pth power of a conjugate of g, $(g^p)^x$, is in P, then it is also in N'.

Now let $\bar{P} = N' \cap P$, let n be the index of P in N, so that n is prime to p, and let ϕ denote the transfer from N into $P/\bar{P}$, θ the transfer from G into $P/\bar{P}$. We shall show that $\bar{P} = g\theta = g\phi = g^n\bar{P} \neq \bar{P}$ and by this contradiction the theorem will be proved.

The first equation $\bar{P} = g\theta$ follows from the fact that $g \in G'$. The second equation follows from the computation below. We first recall from (vii) of Section IV.3 that $g\theta = \prod_{i=1}^{j} (g^{m_i})^{x_i - 1}\bar{P}$, where m_i is the order of $g^{x_i - 1}$ mod P and is thus a power of p. Then $g\theta = abc\bar{P}$, where $a\bar{P}$, $b\bar{P}$, $c\bar{P}$ are, respectively, the products over those i with $x_i \in N$, those i with $x_i \notin N$ and $m_i = 1$, and those i with $x_i \notin N$ and $m_i > 1$. But $c\bar{P} = \bar{P}$ in view of the minimality of the order of g. To see that $b\bar{P} = \bar{P}$ we note first that, since Q is weakly closed in P, when $x \notin N$, there are p^k, $k > 1$, right cosets of P in any double coset PxQ by III.1.z. Furthermore, if $g^{x_i - 1} \in P$, then $g^{(xq) - 1} \in P$ for any $q \in Q$ and $g^{x - 1} = g^{(xq) - 1}$, so that the contribution to $g\phi$ from the double coset PxQ is $(g^{x - 1})^{p^k}\bar{P}$ which is $\bar{P}$ in view of the minimality in the chose of g. Thus $g\theta = a\bar{P}$, and hence $g\theta = g\phi$, as was asserted.

That $g\phi = g^n\bar{P}$ follows from Theorem IV.4.a; and that $g^n\bar{P} \neq \bar{P}$ follows from the fact that n is prime to p. This proves the theorem.

IV.4.c. Corollary. *If G and N are as in Theorem IV.4.b, the maximal abelian p-factor group of G is isomorphic to that of N.*

Proof. By the remark after the proof of Theorem IV.4.a, the maximal p-factor of G is $P\theta$, that of N is $P\phi$; these two are equal by the proof of Theorem IV.4.b, and the corollary follows.

The special case of IV.4.c, where G is finite and Q is the center of P, is due to Grün (cf. [Z]).   In Grün's terminology a group is **p-normal** if the center of one of its Sylow p-subgroups is central in any Sylow p-subgroup containing it.   An easy argument, left to the reader as an exercise, shows that a group is p-normal if and only if the center of a Sylow p-subgroup is weakly closed in the Sylow p-subgroup.

IV.4.d. Corollary.   *Under the hypothesis of Theorem IV.4.b, if also $N' \cap P < P$, then G is different from G' so that G has a proper non-trivial normal subgroup or else is cyclic of prime order.*

5. Normal p-complements

In this section we apply the transfer theory to give the proof of two important theorems stating conditions under which a group has a normal p-complement (as defined below), and then deduce some results on the orders of finite non-abelian simple groups.

IV.5.a. Definition.   Let p be a prime.   A p'-subgroup which is the complement (cf. I.6.e) of a Sylow p-subgroup is a **p-complement**.

We list some elementary facts about normal p-complements.

(i) *If for a prime p, a group G has a normal p-complement M, then M is the only Sylow p'-subgroup of G and is the set of p'-elements of G.   Thus any subgroup and any quotient group of a group with a normal p-complement has a normal p-complement.   Furthermore an extension of a p'-group by a group with a normal p-complement has a normal p-complement.*

(ii) *If a periodic group G has a normal p-complement M, then $G = [M]P$ for some Sylow p-subgroup P of G; the derived group G', is contained in MP', P' is a Sylow p-subgroup of G', and $M \cap G'$ is a normal p-complement for G'.*

IV.5.b. Theorem (*Burnside*).   *Suppose that for some prime p a Hall p-subgroup P of a group G is in the center of its normalizer N; then G has a normal p-complement.*

Proof.   By the hypothesis, P is abelian.   Since P is weakly closed in itself, $G' \cap P = N' \cap P$ by IV.4.b.   If ϕ is the transfer of N into P, then for $g \in P$ it follows from (vii) of Section IV.3 and the fact that P is central in N, that $g\phi = g^n$ with $n = |N:P|$.   Since n is prime to p, $g\phi \neq 1$, and hence, if K is the kernel of ϕ, $K \cap P = 1$.   Thus $N' \cap P = 1$ and finally $G' \cap P = 1$.   The complete inverse image of the Sylow p'-subgroup of G/G' is the normal p-complement of G, and the theorem is proved.

IV.5.c. Theorem (*Frobenius*).   *The finite group G has a normal p-complement for a prime p if and only if each p-subgroup of G is centralized by the p'-elements of its normalizer.*

Proof.   Let P be a Sylow p-subgroup of G, H any subgroup of P, and M a normal p-complement of G.   Then $M \cap \mathfrak{N}(H)$ is the set of p'-elements in the normalizer of H, and H and $M \cap \mathfrak{N}(H)$ are both normal in $\mathfrak{N}(H)$; consequently, since they intersect trivially, they centralize each other. This proves the "only if" statement of the theorem.

Suppose now that each p-subgroup is centralized by the p'-elements of its normalizer: we shall show that G has a normal p-complement. If $P = \mathfrak{Z}(P)$, this conclusion follows from Theorem IV.5.b.   We proceed by induction on the order of P.   Let $N = \mathfrak{N}(Z)$, with Z denoting $\mathfrak{Z}(P)$; then P/Z is a Hall p-subgroup of N/Z of order less than that of P, and a direct check reveals that the hypothesis holds in N/Z.   Hence by the induction assumption there is a subgroup M of N so that $N/Z = [M/Z]P/Z$ with M/Z the normal p-complement of P/Z.   Thus Z is the Sylow p-subgroup of M, so that by Theorem IV.5.b again $M = K \times Z$, where K is the normal p-complement of Z in M.   Then K is the p-complement of P in N, so that, by (ii), $N' \cap P = P'$.

Now in view of the hypothesis together with Theorem IV.2.u, a normal subgroup of one Sylow p-subgroup of G is normal in every

Sylow p-subgroup containing it.   In particular, all Sylow p-subgroups containing Z are in N.   But $N = KP$ where K contains the p'-elements of N, and hence Z is central in N and consequently central in all Sylow p-subgroups containing it.   Thus Z is weakly closed in P and, by Theorem IV.4.b, $G' \cap P = N' \cap P = P'$.   It follows from (ii) again that P' is a Sylow p-subgroup of G' of lower order than that of P. If S is the complete inverse image of the Sylow p'-subgroup of G/G', then P' is a Sylow p-subgroup of S.   By the induction assumption S has a normal p-complement R which is in fact a normal p-complement of G; this is because S is a normal subgroup of G and clearly contains all the p'-elements of G.   This proves the theorem.

For Theorem IV.5.c one could assume that G has a nilpotent (cf. Chapter VI) Hall p-subgroup instead of assuming that G is finite. The proof is as above, replacing "order" by "class."

Theorem IV.5.c has many interesting consequences.   For instance, we have the following proposition on the order of a finite simple group.

IV.5.d. Proposition.   *Let G be a finite simple non-abelian group and let p be the smallest prime divisor of $|G|$; then p^2 divides $|G|$, and if $p = 2$, either* 12, 16, *or* 56 *divides* $|G|$.

The proof of IV.5.d is based on IV.5.c applied to the p-Sylow subgroup of G and is left to the reader; a knowledge of all the groups of order p, 4, and 8 and their automorphism groups is needed (cf. III.1.s, III.2.m, III.4.n, III.3.n).

In view of the recent result of Thompson and Feit [5] that a simple group has even order, we have the following consequence of IV.5.d.

IV.5.e. Proposition.   *If G is a finite simple group, then* 12, 16, *or* 56 *divides* $|G|$.

IV.5.f. Exercise.   *Show that if p, q, r are any primes, a group of order pqr is either isomorphic to Q_8 or is a non-trivial split extension.*

We conclude this section with a theorem from which we deduce a result of Wielandt on normal p-complements.   The latter will be used in Chapter IX.

The statement of the theorem is most conveniently given in terms of the notion of "hypercenter," introduced in Section VI.3. Here we need only note that if $P \neq 1$ is the Sylow p-subgroup of the hypercenter of a group N, then P is normal in N, P has a non-trivial normal subgroup B in the center of N, and P/B is in the hypercenter of N/B.

IV.5.g. Theorem.   *Let p and q be distinct primes dividing the order of a finite group G, and suppose that a Sylow p-subgroup P of G is in the hypercenter of the normalizer of a Sylow q-subgroup Q of G. Then G has a normal p-complement; that is, G has a subgroup K so that $G = [K]P$.*

Proof.   In view of the above remarks the hypothesis implies that there is a subgroup $B \neq 1$ of P central in $\mathfrak{N}(Q)$. We shall show first that B is weakly closed in P. Indeed, since $P \lhd \mathfrak{N}(Q)$, $[P, Q] = 1$, and hence if $g \in G$ and $B^g \leq P$, then both B and B^g are in $\mathfrak{C}(Q)$. Hence $\mathfrak{C}(B) \geq \mathfrak{C}(Q, Q^{g^{-1}})$. By the Sylow q-theorem in $\mathfrak{C}(B)$, there is an $h \in \mathfrak{C}(B)$ so that $Q^{g^{-1}} = Q^h$. Hence $n = hg \in \mathfrak{N}(Q)$ and $B^g = B^{h^{-1}n} = B^n = B$. Thus B is weakly closed in P, as was asserted.

Now the theorem is clearly true in a group of order pq and we proceed by induction, assuming that the theorem is true in all groups of order less than G. If $\mathfrak{N}(B) < G$, then by the induction assumption $\mathfrak{N}(B)$ has a normal p-complement and hence by IV.4.c, G has a normal subgroup M containing P' so that $G/M \cong P/P'$. But then by the induction assumption M has a normal p-complement K which is easily seen to be a normal p-complement of G.

If $\mathfrak{N}(B) = G$ it is easy to check that the hypothesis holds in G/B, and hence by the induction assumption there is a subgroup T of G so that T/B is a normal p-complement of G/B. Since $B \lhd G$, $\mathfrak{C}(B) \lhd G$, and hence, by IV.2.f, $G = \mathfrak{C}(B)\mathfrak{N}(Q)$. Consequently B is a central Hall p-subgroup of T and hence, by IV.5.b, T has a normal p complement K. It follows that $T = K \times B$ and in this case too K is a normal p-complement of G. This proves the theorem.

IV.5.h. Corollary (*Wielandt*).   *Let Π be a set of primes with $|\Pi| > 1$, and suppose that the finite group G has a Hall Π-subgroup H which is a direct product of its Sylow p_i-subgroups P_i for the various primes p_i of Π. If $H = \mathfrak{N}(P_i)$ for each p_i, then G has a normal Π-complement N; that is, $G = [N]H$.*

The important strengthening by Thompson of Theorem IV.5.c for odd primes will be given in IX.3.a.

6. A further result on Sylow theory

In this section we give an application of the transfer theory to get a further result on Sylow theory.

IV.6.a. Theorem (*Wielandt*). *Suppose that the finite group G satisfies the Sylow Γ-theorem for some set Γ of primes and possesses a Hall Γ-subgroup T which centralizes a Sylow p-subgroup P for some prime p not in Γ. If $\Delta = \Gamma \cup \{p\}$, then G satisfies the Sylow Δ-theorem.*

Proof. Let Π and Π^* denote $\{p\}$ or Γ in either order, and let S and S^* denote the Π- and Π^*-groups, respectively, of the pair P, T, so that $P \times T = S \times S^*$. Then in any conjugate class in G of Π-groups, there is a subgroup H in S. We shall show first that if J is a Π^* subgroup in $\mathfrak{N}(H)$, then J is in $\mathfrak{C}(H)$. To do so we let $M = \mathfrak{S}(H, S^*, J)$. Then S^* is in the centralizer C of H in M and H, C, and HC are normal in M. But then $|M/HC|$ is both a Π^*-number (since M/HC is a homomorphic image of J) and not a Π^*-number (since S^* is a Hall Π^*-subgroup of G); thus $|M/CH| = 1$ and $M = HC$. Hence the only automorphisms induced in H by the elements of M are automorphisms whose orders are Π-numbers, and $J \leq \mathfrak{C}(H)$ as was to be shown.

Now if R is a Sylow Δ-subgroup of G, then in view of what was just shown, it follows from Theorem IV.5.c applied to the group R and the prime p that R has a normal p-complement L. Thus $R = [L]Q$, where Q is a p-subgroup and L a Γ-subgroup.

But now by what was shown above again, since Q is in the normalizer of L, Q is in its centralizer, and $R = L \times Q$. Since the Sylow Γ-theorem holds in G, a conjugate of R is $L_1 \times Q_1$ with $L_1 \leq T$. Thus Q_1 and P are in the centralizer D of L_1, and hence, by the Sylow p-theorem in D, a conjugate of Q_1 by an element d in D is in P. But then $(L_1 \times Q_1)^d = L_1 \times Q_1^d \leq T \times P$ and the theorem is proved in view of (i) of Section IV.2.

IV.6.b. Corollary (*Wielandt*).   *If for a set of primes Π, the finite group G has a Hall Π-subgroup which is a direct product of its Sylow p-subgroups for the various primes p of Π, then G satisfies the Sylow Π-theorem.*

7. Complements of normal subgroups

The study of a given group is simplified if the group is known to be a split extension of a normal subgroup; for then it is a semi-direct product of the normal subgroup with a factor group of a subgroup of the group of automorphisms of the normal subgroup. In such a case, the knowledge of the automorphism group of the normal subgroup will suffice to give information about the given group. The groups of order six illustrate this situation (cf. III.4.e). On the other hand, there are groups which have normal subgroups but which are not split extensions, as, for instance, the quaternion group (cf. III.4.i).

In this section we give an important criterion for a group to be a split extension of a normal subgroup—namely, that the order of the normal subgroup be prime to its index. Thus, if the normal subgroup is a Sylow Π-subgroup, there is a Sylow Π'-subgroup which is also a Hall Π'-subgroup. The question of whether the group satisfies the Sylow Π'-theorem will be considered later (cf. VII.2.c and VII.2.i).

We begin with a theorem of Gaschütz which includes an earlier theorem of Schur.

IV.7.a. Theorem (*Gaschütz*).   *Suppose that the group G has a normal abelian subgroup A of finite exponent k and subgroups U and S so that $U = [A]S$. If the index j of U in G is prime to the exponent k of A, then G is a split extension of A.*

Proof.   Let W be a right transversal of U in G. Then $SW = T$ is a right transversal of A in G, and since S is a group, $ST = T$. Thus $G = AT$ and since A is normal, T is also a left transversal and $G = TA$ also. We define the representative map τ and the projection map α from G to T and A, respectively, by the equation $g = (g\tau)(g\alpha)$ with $g\tau \in T$, $g\alpha \in A$ uniquely determined as in IV.3.b.

Now for $s \in S$, $w \in W$, $t \in T$, $(wt)\alpha = (swt)\alpha$, and since for all $x \in G$, w_1 and $w_2 \in W$, $w_1 x$ and $w_2 x$ are in the same right coset of U in G if and only if $w_1 = w_2$, it follows that if $x \in T$, then

(i) $$\prod_{w \in W} (wt)\alpha = \prod_{w \in W} ((wx)\tau\, t)\alpha.$$

The order of the multiplication in (i) is irrelevant since A is abelian. Furthermore, if x, y and t are in T,

$$(xy)t = (xy)\tau(xy)\alpha t = (xy)\tau t((xy)\alpha)^t$$

and $((xy)t)\alpha = ((xy)\tau t)\alpha((xy)\alpha)^t$. Also $x(yt) = x(yt)\tau(yt)\alpha$ and $(x(yt))\alpha = (x(yt)\tau)\alpha(yt)\alpha$. Since $(x(yt))\alpha = ((xy)t)\alpha$, it follows that

(ii) $$(x(yt)\tau)\alpha = ((xy)\tau t)\alpha((xy)\alpha)^t((yt)\alpha)^{-1}.$$

Now let the integer h be chosen so that $hj \equiv -1 \bmod k$ (k is the exponent of A), and for $t \in T$ consider the new transversal $T^* = \{t\prod_{w \in W} ((wt)\alpha)^h\}$. We shall show that T^* is a group. First we observe that for x and $t \in T$,

$$[x \prod ((wx)\alpha)^h][t \prod ((wt)\alpha)^h] = (xt)\tau(xt)\alpha(\prod ((wx)\alpha)^h)^t \prod ((wt)\alpha)^h.$$

with the products taken over all $w \in W$. On the other hand, in view of (ii),

$$(xt)\tau\, (xt)\alpha \prod ((w(xt)\tau)\alpha)^h$$
$$= (xt)\tau\, (xt)\alpha \prod (((wx)\tau\, t)\alpha)^h \prod (((wx)\alpha)^t)^h \prod (((xt)\alpha)^{-1})^h.$$

It follows from (i) and the fact that $\prod (xt)\alpha = ((xt)\alpha)^j$ that the right sides of the last two equations are the same. Hence T^* is a semi-group. Therefore by (iii) of Section IV.3, T^* is a group, $G = [A]T^*$, and the theorem is proved.

IV.7.b. Corollary (*Schur*). *If the group G has a normal abelian subgroup A whose index in G is prime to its exponent, then there is a subgroup B of G so that $G = [A]B$.*

For finite groups Schur's theorem (Corollary IV.7.b) can be extended to the case where the normal subgroup is arbitrary.

IV.7.c. Theorem (*Schur-Zassenhaus*). *If a finite group G has a normal subgroup A whose order is prime to its index, then G is a split extension of A.*

Proof. We shall first show that A is not contained in the Frattini subgroup $\Phi(G)$. Indeed suppose it were the case that $A \leq \Phi(G)$; by IV.2.g, A is then the direct product of its non-trivial Sylow p-subgroups, and it follows from III.1.t that $A' < A$. Then by IV.7.b, G has a subgroup W containing A' such that G/A' is $[A/A']W/A'$. Thus G is AW with $W \cap A = A'$; consequently W is proper in G and is contained in a maximal proper subgroup M of G. But this is a contradiction since $G = AW = AM$ and $A \leq \Phi(G) \leq M$. We conclude that $A \nleq \Phi(G)$.

We proceed now by induction on $|G|$ noting that the theorem is true for $|G| = 1$ and that in view of the above, G has a maximal subgroup M so that $G = AM$. Then $G/A \simeq M/M \cap A$, and by the induction assumption M has a subgroup S of order $|M/M \cap A|$ $= |G/A|$. In view of the order of S, $G = [A]S$ and the proof is complete.

8. Further splitting theorems

The next theorem gives a criterion for the splitting of a group in terms of the splitting of its Sylow subgroups.   First we give a lemma whose proof is left to the reader.

IV.8.a. Lemma.   *Let the group G be a split extension $[A]H$ with A the direct product of two normal subgroups B and C of G.   If, for some set of primes Π, B is a Sylow Π-subgroup of A and P is a Sylow Π-subgroup of G, then $P \cap A = B$ and $P = [P \cap A](P \cap CH)$.*

IV.8.b. Theorem (*Gaschütz*).   *If the normal abelian subgroup A has finite exponent k and finite index in the group G, then G splits over A if and only if for each prime p dividing k each Sylow p-subgroup P splits over $P \cap A$.*

Proof. If G splits over A, then each of its Sylow p-subgroups P splits over $P \cap A$ by Lemma IV.8.a.

The converse will be proved by induction on k, the statement being true for k a prime by IV.7.a.   Suppose P is a Sylow p-subgroup of G,

p dividing k, such that P splits over $P \cap A$. Let B be the Sylow p'-subgroup of A so that $A = (P \cap A) \times B$ with B characteristic in A and hence normal in G. Then by Theorem IV.7.a applied to G/B with PB/B in place of U, there is a subgroup H of G containing B so that $G/B = [A/B]H/B$. Hence $G = AH$ with $H \cap A = B$. But for primes $q \neq p$, q dividing k, the Sylow q-subgroups of H are Sylow q-subgroups of G, and hence by the induction argument ($P \cap A \neq 1$ since p divides k) $H = [B]K$ for some subgroup K. But then $G = AH$ $= ABK = AK$ with $A \cap K \leq B \cap K = 1$ so that $G = [A]K$ and the theorem is proved.

Before giving the next splitting theorem we need a theorem giving some conditions under which the complements of a normal subgroup are conjugate.

IV.8.c. Theorem.   *Let the group G be a split extension $[A]B$ with B a finite Π-group for some set of primes Π, and A an abelian group of exponent k with k a Π'-number.   Then any Π-subgroup of G is conjugate to a subgroup of B by an element of A.*

Proof.   The subgroup B is a right transversal of A in G and we let the projection map α and the representative map β be defined from G onto A and B, respectively, by the equation $g = (g\beta)(g\alpha)$ for $g \in G$, $g\alpha \in A$, $g\beta \in B$.   If C is any Π-subgroup, let $j \in J$ index the cosets of A in AC, and for $j \in J$ let c_j be the element of C in the corresponding coset.   Then the elements $b_j = c_j\beta$, $j \in J$ form a subgroup of B since $B \cap AC$ is a subgroup.   Furthermore, if $a_j = c_j\alpha$ for $j \in J$, then $(c_ic_j) = a_i^{b_j}a_j$.   Since for a fixed j, c_ic_j ranges through C as c_i does, it follows that $\prod_{i \in J} a_i^{b_j}a_j = \prod_{i \in J} a_i$.   If now h is chosen so that $h|J| \equiv 1$ mod k and if d denotes $\prod_{i \in J} a_i^h$, then the last equation becomes $d^{b_j}a_j$ $= d$ when both sides are raised to the hth power.   But then $(b_j^{-1})^d b_j a_j = 1$ or $c_j = b_j^d$.   Since this holds for each $j \in J$, C is a conjugate of a subgroup of B by the element d of A, as was to be shown.

For finite groups the above theorem may be restated as follows.

IV.8.d. Corollary.   *If the finite group G is a split extension $[A]B$, with B a Π-subgroup for some set of primes Π and A an abelian Π'-subgroup, then G satisfies the Sylow Π-theorem.*

The hypothesis in IV.8.d that A be abelian will be removed later (cf. VII.2.c and VII.2.i).

The next theorems of this section give conditions which imply that a group splits when a normal subgroup splits.

IV.8.e. Theorem.   *Suppose that the group G has a normal subgroup M which is a split extension $[A]H$ of an abelian group A by a subgroup H intravariant in M; if the center of M intersects A in 1, then $G = [A]\mathfrak{N}(H)$.*

Proof.   Let $N = \mathfrak{N}(H) \cap M$ and let $D = N \cap A$.   Then $D \lhd N$ since $A \lhd M$, and $[D, H] \leq H \cap A = 1$.   But $[D, A] = 1$ since A is abelian and hence $[D, M] = 1$.   Thus $D \leq \mathfrak{Z}(M) \cap A = 1$, and hence $\mathfrak{N}(H) \cap A = 1$.   By IV.2.e, $G = M\mathfrak{N}(H)$; and since $\mathfrak{N}(H) > H$, $G = A\mathfrak{N}(H)$.   But $\mathfrak{N}(H) \cap A = 1$ and $G = [A]\mathfrak{N}(H)$ as the theorem asserts.

In view of IV.7.b and IV.8.c, Theorem IV.8.e has the following consequences.

IV.8.f. Corollary.   *Suppose that the group G has an abelian normal subgroup A contained in the normal subgroup M of G; if the exponent k of A is prime to the index of A in M, and if the center of M intersects A in 1, then G splits over A.*

IV.8.g. Corollary.   *Suppose that the group G has a normal subgroup M, which has a unique minimal proper non-trivial normal subgroup A with A abelian of exponent prime to its index in M.   Then G splits over A.*

Proof.   By IV.7.b and IV.8.c, $M = AH$ with H intravariant in M. Because of its uniqueness A is normal in G.   Since $\mathfrak{Z}(M) \cap A$ is normal in M, by the minimality of A either $\mathfrak{Z}(M) \cap A = A$ or $\mathfrak{Z}(M) \cap A = 1$.   If $\mathfrak{Z}(M) \cap A = A$, $[H, A] = 1$ and $M = H \times A$ with $H \neq 1$, since A is proper in M.   But this is contrary to the uniqueness of A.   Thus $\mathfrak{Z}(M) \cap A = 1$ and the corollary follows from Theorem IV.8.e.

The condition in IV.8.f and IV.8.g that the exponent of A is prime to the index of A in M is replaced in the following theorem by the condition that M/A is a direct product of its Sylow p-subgroups.   The proof will depend on a proposition from Chapter VI and on the following lemma, the easy proof of which is left to the reader.

IV.8.h. Lemma.   *If A, B, and C are normal subgroups of a group G with $A = B \times C$, and if the center of G intersects A in 1, then the center of G/C intersects A/C in 1.*

IV.8.i. Theorem.   *Suppose that the group G has an abelian normal subgroup A of finite exponent and of finite index in the normal subgroup M of G.   If M/A is the direct product of its Sylow p-subgroup for the primes dividing $|M/A|$, and if the center of M intersects A in 1, then G splits over A.*

Proof.   We shall first consider the case where A is a p-group for some prime p.   Then by the hypothesis, $M/A = P/A \times QA/A$ with P the unique Sylow p-subgroup of M and Q a p'-subgroup of M whose existence is guaranteed by IV.7.b in the group QA, the complete inverse image of QA/A.   Thus $QA = [A]Q$ and furthermore Q is intravariant in $[A]Q$ by IV.8.c.   Since AQ is normal in M, $M = A\mathfrak{N}(Q)$ by IV.2.e.   It is now only necessary to show that $R = 1$ with R denoting $A \cap \mathfrak{N}(Q)$.   Since P is normal in M and P contains R, it follows that $[R, Q] \leq Q \cap P = 1$ and hence that $R = A \cap \mathfrak{C}(Q)$.   Thus $R = A \cap \mathfrak{Z}(QA)$ (A is abelian) and hence R is normal in M, since A, QA, and $\mathfrak{Z}(QA)$ are normal in M.   It follows that $R \lhd P$ and hence by VI.1.g that $R = 1$, since otherwise $R \cap \mathfrak{Z}(P)$ would be a non-trivial subgroup of the center of M ($M = PQ$) contrary to the hypothesis of the theorem.   This proves the theorem when A is a p-group and in particular when A has exponent p.

We proceed by induction on the exponent of A.   Suppose then that $A = B \times C$ with B the Sylow p-subgroup of A, $B \neq 1$, and C the Sylow p'-subgroup of A, $C \neq 1$.   In view of Lemma IV.8.h, the hypotheses of the theorem hold in G/C so that $G/C = [A/C]L/C$.

But then the hypotheses of the theorem also hold in L with the normal abelian subgroup C of lower exponent than that of A, and hence there is a subgroup J with $L=[C]J$.   Then since $G=AL$ with $L \cap A=C$, it follows that $G=AJ$ with $A \cap J \leq C \cap J=1$.   Thus $G=[A]J$ and the theorem is proved.

We conclude this section with a general theorem from which we can deduce a splitting theorem as well as the useful theorem of Maschke known as the theorem of complete reducibility.

IV.8.j. Theorem.   *Let V be an abelian group, let G be a finite group of automorphisms of V, and suppose that each element of V has a unique nth root with $n=|G|$.   Then any direct factor of V which is mapped into itself by G has a complement with the same property.*

Proof.   Let M be a direct factor of V, so that there is a $K < V$ with $V = M \times K$; and let θ be the projection of V onto M determined by this decomposition of V.   Then both θ and the map ϕ which assigns to each element of V its unique nth root are clearly homomorphisms.   If now σ is the map defined by the equation $v\sigma = (\prod_{\gamma \in G} (v\gamma\theta)\gamma^{-1})\phi$ for $v \in V$, then σ is also a homomorphism which maps V onto M and is the identity on M.   The kernel of σ is a subgroup N which intersects M in 1; for $m\sigma = m$ when $m \in M$ and $n\sigma = 1$ when $n \in N$.   Then if $v \in V$, $v\sigma \in M$, and $v\sigma^2 = v\sigma$ so that $v(v^{-1}\sigma) \in N$ and $v \in NM$.   Thus N is a complement of M in V.

There only remains to show that $N\beta \leq N$ for each $\beta \in G$.   But if $n \in N$, then $n\beta\sigma = (\prod_{\gamma \in G} ((n\beta)\gamma\theta)\gamma^{-1})\phi = (\prod_{\beta\gamma \in G}(n(\beta\gamma)\theta)\gamma^{-1}\beta^{-1})\beta\phi = 1\beta\phi = 1$ and hence $n\beta \in N$ so that $N\beta \leq N$ as was to be shown.

The splitting theorem that can be deduced from IV.8.j, together with IV.7.b, is as follows.   The few details of the proof as well as those of its corollary and of IV.8.m below are left for exercises.

IV.8.k. Theorem.   *If the group G has a normal abelian subgroup A whose index in G is prime to its exponent, and if B is a direct factor of A normal in G, then B has a complement T in G (or G splits over B), and T splits over $T \cap A$.*

IV.8.1. Corollary.   *Let the group G be a split extension $[Q]S$ where Q is an elementary abelian q-group and S is finite with $|S|$ prime to q. Then Q is a direct product $\prod_{\alpha \in M} Q_\alpha$ with each Q_α a finite minimal normal subgroup of G as well as of $\mathfrak{S}(Q_\alpha, S)$.*

The theorem of complete reducibility is as follows.

IV.8.m. Theorem (*Maschke*).   *If G is a finite group of linear transformations of a vector space V over a field F whose characteristic does not divide the group order t, and if M is a subspace of V such that $Mg \leq M$ for each $g \in G$, then there is complementary subspace N of V such that $Ng \leq N$ for all $g \in G$; as a consequence, V is a direct sum of subspaces W, each minimal in that $WG \leq W$.*

Chapter V

FREE GROUPS AND FREE PRODUCTS

Free groups were introduced in Section I.5 and their importance in the general theory of groups was seen to stem from the fact that every group is a homomorphic image of a free group (cf. I.5.h). The study of free groups is continued in this chapter. It is seen that two free groups are isomorphic if and only if they have the same rank, and it is shown that a subgroup of a free group is a free group; also given are two theorems about the rank of a subgroup of a free group in terms of its index.

The free product and the free product with an amalgamated subgroup are also introduced, and some of the basic facts about them are proved. As applications of the theory developed, the theorem is then proved that a group with two isomorphic subgroups may be embedded in a group in which the two subgroups are conjugate. Finally, an example is given of a group in which any two non-identity elements are conjugate; also given is an example of a two-generator group with one relation which is isomorphic to a proper factor group of itself.

1. Subgroups of free groups

We begin with a criterion for a group to be a free group and a set of its generators to be a free set of generators.

V.1.a. Criterion. *Let Y be a set of generators of a group G, Y disjoint from Y^{-1}, and let K denote $Y \cup Y^{-1}$. Then G is a free group on the free generators Y if each product $k_1 \cdots k_n$ of elements k_i of K is different from 1 when $k_i k_{i+1} \neq 1$ for $i = 1, \cdots, n-1$.*

Proof. Let θ be a one-one map from Y onto a set M. Then by I.5.h, θ^{-1} is a homomorphism of $\mathfrak{G}(M)$ onto G. In view of the condition and Theorem I.5.r, the kernel of θ^{-1} is 1 and hence θ^{-1} is an isomorphism of $\mathfrak{G}(M)$ onto G. Thus G is a free group and Y is a free set of generators for G as was asserted.

The following proposition will be needed for the main theorem of this section.

V.1.b. Proposition. *Let X be a set of generators of a group G, let H be a subgroup of G, and let T be a right transversal containing 1 of H in G; then $TXT^{-1} \cap H$ is a set of generators of H.*

Proof. Let η and τ be the maps defined by the equation $g = (g\eta)(g\tau)$ for $g \in G$ with $g\eta \in H$, $g\tau \in T$. Then an element of H has the form $(m_1 m_2 \cdots m_n)\eta$ with $m_1, \cdots, m_n \in X \cup X^{-1}$, and n a natural number. We shall show by induction on n that $(m_1 \cdots m_n)\eta$ is a product of elements from $T(X \cup X^{-1})T^{-1} \cap H$. For $n = 1$ we have $m_1\eta = 1m_1(m_1\tau)^{-1}$, and we suppose that for $n > 1$, r denotes $m_1 \cdots m_{n-1}$ and that $r\eta$ is a product of elements of $T(X \cup X^{-1})T^{-1} \cap H$. Then $m_1 \cdots m_n = (r\eta)(r\tau)m_n$ and by (vi) of Section IV.3, $(m_1 \cdots m_n)\eta = r\eta(((r\tau)m_n)\eta)$. But $((r\tau)m_n)\eta = (r\tau)m_n(((r\tau)m_n)\tau)^{-1}$ so that $((r\tau)m_n)\eta$ is also in $T(X \cup X^{-1})T^{-1} \cap H$, and the proof is complete.

Proposition V.1.b has the following interesting and important consequence.

V.1.c. Corollary. *A subgroup of finite index in a finitely generated group is finitely generated.*

We now give the important theorem that a subgroup of a free group is free. Our proof is a modification of Schreier's method of proof; other proofs have been given by Nielsen, Levi (cf. Section 3 below), and Hurewicz, to mention a few.

V.1.d. Theorem. *A subgroup of a free group is free.*

Proof. Let $G = \mathfrak{G}(X)$ be a free group, let H be a non-trivial subgroup of G (the trivial group is free by convention), and let M denote

$X \cup X^{-1}$ so that if $M^0 = 1$, $G = \bigcup_{n=0}^{\infty} M^n = \bigcup_{n=0}^{\infty} HM^n$. Then for $n = 1, 2, \cdots$, let Q_n denote the set complement of $\bigcup_{k=0}^{n-1} HM^k$ in $\bigcup_{k=0}^{n} HM^k$. We now select a right transversal of H in G as follows. Let $T_0 = \{1\}$, and suppose T_n already chosen to contain exactly one element of each right coset of H in Q_n. Then $Q_{n+1} \subseteq HT_n M$ and we choose T_{n+1} so that if an element of T_{n+1} is written as a reduced word in $\mathfrak{G}(X)$ (cf. I.5.q), namely $m_1 m_2 \cdots m_{n+1}$ with $m_i \in M$, then $m_1 m_2 \cdots m_n$ is also in T. This property will be called the **Schreier property**. Finally the desired transversal is $T = \bigcup_{n=0}^{\infty} T_n$.

We shall show that the set Y of non-trivial elements of $H \cap TXT^{-1}$ is a free set of generators for H, and consequently that H is a free group. It follows from V.1.b that Y is a generating set for H. If we let K denote $Y \cup Y^{-1}$, we can conclude from V.1.a that Y is a free set of generators for H if we show that Y is disjoint from Y^{-1} and that a product $k_1 \cdots k_n$ of elements k_i of K is not 1 if for each $i = 1, \cdots, n-1$, $k_i k_{i+1} \neq 1$. We do this by considering the reduced words of $\mathfrak{G}(X)$ expressing the products of the form $k_1 \cdots k_n$. First we show the following:

(1) *If $k \in K$ and $k = smt^{-1}$ with s, $t \in T$, $m \in M$, then sm and tm^{-1} are not in T; consequently m^{-1} is not the last symbol of the reduced word expressing s, and m is not the last symbol of the reduced word expressing t.*

For sm in T would imply (since $smt^{-1} \in H$) that $sm = t$ and hence that $smt^{-1} = 1$ contrary to the fact that $1 \notin K$; a similar argument shows that tm^{-1} is not in T and that m is not the last symbol of the reduced word expressing t. The second assertion of (1) follows from the first and the Schreier property.

We next show:

(2) *If for $i = 1, 2$, $k_i \in K$ and $k_i = s_i m_i t_i^{-1}$ with s_i, $t_i \in T$, $m_i \in M$, then the reduced word expressing $m_1 t_1^{-1} s_2 m_2$ begins with m_1 and ends with m_2 unless $s_2 = t_1$, $m_1 = m_2^{-1}$, $t_2 = s_1$, and hence $k_1 k_2 = 1$.*

If t_1^{-1} and s_2 are written as reduced words, we consider the possible cancellation (cf. Theorem I.5.r and the remark following it) of inverse pairs in $m_1 t_1^{-1} s_2 m_2$. If m_2 does not appear at the end of the reduced word expressing $m_1 t_1^{-1} s_2 m_2$, then all the symbols of $s_2 m_2$ must have been cancelled.   They cannot have been cancelled by those of t_1^{-1}; for, if that were the case, $s_2 m_2$ would be in T by the Schreier property, but that would be contrary to (1).   If all the symbols of $s_2 m_2$ had been cancelled by $m_1 t_1^{-1}$, then s_2 must equal t_1, m_1 must equal m_2^{-1}, and (since $s_1 \in H t_1 m_1^{-1} = H s_2 m_2$, $t_2 \in H s_2 m_2$) $s_1 = t_2$ so that $k_1 k_2 = s_1 m_1 t_1^{-1} s_2 m_2 t_2^{-1} = 1$.   A similar argument shows that m_1 must begin the reduced word expressing $m_1 t_1^{-1} s_2 m_2$ unless $s_1 = t_2$, $m_1 = m_2^{-1}$, $t_1 = s_2$, and hence $k_1 k_2 = 1$; thus (2) is proved.

As an immediate consequence of (1) and (2) we see that Y is disjoint from Y^{-1}.   For in the contrary case, if there were a $k \in K$ which had the form sxt^{-1} and $s_1 x_1^{-1} t_1^{-1}$ with $s, s_1, t, t_1 \in T$, $x, x_1 \in X$, then $sxt^{-1} t_1 x_1 s_1^{-1}$ would be 1 contrary to the fact that its expression as a reduced word must contain x and x_1 in view of (1) and (2).

We say that the symbol m_i is the **significant factor** in the expression $s_i m_i t_i^{-1}$, and prove the following statement from which the proof of the theorem will follow:

(3) *If n is an arbitrary natural number and if for $i = 1, \cdots, n$, $k_i \in K$ and $k_i = s_i m_i t_i^{-1}$ with $s_i, t_i \in T$, $m_i \in M$, then the reduced word expressing $k_1 \cdots k_n$ contains all the significant factors $m_1, \cdots, m_n$, provided that $k_i k_{i+1} \neq 1$ for each $i = 1, \cdots, n - 1$.*

The proof of (3) is by induction on n, the case $n = 1$ following directly from (1).   If $n > 1$ and (3) is assumed true for $n - 1$, then the reduced word expressing $k_1 \cdots k_{n-1}$ has the form $z m_{n-1} t_{n-1}^{-1}$, where z is a reduced word containing the symbols $m_1, \cdots, m_{n-2}$, and t_n^{-1} denotes the reduced word expressing t_n^{-1}.   Then $z m_{n-1} t_{n-1}^{-1} s_n m_n t_n^{1}$ is a word expressing $k_1 \cdots k_n$, and by (2) and the remark after I.5.r, the reduced word expressing $k_1 \cdots k_n$ must contain all the significant factors m_i as is asserted in (3).

Statement (3) implies directly the second condition mentioned above, needed to apply V.1.a and the proof of the theorem is complete.

2. The ranks of some subgroups of free groups

We first show that the rank (cf. I.5.d) of a free group is the same as the torsion-free rank of the group modulo its derived group, and hence that rank determines a free group up to isomorphism.   We begin with an easy proposition, the proof of which is left to the reader (cf. II.6.c).

V.2.a. Proposition.   *If $G = \mathfrak{G}(M \mid R)$, then G/G' is isomorphic to $\mathfrak{G}(M \mid R, [m, n], m, n \in M)$; in particular, if F is a free group $\mathfrak{G}(M)$, then F/F' is a free abelian group on the elements mF' with m ranging over M.*

V.2.b. Corollary.   *The rank of a free group $F = \mathfrak{G}(M)$ is equal to the torsion-free rank of the abelian group F/F'.*

As a consequence of V.2.b and the fact that two free abelian groups are isomorphic if and only if they have the same rank, we have the following proposition.

V.2.c. Proposition.   *Two free groups are isomorphic if and only if they have the same rank.*

We now give some theorems on the rank of some subgroups of free groups.

As a corollary of the proof of V.1.d we have the following proposition.

V.2.d. Proposition.   *The derived group of a two-generator free group has countable infinite rank.*

Proof.   If the group F is $\mathfrak{G}(a, b)$, then the set of all $a^m b^n$ with m, n integers is a transversal of F' in F with the Schreier property; and the set of elements $(a^m b^n) a (a^{m+1} b^n)^{-1}$ with $n \neq 0$ is a countable infinite set of free generators of F'.

It follows from V.2.d and V.2.c that a countable free group can always be embedded in a two-generator free group. We already noted (cf. III.5.j) that a countable group can always be embedded in a two-generator group.

Our next theorem gives the rank of a subgroup of finite index in a finitely generated free group.

V.2.e. Theorem (*Schreier*).   *If H is a subgroup of finite index j in a free group $F = \mathfrak{G}(x_1, \cdots, x_n)$, then H has rank $1 + j(n-1)$.*

Proof. We use the transversal with the Schreier property and the notation in the proof of V.1.d. Then $|T|=j$, $|M|=2n$, and since $s \in T$ and $m \in M$ determine $t \in T$ in the element smt^{-1} of H it follows that there are $2nj$ expressions smt^{-1} with s, $t \in T$, $m \in M$, and $smt^{-1} \in H$. We wish to determine how many of these are 1. If $smt^{-1}=1$, then its inverse $tm^{-1}s^{-1}=1$ and hence the expressions representing 1 are paired. Now the shorter (cf. Section 1.5) of the two reduced words expressing s and t is obtained from the longer by cancellation of the symbol m or m^{-1} since $sm=t$ and $tm^{-1}=s$. On the other hand, to each non-trivial $s \in T$ there is exactly one $m \in M$ so that the reduced word expressing sm is shorter than that expressing s. Hence to each of the $j-1$ non-trivial elements $s \in T$ there is exactly one pair of expressions smt^{-1}, $tm^{-1}s$ of H representing 1. Thus there are $2nj-2(j-1)=2j(n-1)+2$ expressions representing elements of K. By (2) in the proof of V.1.d, two different such expressions represent different words of K and hence $|K|=2j(n-1)+2$. It follows that $|Y|=j(n-1)+1$ and the theorem is proved.

We conclude this section with a theorem which includes V.2.d as a special case.

V.2.f. Theorem (*Schreier*). *If a free group $F=\mathfrak{G}(X)$ has a non-trivial normal subgroup H of infinite index, then H has infinite rank.*

Proof. Since H has infinite index in F, X contains at least two symbols b and c. Let T be a right transversal of H in F with the Schreier property so that the set Y of non-trivial elements of $H \cap TXT^{-1}$ is a free set of generators for H as in the proof of V.1.d. Let $x_1 \cdots x_k$ (with $x_i \in X \cup X^{-1}$) be the reduced word expressing a fixed element t of T; we may suppose without loss of generality that x_k is not b or b^{-1}. If h is a non-trivial element of H, then for a suitable integer n, its conjugate $m=h^{b^n}$ is an element of H whose expression as a reduced word in X begins with b^{-1} and ends with b. It follows that the reduced word $x_1 \cdots x_r$ expressing tmt^{-1} begins with $x_1 \cdots x_k$. We then let s be maximal so that $k \le s \le r$ and so that $x_1 \cdots x_s$ (which is the beginning of the expression $x_1 \cdots x_r$) is an element of T. Since 1 is the element of T in the coset H, it follows that $s < r$ and hence that $x_1 \cdots x_{s+1}$ is not in T.   Let w be the element of T in the coset of $x_1 \cdots x_{s+1}$; then $(x_1 \cdots x_s) x_{s+1} w^{-1}$ or its inverse is a non-trivial element of Y (which we obtained from t).

Since T is infinite, either X is infinite (so that there are an infinite number of choices for b to give an infinite subset of Y using the above construction) or else the lengths of the reduced words expressing the elements of T are unbounded.   In the latter event, it is clear from the construction above that the lengths of the reduced words expressing the elements of Y are unbounded and hence that Y is infinite.   This proves the theorem.

3. A theorem of Levi on subgroups of a free group

The main object of this section is to give a theorem (V.3.c below) which will be used later to deduce Magnus' theorem (VI.2.g in the next chapter) that a free group is residually nilpotent.   The proof of Theorem V.3.c uses the method of Nielsen as adopted by Levi to prove that a subgroup of a free group is free.   Accordingly we begin with a second proof of Theorem V.1.d based on the well-ordering of the group elements in terms of the lengths of their expressions as reduced words.

A second proof of Theorem V.1.d: Let F be a free group $\mathfrak{G}(X)$, let $M = X \cup X^{-1}$, and let F be given a well-ordering denoted by $<$ subject only to the condition that if $f, g \in F$, $f < g$ when $L(f)$ is less than $L(g)$ (here $L(f)$ is the length as in Section I.5 of the reduced word in M expressing f).

Since a reduced word $u \neq 1$ of length $2t$ has a unique representation in the form ab^{-1} with $L(a) = t = L(b)$, the elements a and b will be called the **halves** of u.   It is clear that u and u^{-1} have the same halves and, since $u \neq 1$, the two halves will be unequal.   When $a < b$, a will be called the **first half**, b the **second half**, and, if $b = v_1 \cdots v_t$ with v_i in M, v_t^{-1} will be called the **significant factor** of u; when $b < a$, b will be called the **first half**, a the **second half**, and, if $a = m_1 \cdots m_k$ with $m_i \in M$, m_k will be called the **significant factor** of u.

Similarly a reduced word $u \neq 1$ of length $2t+1$ has a unique representation acb^{-1} with $L(a) = t = L(b)$ and with $c \in M$.   Again the elements a and b will be called the **halves** of u, and c will be called the **middle**.   Both u and u^{-1} have the same halves (which may be equal), and in this case the **first half** refers to either half which is not greater than the other half, the **second half**.   The middle, c, is the **significant factor** of u.

The set of pairs of non-identity elements f, f^{-1} of F is now ordered, first by length of f, and then for inverse pairs of words of the same length, lexicographically in terms of the ordering of F, first by first halves, then by second halves, and then by middles for pairs of words of odd length.

Now we pick out a set Y of free generators h_λ for λ in some set L by choosing a member h_1 of the first pair whose elements are in H and then by continuing to choose one element h_λ from the first pair whose elements are in H but not in the subgroup generated by the h_λ already chosen.   To show that Y is a set of free generators of H it is sufficient in view of V.1.a to show that if $w = k_1 k_2 \cdots k_s$ is a product of elements k_i of $K = Y \cup Y^{-1}$ with $k_i k_{i+1}$ not 1 for $i = 1, 2, \cdots, s-1$, then $w \neq 1$. We shall show this by showing that the significant factor of each k_i appears in the expression of w as a reduced word in M.   It is clear that this is true for $s = 1$ and we assume inductively that it is true for every product of fewer than s factors k_i.   Then if the significant factors of k_{s-1} were not to appear in the reduced form of w as a word in M it would also fail to appear in the reduced form of the word $k_{s-1}k_s$.

But $k_{s-1}k_s$ is in H and we shall show that $k_{s-1}k_s$ is a member of an inverse pair either less than that containing k_{s-1} or that containing k_s, contrary to the way in which Y was chosen.   To show this, we note first that if x and y are reduced words in M, then $L(xy) < L(y)$ if and only if more than half of the symbols of x cancel symbols of y in the product xy and that a similar criterion holds for $L(xy)$ to be less than $L(x)$.   Hence $L(k_{s-1}k_s)$ will be less than $L(k_s)$ or less than $L(k_{s-1})$ unless at most half the symbols of k_{s-1} and at most half the symbols of k_s are cancelled in the product $k_{s-1}k_s$.   Thus we need only consider this case, and since the significant factor of k_{s-1} is cancelled, this means we need only consider the case where precisely the second half of k_{s-1} is cancelled.   Thus, if $k_{s-1} = ab^{-1}$ with a and b reduced words in M and $L(a) = L(b)$, then $a < b$ (since the significant factor of k_{s-1} is in b), and if $k_s = bz$, then $L(b) = L(z)$ and $k_{s-1}k_s = az$.   But now it is clear that the pair containing $k_{s-1}k_s$ is less than that containing k_s; for the element az has a smaller half on the left than the left half of bz, whereas the right half of bz is equal to that of az.   A similar argument leads to a contradiction if the significant factor of k_s fails to appear in the reduced form of w.   We conclude that Y is a set of free generators of H as was asserted, and our second proof of Theorem V.1.d is complete.

We need two lemmas before giving the main theorem of this section.

V.3.a. Lemma.   *If* $X=\{x_\alpha, \alpha \in A\}$ *is a free set of generators of a free group* $F=\mathfrak{G}(X)$, *then for* $\alpha, \beta \in A$, $\alpha \neq \beta$, *and* $\epsilon = \pm 1$, *the maps* $\theta_{\alpha\beta^\epsilon}$ *induced on* F *by the equations* $x_\alpha \theta_{\alpha\beta^\epsilon} = x_\alpha x_\beta^\epsilon$, $x_\gamma \theta_{\alpha\beta^\epsilon} = x_\gamma$ *for* $\gamma \in A$, $\gamma \neq \alpha$, *are automorphisms of* F *and hence in particular* $\{x_\alpha x_\beta, x_\gamma, \gamma \in A, \gamma \neq \alpha\}$ *is a free set of generators of* F.   *Also automorphisms of* F *are the maps* ψ_α *induced on* F *by the equations* $x_\alpha \psi_\alpha = x_\alpha^{-1}$, $x_\gamma \psi_\alpha = x_\gamma$ *for* $\gamma \neq \alpha$; *and the maps* $\phi_{\alpha\beta}$ *induced on* F *by the equations* $x_\alpha \phi_{\alpha\beta} = x_\beta$, $x_\beta \phi_{\alpha\beta} = x_\alpha$, $x_\gamma \phi_{\alpha\beta} = x_\gamma$ *for* $\gamma \neq \alpha$, $\gamma \neq \beta$.

Proof.   It is clear from I.5.h that $\theta_{\alpha\beta^\epsilon}$ is a homomorphism of F onto F.   Since $\theta_{\alpha\beta^{-1}}$ is the inverse of $\theta_{\alpha\beta}$, it follows that each $\theta_{\alpha\beta^\epsilon}$ is an automorphism and the first statement of the lemma follows.   A similar argument shows that ψ_α and $\phi_{\alpha\beta}$ are also automorphisms.

It is of interest to note here (for a proof cf., for instance, [H]) that if A is finite, the automorphisms described in Lemma V.3.a generate the automorphism group of F.

Our next lemma is based on the second proof of Theorem V.1.d above.

V.3.b. Lemma.   *Let* H *be a subgroup of a free group* $F=\mathfrak{G}(X)$, *let* M *be a proper characteristic subgroup of* H, *and let* s *and* t *be the minima of the lengths of the reduced words in* X *expressing the non-trivial elements of* H *and* M, *respectively; then* $s < t$.

Proof.   We use the set Y of free generators of H chosen in the second proof of Theorem V.1.d above, and let $w = k_1 \cdots k_s$ be a product of elements $k_i \in Y \cup Y^{-1}$ with $k_i k_{i+1} \neq 1$ for $i = 1, \cdots, s-1$. Then since each of the significant factors of the k_i appears in the reduced form of w as a word in $X \cup X^{-1}$, it follows that if $s=2$, $L(w) \geq L(k_i)$, and that if $s > 2$, $L(w) > L(k_i)$.

Now since any element of the form $k_1 k_2$ is a member of a free set of generators of H by V.3.a, it follows that no such element is in the proper characteristic subgroup M of H. Thus each non-trivial element of M must have length greater than some generator y_i of H, and hence must have length greater than s. It follows that $t > s$ and the lemma is proved.

The main theorem of this section is now immediate.

V.3.c. Theorem (*Levi*).   *If for each $i = 1, 2, \cdots, F_i$ is a free group such that F_{i+1} is a proper characteristic subgroup of F_i, then $\bigcap_{i=1}^{\infty} F_i = 1$.*

Proof.   Let $F_1 = \mathfrak{G}(X)$, and for each i, let m_i be the minimum of the lengths of the reduced words in X expressing the non-trivial elements of F_i. Then by V.3.b, $m_1 < m_2 < \cdots$ and the theorem follows.

4. Free products

For each α in an index set A let G_α be a group. We treat the elements of all the groups G_α as symbols and consider the set of words in these symbols. The product of two words is obtained by juxtaposition as in Section I.5; when two adjacent elements (or symbols) of a word belong to the same group G_α, they may be replaced by their product. It turns out that this set of words with this product operation and an appropriate inverse operation is a group, the free product of the G_α.

The object of this section is to introduce the free product of a set of groups and to develop some of its important properties. Our definition will be made in terms of a set of generators and relations for each of the given groups, but it will be seen that the free product depends in fact only on the given groups regardless of the generators and relations chosen to express them.

V.4.a. Definition.   For each α in an index set A let G_α be a given group and suppose that it is described by means of certain generators and relations, thus $G_\alpha = \mathfrak{G}(X_\alpha \mid M_\alpha)$. If for $\alpha, \beta \in A$, X_α is disjoint from X_β, then $\mathfrak{G}(\bigcup_{\alpha \in A} X_\alpha \mid \bigcup_{\alpha \in A} M_\alpha)$ is the **free product of the groups** G_α; it will be denoted by $\prod^*_{\alpha \in A} G_\alpha$, or if A is the set $\{1, \cdots, n\}$, by $G_1 * \cdots * G_n$. Each group G_α will be regarded as a subgroup of $\prod^*_{\alpha \in A} G_\alpha$ in the obvious way.

V.4.b. Example. If X is a set of symbols, then the free group $\mathfrak{G}(X)$ is isomorphic to the free product of the infinite cyclic groups $\mathfrak{G}(x)$ with $x \in X$.

Immediately obvious from the definition and Theorem 1.5.g is the following proposition.

V.4.c. Proposition. *If K is a group containing subgroups G_α for α in some set A, then there is a homomorphism from $\prod^*_{\alpha \in A} G_\alpha$ onto the subgroup $\mathfrak{G}(\bigcup_{\alpha \in A} G_\alpha)$ of K, which maps each subgroup G_α of the free product isomorphically onto the subgroup G_α of K.*

An important property of the free product is given in the following theorem. The proof is based on ideas similar to those of Section I.5, particularly, 1.5.g and I.5.h, and is left as an exercise for the reader.

V.4.d. Theorem. *Suppose that a group G is generated by some of its subgroups G_α with α in an index set A. Then $G \cong \prod^*_{\alpha \in A} G_\alpha$ if and only if for each group K and each set of homomorphisms ϕ_α of G_α into K, consisting of one homomorphism for each $\alpha \in A$, there exists a homomorphism ϕ of G into K so that for each $\alpha \in A$, ϕ restricted to G_α is equal to ϕ_α.*

It is an immediate consequence of V.4.d that the free product depends only on the groups G_α and is independent of the generators and relations chosen to express them.

Another important property of the free product which is derived easily from its description in terms of generators and relations is the following.

V.4.e. Theorem. *Let G be the free product $\prod_{\alpha \in A}^{*} G_\alpha$, and for $\alpha \in A$ let H_α be the normal closure of the subgroup of G generated by all G_β with $\beta \in A$, $\beta \neq \alpha$; then $G/H_\alpha \cong G_\alpha$.*

For each α in an index set A, let G_α be a group $\mathfrak{G}(X_\alpha \mid R_\alpha)$, and let the free product $G = \prod_{\alpha \in A}^{*} G_\alpha$ be given as $\mathfrak{G}(X \mid R)$ where $X = \bigcup_{\alpha \in A} X_\alpha$ and $R = \bigcup_{\alpha \in A} R_\alpha$. Then an element $g \in G$ may be expressed as a word in X; let the symbols of this word be grouped in parentheses so that each parenthesis contains symbols of only one X_α and so that the symbols of adjacent parentheses belong to different X_α. If X_{α_i} contains the symbols of the ith parenthesis, let g_{α_i} be the element of G_{α_i} which is expressed by these symbols; then the non-trivial element g of G may be described as a product $g_{\alpha_1} \cdots g_{\alpha_k}$ of non-trivial element g_{α_i} of G_{α_i} for $i = 1, \cdots, k$ and such that for $i = 1, \cdots, k-1$, $\alpha_i \neq \alpha_{i+1}$. Such an expression is a **normal form** of the element g. We now show that each non-trivial element g of G has precisely one normal form.

V.4.f. Theorem. *Each non-trivial element of a free product $G = \prod_{\alpha \in A}^{*} G_\alpha$ has exactly one normal form.*

Proof. In view of the remarks above, each non-trivial element of G has at least one normal form. If an element had two different normal forms, it would follow directly that the identity could be expressed as a product $h_{\alpha_1} \cdots h_{\alpha_n}$ with h_{α_i} a non-trivial element of G_{α_i} for each $i = 1, \cdots, n$ and with $\alpha_i \neq \alpha_{i+1}$ for $i = 1, \cdots, n-1$. On the other hand, we shall show that in each such word in the class of the identity, at least one h_{α_j} is trivial, and by this contradiction the theorem will be proved. To show this we let $k_{\alpha_1} \cdots k_{\alpha_m}$ be a product of elements k_{α_j} of G_{α_j} so that for $j = 1, \cdots, m-1$, $\alpha_j \neq \alpha_{j+1}$, and so that at least one k_{α_j} is in the class of the identity of G_{α_j} and hence of G. Then it is obvious that any expression obtainable from this product by means of an insertion of a word of $R = \bigcup_{\alpha \in A} R_\alpha$ has the same property. Accordingly we need only show that each word in the class of the identity may be obtained from the empty word by means of insertions alone. Indeed it is clear (since each deletion and insertion involves the symbols of only one X_α) that the first deletion in a sequence of operations taking the empty word to a word in its class may be combined with the insertions involving the symbols deleted to be replaced by one insertion. In this fashion all the deletions may be replaced by insertions and we see that a word in the class of the identity cannot be a product of non-trivial h_{α_j}, and hence that each non-trivial element has exactly one normal form.

Theorem V.4.f brings out the point again that the free product is independent of the choice of generators and relations to express the groups G_α.

V.4.g. Definition, Let g be an element of the free product $\prod_{\alpha \in A}^* G_\alpha$; if $g = g_{\alpha_1} \cdots g_{\alpha_n}$ with $g_{\alpha_i} \in G_{\alpha_i}$ and if $\alpha_i \neq \alpha_{i+1}$ for $i = 1, \cdots, n-1$, then $g_{\alpha_1} \cdots g_{\alpha_n}$ is the **normal form** of g and n is the **length** of g. The empty word is the **normal form** of 1 and its **length** is zero.

In view of Theorem V.4.f we see that the elements of the free product may be thought of in terms of their normal forms, the normal form of the product of two elements being obtained by writing down their normal forms in order and combining where possible the elements of the first normal form with those of the second. Theorem V.4.f has the following easy consequences, the proofs of which are good exercises for the reader.

V.4.h. Proposition. *If G_α and G_β, $\alpha \neq \beta$, are regarded as subgroups of $\prod_{\alpha \in A}^* G_\alpha$, then $G_\alpha \cap G_\beta = 1$.*

V.4.i. Theorem. *The center of a free product of two or more non-trivial groups is 1.*

V.4.j. Theorem. *An element of finite order of a free product $\prod_{\alpha \in A}^* G_\alpha$ is conjugate to an element of one of the G_α; in particular a free product of non-trivial torsion-free groups is torsion-free.*

Theorem V.1.d has a generalization for free products as follows.

V.4.k. Theorem (*Kurosh*). *If H is a subgroup of a free product $\prod_{\alpha \in A}^{*} G_{\alpha}$, then H is a free product of a free group and some conjugates of some subgroups of the G_{α}.*

The reader is referred to [19] for a recent proof of Theorem V.4.k and for references to other proofs.

We have already seen (V.4.b) that $C_{\infty} * C_{\infty}$ is a free group on two generators.   The remainder of this section will be devoted to a study of $C_2 * C_2$ and $C_2 * C_3$ and to relate these groups to groups encountered earlier.   The properties of these groups will be listed in a series of propositions; most of the proofs are left to the reader as exercises.

V.4.l. Proposition.   *The infinite dihedral group of I.5.m is isomorphic to $C_2 * C_2$.*

V.4.m. Proposition.   *Let $G = \mathfrak{G}(a, b \mid aba = bab)$ (so that G is the group of the trefoil knot as in I.5.p), let $x = ab^2$ and $y = ab$.   Then $x^2 = y^3$ is in the center of G, G is generated by x and y, G is isomorphic to $\mathfrak{G}(x, y \mid x^2 = y^3)$, $G/(y^3) \cong C_3 * C_2$, and finally (cf. V.4.i), (y^3) is the center of G.*

Now (cf. III.8.a) let $S(J, 2)$ denote the group of 2 by 2 matrices with integer entries and determinant 1, and let $P(J, 2)$ denote $S(J, 2)$ modulo its center (it is not hard to prove that the center consists of $\pm I_2$, with I_2 the 2 by 2 identity matrix).   We first need the following fact about $S(J, 2)$.

V.4.n. Lemma. $S(J, 2)$ *is generated by* $t = \begin{pmatrix} 0 & 1 \\ -1 & 0 \end{pmatrix}$ *and*

$$u = \begin{pmatrix} 0 & -1 \\ 1 & 1 \end{pmatrix}.$$

Proof.   Since the matrices of $S(J, 2)$ have determinant 1, those with a zero in the left column have either the form

$$\pm \begin{pmatrix} 1 & n \\ 0 & 1 \end{pmatrix} \quad \text{or} \quad \pm \begin{pmatrix} 0 & 1 \\ -1 & -n \end{pmatrix}$$

with n an integer.   Then since $t^2 = -I_2$, they are either $(tu)^n$, $t^2(tu)^n$, or $t(tu)^n$, $t^3(tu)^n$, and hence are in $\mathfrak{G}(t, u)$.

Suppose now that there is an element $v = \begin{pmatrix} a & b \\ c & d \end{pmatrix}$ of $S(J, 2)$ not in $\mathfrak{S}(t, u)$. Then neither a nor c is zero and we let v be chosen outside $\mathfrak{S}(t, u)$ so that the sum of the absolute values of the entries of the left column of v are minimal. If $|a| \geq |c|$, an integer r may be chosen so that $|a + rc| < |a|$. But then $(tu)^r v$ is not in $\mathfrak{S}(t, u)$; on the other hand,

$$(tu)^r v = \begin{pmatrix} 1 & r \\ 0 & 1 \end{pmatrix} \begin{pmatrix} a & b \\ c & d \end{pmatrix} = \begin{pmatrix} a + rc & b + rd \\ c & d \end{pmatrix}$$

and $|a + rc| + |c| < |a| + |c|$ contrary to the choice of v. If $|a| < |c|$, an integer s may be chosen so that $|sa + c| < |a|$; then since

$$(t^3 u^{-1})^s = \begin{pmatrix} 1 & 0 \\ s & 1 \end{pmatrix}$$

and since

$$\begin{pmatrix} 1 & 0 \\ s & 1 \end{pmatrix} \begin{pmatrix} a & b \\ c & d \end{pmatrix} = \begin{pmatrix} a & b \\ sa + c & sb + d \end{pmatrix},$$

it follows that the latter element is not in $\mathfrak{S}(t, u)$ again contrary to the choice of v. We conclude that $S(J, 2) = \mathfrak{S}(t, u)$ as the lemma asserts.

V.4.o. Proposition. *The free product $C_2 * C_3$ is isomorphic to $P(J, 2)$.*

Proof. Let $C_2 * C_3$ be given as $\mathfrak{G}(x, y \mid x^2 = y^3 = 1)$, let $P(J, 2)$ be generated by $t \equiv \begin{pmatrix} 0 & 1 \\ -1 & 0 \end{pmatrix}$ and $u \equiv \begin{pmatrix} 0 & -1 \\ 1 & 1 \end{pmatrix}$ (cf. V.4.n), let ϕ be defined on $\{x, y\}$ by the equations $x\phi = t$, $y\phi = u$, and let θ be the obvious extension of ϕ to $C_2 * C_3$. Then, since $t^2 = 1$ and $u^3 = 1$, by V.4.c, θ is a homomorphism of $C_2 * C_3$ onto $P(J, 2)$. Now the elements of $C_2 * C_3$ are products of xy and xy^{-1} either preceded or followed by x; and hence an element is in the kernel of θ only if a similar product in t, tu, and tu^{-1} is 1 or equivalently if a product of tu and tu^{-1} is $1 \equiv \begin{pmatrix} 1 & 0 \\ 0 & 1 \end{pmatrix}$ or $t \equiv \begin{pmatrix} 0 & 1 \\ -1 & 0 \end{pmatrix}$. On the other hand,

$$tu \equiv \begin{pmatrix} 1 & 1 \\ 0 & 1 \end{pmatrix}, \quad tu^{-1} \equiv \begin{pmatrix} 1 & 0 \\ 1 & 1 \end{pmatrix}$$

and hence, in any product of these two matrices, the sum of the coefficients is greater than 2. Thus the only element of $C_2 * C_3$ in the kernel of θ is 1, and θ is an isomorphism as the proposition asserts.

Since the groups $P(K, 2)$ of III.8.a, with K a finite prime field, are homomorphic images of $P(J, 2)$, we have the following interesting consequence of III.8.f.

V.4.p. Proposition. $C_2 * C_3$ has an infinite number of normal subgroups of finite index, and an infinite number of simple, homomorphic images.

5. Generalized free products

The notion of free product with an amalgamated subgroup is a generalization of the ordinary free product as developed in the last section. The ordinary free product is a free product in which the amalgamated subgroup is the trivial subgroup. The ideas underlying the notion of this generalized free product are developed here.

V.5.a. Definition.   For each α in an index set A let G_α be a group with subgroup K_α, and let ϕ_α be an isomorphism from a given group K onto K_α. If for each $\alpha \in A$, G_α is given by $\mathfrak{G}(X_\alpha \mid R_\alpha)$, and if X_α is disjoint from X_β when α is different from β with $\beta \in A$, then $\mathfrak{G}(\bigcup_{\alpha \in A} X_\alpha \mid \bigcup_{\alpha \in A} R_\alpha, \ k_\beta = k_\alpha \phi_\alpha^{-1} \phi_\beta$ for $k_\alpha \in K_\alpha$, $k_\beta \in K_\beta$, $\alpha, \ \beta \in A)$ is the **free product** of the groups G_α with the subgroups K_α **amalgamated** according to the isomorphisms $\phi_\alpha^{-1} \phi_\beta$, or, more briefly, the **free product** of the G_α with **amalgamated subgroup** K.

At this stage it is not clear that the free product of non-trivial groups G_α with an amalgamated subgroup is always non-trivial; it will be seen later that such a free product contains an isomorphic copy of each G_α, and that the intersection of any two of the G_α is the amalgamated subgroup.

V.5.b. Examples.   The free product $\prod_{\alpha \in A}^{*} G_\alpha$ is the free product of the G_α with the trivial subgroups amalgamated according to the obvious isomorphisms. The group (cf. V.4.m) of the trefoil knot

$\mathfrak{G}(x, y \mid x^2 = y^3)$ is the free product of two infinite cyclic groups $\mathfrak{G}(x)$ and $\mathfrak{G}(y)$ with the subgroup of index two of the first amalgamated with the subgroup of index three of the second according to the isomorphism mapping x^2 to y^3. The quaternion group Q_8 is a homomorphic image of the free product of two cyclic groups of order 4 with their subgroups of order two amalgamated in the obvious way.

Although the generalized free product was defined above in terms of generators and relations, it is in fact independent of their choice (see V.5.h below) just as is the case with the ordinary free product. Immediately obvious is the following analogue of V.4.c.

V.5.c. Proposition.   *Let K be a group containing subgroups G_α for α in some set A; for each α let H_α denote $\bigcap_{\alpha \in A} G_\alpha$ as a subgroup of G_α, and let P denote the free product of the G_α with the subgroups H_α amalgamated according to the obvious isomorphisms.   Then there is a homomorphism from P onto K which maps each subgroup G_α of K isomorphically onto the corresponding subgroup G_α of K.*

Now for each α in a set A let G_α be a group with subgroup H_α, and suppose that for each $\alpha \in A$ there is an isomorphism ϕ_α from a group H onto H_α.   We shall follow B. H. Neumann and construct the **permutational product** of the groups G_α as follows.   For each $\alpha \in A$ let T_α be a left transversal containing 1 of H_α in G_α, and let the maps τ_α and η_α be defined by the equation $g = (g\tau_\alpha)(g\eta_\alpha)$ for $g \in G_\alpha$ with $g\tau_\alpha \in T_\alpha$ and $g\eta_\alpha \in H_\alpha$.   Let V be the cartesian product of all the sets T_α and H.   Thus the elements of V have the form $(\cdots, t_\alpha, \cdots, h)$ with $h \in H$ and $t_\alpha \in T_\alpha$.   For each α and each element g_α of G_α, let ρ_{g_α} be the map defined on V by the equation $(\cdots, t_\beta, \cdots, t_\alpha, \cdots, h)\rho_{g_\alpha}$
$= (\cdots, t_\beta, \cdots, k\tau_\alpha, \cdots, (k\eta_\alpha)\phi_\alpha{}^{-1})$, with k denoting $t_\alpha(h\phi_\alpha)g_\alpha$.   Now each G_α has the form $T_\alpha H_\alpha$ and may be identified with the subset R_α of V consisting of those elements with $t_\beta = 1$ for $\beta \neq \alpha$, $\beta \in A$.   The action of ρ_{g_α} on R_α is then clearly the same as the action of ρ_{g_α} as a right multiplication (cf. Section I.1) of G_α.   It then follows easily that if ρ_{G_α} denotes the set of maps ρ_{g_α} with g_α in a fixed G_α, then ρ_{G_α} is isomorphic (cf. I.3.c) to G_α.   Furthermore, if $\alpha \neq \beta$, $\rho_{g_\alpha} = \rho_{g_\beta}$ if and only if $g_\alpha \in H_\alpha$, $g_\beta \in H_\beta$ and $g_\alpha \phi_\alpha{}^{-1}\phi_\beta = g_\beta$; thus $\rho_{G_\alpha} \cap \rho_{G_\beta} = \bigcap_{\alpha \in A} \rho_{G_\alpha}$

and is a subgroup isomorphic to H.   The subgroup K of the group of all one-one maps of V onto itself, which is generated by all the ρ_{G_α} is the **permutational product** of the G_α with the subgroups H_α **amalgamated**.

We summarize the results above in the following theorem.

V.5.d. Theorem (*B. H. Neumann*).   *If for each α in a set A, G_α is a group with a subgroup H_α isomorphic to a given group H, the permutational product of the groups G_α with the subgroups H_α amalgamated is a group generated by the G_α (strictly speaking, isomorphic copies of the G_α) in such a way that the intersection of any two G_α is equal to the intersection of all the G_α and is isomorphic to H.*

In view of V.5.d and the properties of the homomorphism of V.5.c, we have the following important result.

V.5.e. Theorem (*Schreier*).   *The free product of a set of groups G_α, α in some set A, with an amalgamated subgroup H, is a group generated by (copies of) the G_α in such a way that the intersection of any two G_α is equal to the intersection of them all and is isomorphic to H.*

The reader is referred to the essay (cf. [20]) by B. H. Neumann on free products of groups with amalgamations for a more detailed study of generalized free products.   Here we only give two examples to show that the amalgamation of more than one subgroup is not in general possible.

V.5.f. Examples (cf. [20]).   The symmetric group on four symbols S_4, and the cyclic group of order six $C_6 = C_2 \times C_3$, each has subgroups of order two and of order three.   But since S_4 has no element of order six, there can be no group containing S_4 and $C_2 \times C_3$ with a subgroup of order two and also a subgroup of order three amalgamated. We can argue further.   We consider the alternating group A_4 which is a split extension $[K_4]C_3$, and a Sylow 2-subgroup of S_4 which is a dihedral group D_8 of the form $[K_4]C_2$, and we form the free product

H of $[K_4]C_3$ and $[K_4]C_2$ with K_4 amalgamated. Then a generator of C_3 cannot commute with a generator of C_2 (as subgroups of H); for if they did commute, then by the properties of the homomorphism of V.5.c mapping H onto S_4, S_4 would have an element of order 6. We can conclude from this type of argument that there exists no group generated by the three groups $A_4 = [K_4]C_3$, $D_8 = [K_4]C_2$, and $C_6 = C_2 \times C_3$, with the common subgroups K_4, C_3, and C_2, amalgamated in pairs.

We return to the study of the free product with one amalgamated subgroup and show that the elements may be given a normal form. We begin with a lemma, the proof of which is modeled after that of Theorem V.4.f; it is left to the reader.

V.5.g. Lemma.   *Let G be the free product of the groups G_α with the amalgamated subgroup K as in V.5.a, that is, G is the group*

$$\mathfrak{G}(\bigcup_{\alpha \in A} X_\alpha \mid \bigcup_{\alpha \in A} R_\alpha, \; k_\beta = k_\alpha \phi_\alpha{}^{-1} \phi_\beta \text{ for } k_\alpha \in K_\alpha, \; k_\beta \in K_\beta, \; \alpha, \; \beta \in A);$$

and let the element g of G be expressed as a word $g_{\alpha_1} \cdots g_{\alpha_n}$ with g_{α_i} a word in X_{α_i} and $X_{\alpha_i} \neq X_{\alpha_{i+1}}$ for $i = 1, \cdots, n-1$. If g is in K, then at least one of the g_{α_i} represents an element of K_{α_i}.

V.5.h. Theorem (*Schreier*).   *Let G be the free product of groups G_α (α in an index set A) with subgroups K_α amalgamated according to some isomorphisms ϕ_α; and for each $\alpha \in A$, let T_α be a right transversal of K_α in G_α. Then each element $g \in G$ has a unique expression in the form $k t_{\alpha_1} \cdots t_{\alpha_n}$ with k in the common subgroup K, with $t_{\alpha_i} \in T_{\alpha_i}$, $t_{\alpha_i} \notin K_{\alpha_i}$, for $i = 1, \cdots, n$, and with $G_{\alpha_i} \neq G_{\alpha_{i+1}}$ for $i = 1, \cdots, n-1$.*

Proof.   It is clear that each element of G can be written as a product $g_{\alpha_1} \cdots g_{\alpha_n}$ with $g_{\alpha_i} \in G_{\alpha_i}$ and $G_{\alpha_i} \neq G_{\alpha_{i+1}}$ for $i = 1, \cdots, n-1$. If $n = 1$ the element has the form $g_{\alpha_1} = k_{\alpha_1} t_{\alpha_1}$ with $k_{\alpha_1} \in K_{\alpha_1} = K$, and $t_{\alpha_1} \in T_{\alpha_1}$. We shall show by induction on n that each element has at least one such expression as in the theorem. Indeed, by the induction assumption $g_{\alpha_2} \cdots g_{\alpha_n}$ may be written $k_2 t_{\alpha_2} \cdots t_{\alpha_n}$ and hence g has the expression $(g_{\alpha_1} k_2) t_{\alpha_2} \cdots t_{\alpha_n}$; but k_2 may be replaced by an element of G_{α_1}

and $g_{\alpha_1} k_2$ then has the form $k t_{\alpha_1}$, so that finally g has the form $k t_{\alpha_1} \cdots t_{\alpha_n}$ as was to be shown.

To show the uniqueness of the above expression, we suppose that g also has the form $k_1 s_{\alpha_1} \cdots s_{\alpha_m}$ where without loss of generality $s_{\alpha_m} \neq t_{\alpha_n}$ (since otherwise we could consider the element $g t_{\alpha_n}{}^{-1}$ and so on). Then $s_{\alpha_1} \cdots s_{\alpha_m} t_{\alpha_n}{}^{-1} \cdots t_{\alpha_1}{}^{-1}$ is an element of K which can be expressed as a product of g_{α_i} with each g_{α_i} in G_{α_i} but not in K_{α_i} (if s_{α_m} and $t_{\alpha_n}{}^{-1}$ are in the same G_α, their product is not in K_α), and adjacent G_{α_i} distinct. But this is contrary to V.5.g and the theorem is proved.

V.5.i. Definition. The expression $k t_{\alpha_1} \cdots t_{\alpha_n}$ in Theorem V.5.h is the **normal form** of the element g (it is of course dependent only on the choice of the transversals T_α); and n is the **length** of g (it is independent of the choice of the transversals T_α).

Immediately obvious is the following.

V.5.j. Proposition. *An element of the free product of groups G_α with amalgamated subgroup K has length 1 if and only if it is in one of the G_α but not in K_α; it has length zero if and only if it is in K.*

It is now easy to prove the following theorem about the elements of finite order in a generalized free product (cf. V.4.j).

V.5.k. Theorem. *Let G be the free product of groups G_α with amalgamated subgroup K, and let g be an element of finite order in G; then g is conjugate to an element of length less than or equal to 1.*

Proof. Suppose that b is an element of minimal length in its conjugate class in G and that this length is greater than 1. Thus b has the normal form $k t_1 \cdots t_n$ with $n > 1$. Then t_n and t_1 belong to different G_α; for otherwise $b^{t_n{}^{-1}}$ would have length less than n contrary to the minimality of the length of b. Since t_1 and t_n belong to different G_α, it follows inductively that the length of b^m is mn and hence that b has infinite order. The theorem now follows immediately.

V.5.1. Corollary. *The free product of torsion-free groups with an amalgamated subgroup is torsion-free.*

We can also prove the following theorem now.

V.5.m. Theorem. *Let G be the free product of finitely many (but more than one) finite groups G_i with proper subgroups K_i amalgamated; then G has a normal subgroup of finite index and hence G is not simple.*

Proof. It is clear (as in the proof of V.5.k) that an element of length two has infinite order and hence that G is infinite. On the other hand the permutational product of the G_i with the subgroups K_i amalgamated is finite and hence G has a finite homomorphic image. This proves the theorem.

6. Applications of the generalized free product

In this section we show how to embed a group with a family of pairs of isomorphic subgroups into a group in which each pair of isomorphic subgroups is conjugate. Then we apply this result to construct a group in which any two non-trivial elements are conjugate. Finally we give a recent interesting example of a non-Hopf group (cf. [3]), that is, a group isomorphic to a proper factor group of itself.

V.6.a. Theorem (*Higman, Neumann, and Neumann*). *For α in some index set M, let the group G have subgroups A_α and B_α, and suppose that for each α in M there is an isomorphism ψ_α defined on A_α so that $A_\alpha \psi_\alpha = B_\alpha$; then there exists a group H containing G as well as elements h_α so that $a_\alpha{}^{h_\alpha} = a_\alpha \psi_\alpha$ for each $\alpha \in M$ and each $a_\alpha \in A_\alpha$. Furthermore, if G is torsion-free, then so also is H.*

Proof. For each $\alpha \in M$ let θ_α be an isomorphism of G onto a group G_α and let H_1 be the semi-direct product of $G \times \prod_{\alpha \in M} G_\alpha$ with a free abelian group $\prod_{\alpha \in M} (s_\alpha)$ with each s_α acting as the isomorphism θ_α on G and $\theta_\alpha{}^{-1}$ on G_α so that s_α induces an automorphism of order two which permutes G with G_α; thus each element of $\prod_{\beta \in M, \beta \neq \alpha} G_\beta$ commutes with s_α, whereas if $g \in G$, $g_\alpha \in G_\alpha$, and $(g, g_\alpha) \in G \times G_\alpha$, then $(g, g_\alpha)^{s_\alpha} = (g_\alpha \theta_\alpha{}^{-1}, g\theta_\alpha)$. Similarly, let γ be an isomorphism from G onto a group F, and for each $\alpha \in M$ let ϕ_α be an isomorphism of F onto a group F_α, and let H_2 be the semi-direct product of $F \times \prod_{\alpha \in M} F_\alpha$ with a free abelian group $\prod_{\alpha \in M} (t_\alpha)$ with each t_α acting as the isomorphism ϕ_α on F and $\phi_\alpha{}^{-1}$ on F_α so that t_α induces an automorphism of order two which permutes F with F_α; thus each element of $\prod_{\beta \in M, \beta \neq \alpha} F_\beta$ commutes with t_α, whereas if $f \in F$, $f_\alpha \in F_\alpha$, and $(f, f_\alpha) \in F \times F_\alpha$, then $(f, f_\alpha)^{t_\alpha} = (f_\alpha \phi_\alpha{}^{-1}, f\phi_\alpha)$.

Then there is an isomorphism σ from the subgroup $G \times \prod_{\alpha \in M} A_\alpha \theta_\alpha$ of H_1 onto the subgroup $F \times \prod_{\alpha \in M} B_\alpha \phi_\alpha$ of H_2 so that if $g \in G$ and $a_\alpha \theta_\alpha \in A_\alpha \theta_\alpha$ (as elements of H_1), then $g\sigma = g\gamma$ and $a_\alpha \theta_\alpha \sigma = a_\alpha \psi_\alpha \gamma \phi_\alpha$. If H is the free product of H_1 and H_2 with the subgroups $G \times \prod_{\alpha \in M} A_\alpha \theta_\alpha$ and $F \times \prod_{\alpha \in M} B_\alpha \gamma \phi_\alpha$ amalgamated according to the isomorphism σ, then in G as a subgroup of H, we have $a_\alpha{}^{s_\alpha t_\alpha} = a_\alpha \psi_\alpha$ for each $\alpha \in M$ and $a_\alpha \in A_\alpha$; and the first statement of the theorem follows.

It is clear that H_1 and H_2 are torsion-free when G is torsion-free. Hence in this case H is torsion-free in view of V.5.1, and the second statement of the theorem is also proved.

V.6.b. Theorem (*Higman, Neumann, and Neumann*). *Let n be a fixed integer or infinity. Then any group G can be embedded in a group in which all the elements of order n are conjugate.*

Proof. By V.6.a, G can be embedded in a group G_1 in which all the elements of order n of G are conjugate. Then for each $k \geq 1$, G_k can be embedded in a group G_{k+1} so that the elements of order n of G_k are conjugate in G_{k+1}. The ascending union $G_\infty = \bigcup_{k=1}^{\infty} G_k$ is a group so that any two elements of G_∞ are conjugate in G_∞. This proves the theorem.

V.6.c. Corollary (*Higman, Neumann, and Neumann*). *There exists a group so that any two elements not the identity are conjugate.*

Proof. Let G be any torsion-free group and let n denote infinity. Then the groups G_k in the proof of V.6.b are torsion-free by V.6.a.

Hence G_∞ is torsion-free and any two elements not 1 are conjugate in G_∞. This proves the theorem.

By way of contrast with V.6.c, the only finite group with only one class of non-identity elements has order two.

We now give the following example of a non-Hopf group (i.e., a group isomorphic to a proper factor of itself) which is due to Baumslag and Solitar. For other examples and a further discussion of Hopf groups, the reader is referred to [11] and [21].

V.6.d. Theorem.   *Let G denote the group $\mathfrak{G}(a, h \mid (a^h)^2 = a^3)$, and let σ denote the extension to G of the map defined by the equations $a\sigma = a^2$ $h\sigma = h$.   Then σ is a homomorphism of G onto G which is not an isomorphism; and hence G is a non-Hopf group.*

Proof.   Since $(a\sigma^{h\sigma})^2 = (a^{2h})^2 = a^6 = (a\sigma)^3$, it follows from I.5.g that σ is a homomorphism of G onto the subgroup $\mathfrak{S}(a\sigma, h\sigma)$ of G. Since $a^2 \in G\sigma$ and $a\sigma^{h\sigma} = a^3 \in G\sigma$, it follows that $\mathfrak{S}(a\sigma, h\sigma) = G$ and that σ is a homomorphism from G onto G. Now $a\sigma = a^2$ and $a\sigma^{h\sigma} = a^3$; hence $a\sigma$ and $a\sigma^{h\sigma}$ generate an abelian subgroup of $G\sigma$. We shall show that a and a^h do not generate an abelian subgroup of G and from this it will follow that σ is not an isomorphism and the theorem will be proved.

To show that the subgroup generated by a and a^h is not abelian we proceed as follows. Let A_1 and B_1 be infinite cyclic groups generated by elements a_1 and b_1, respectively; and let K_1 be the free product of A_1 and B_1 with the subgroups $(a_1{}^3)$ and $(b_1{}^2)$ amalgamated according to an isomorphism which maps $b_1{}^2$ onto $a_1{}^3$. Then by V.6.a there is a group H_1 containing K_1 and an element h_1 so that $a_1{}^{h_1} = b_1$. If the element a^h of G is denoted by b, then G can be described by the three generators and two relations $\mathfrak{G}(a, b, h) \mid a^h = b, b^2 = a^3)$. It is now clear that the extension ϕ to G of the map defined by the equations $a\phi = a_1$, $b\phi = b_1$, $h\phi = h_1$ is a homomorphism of G onto the subgroup G_1 of H_1 generated by K_1 and h_1. Now the restriction of ϕ to the subgroup K of G generated by a and $b = a^h$ is a homomorphism onto K_1 which obviously has an inverse onto G and hence is an isomorphism. Thus K is isomorphic to a non-abelian free product and the proof of the theorem is complete.

Chapter VI

NILPOTENT GROUPS AND
RELATED TOPICS

In Chapter II we studied an important class of groups, the abelian groups; and we observed in Section III.1 that a group is abelian if and only if it is equal to its center. It turns out that non-trivial abelian groups are nilpotent of class 1, if we define a group to be nilpotent of class n, inductively, as follows: a group is **nilpotent of class n** $(n > 0)$ if modulo its center it is nilpotent of class $n-1$ (the trivial group is defined to be nilpotent of class 0). It follows from this definition and from III.1.r that each finite p-group is nilpotent (of some class); thus the class of nilpotent groups includes many interesting types of groups. In particular, the groups of order p^4 when p is a prime and the quaternion groups (see VI.4.b) below will be studied in this chapter.

Our definition of nilpotency will actually be made to depend on the fact that one of the members of the lower central series (see VI.1.a and VI.1.b below) is trivial, and it will be shown that this definition is equivalent to the one given above. Various criteria are given that a finite group be nilpotent, and in some instances these criteria will be extended to some types of infinite groups.

We shall show in this chapter that any group has a unique maximal locally nilpotent normal subgroup, the **Hirsch-Plotkin radical**: and in particular shall show that a group satisfying the normalizer condition is its own Hirsch-Plotkin radical. Finally we shall give some results stating conditions which imply that an element is in the Hirsch-Plotkin radical.

1. Nilpotent groups

VI.1.a. Definition. The **lower central series** of a group G is the chain of subgroups, $G = G^1$, $G^2 = [G, G]$, $\cdots$, $G^n = [G^{n-1}, G]$, $\cdots$, $G^\omega = \bigcap_{n=1}^{\infty} G^n$, $G^{\omega+1}$, $\cdots$, continued transfinitely if necessary.

The following facts are immediately obvious.

(i) *The members of the lower central series of a group G are fully invariant in G.*

(ii) *There is an ordinal α so that $G^\alpha = G^{\alpha+1}$. If for some natural number n, $G^n = G^{n+1}$, then $G^{n+r} = G^n$ for each natural number r, $G^n = G^\omega$, and the lower central series has only a finite number of distinct terms; in particular if G is a finite group, there is an n so that $G^n = G^\omega$.*

VI.1.b. Definition. The group G is **nilpotent** if for some non-negative integer n, $G^{n+1} = 1$; G is nilpotent of **class n, has class n,** or is a **class n group,** if n is the least integer so that $G^{n+1} = 1$.

(iii) *A non-trivial abelian group is nilpotent of class 1.*

(iv) *A subgroup of a nilpotent group of class n is nilpotent of class at most n.*

(v) *A cartesian product of nilpotent groups of class at most n is nilpotent of class at most n.*

Since our definition of nilpotency is given in terms of commutators, a knowledge of the behavior of commutators under homomorphism is important. Accordingly, the following continuation of the statement of Theorem I.3.t is fundamental to the further study of nilpotent groups.

VI.1.c. Theorem. *In the notation of I.3.t, the following statement holds: If A and B are in $\mathscr{S}$, then $K[A, B]\theta = [A\theta, B\theta]$.*

The proof of VI.1.c is direct, as is also the proof of its corollaries below; they are left to the reader.

VI.1.d. Corollary.   *If G is a group and k and n integers with $1 \le k \le n$, then $(G/G^n)^k = G^k/G^n$.*

VI.1.e. Corollary.   *If G is a nilpotent group of class n and θ is a homomorphism of G, then $G\theta$ is nilpotent of class at most n.*

In view of (iv), VI.1.e, and (v), we have the following consequences of I.8.u.

VI.1.f. Theorem.   *The nilpotent groups of class at most n constitute a variety.*

In order to simplify the printing it is convenient at this point to introduce the following notation. Whether $A, B, C, \cdots, N$ are subgroups, subsets, or elements, we write $[A, B, C]$ for $[[A, B], C]$ and $[A, B, C, \cdots, N]$ for $[\cdots[A, B], C], \cdots, N]$; it should be emphasized that the "norming" is from the left and that $[A, B, C]$ does not denote $[A, [B, C]]$. We shall also use the notation $[A, nB]$ $(n > 0)$ to denote $[A, (n-1)B, B]$, it being understood that $[A, 0B] = A$.

We can now easily give the proof of the following proposition.

VI.1.g. Proposition.   *A normal non-trivial subgroup H of a nilpotent group G intersects the center of G in a non-trivial subgroup; in particular a non-trivial nilpotent group always has a non-trivial center.*

Proof. Since H is non-trivial $[H, 0G] \ne 1$. Let k be the least integer so that $[H, kG] = 1$. Then $[H, (k-1)G]$ is a non-trivial subgroup of the center of G as the proposition asserts.

By way of contrast with VI.1.g we have the following criterion for a group to be nilpotent.

VI.1.h. Proposition.   *Let G be a group and let Z be a non-trivial subgroup in the center of G; if G/Z is nilpotent, then so also is G.*

Proof. Since G/Z is nilpotent, there is a natural number n so that $(G/Z)^n = 1$. This means that $G^n \le Z$ and then, since Z is central that $G^{n+1} = 1$. Thus G is nilpotent as was to be shown.

In view of III.1.r and VI.1.h an easy induction gives the following important theorem.

VI.1.i. Theorem.   *If p is a prime, a finite p-group is nilpotent.*

Theorem VI.1.i has the following corollary which follows immediately from (v).

VI.1.j. Corollary.   *A finite group is nilpotent if it is the direct product of its Sylow p-subgroups.*

The identities of the next proposition are basic to the study of nilpotent groups (the reader is reminded here that a^c denotes $c^{-1}ac$).

VI.1.k. Proposition.   *If a, b, c are any elements of a group G, then*

(1*) $[a, bc] = [a, c][a, b]^c$;

and

(2*) $[ac, b] = [a, b]^c[c, b]$.

If $[a, b]$ commutes with c, then

(1) $[a, bc] = [a, c][a, b]$

and

(2) $[ac, b] = [a, b][c, b]$.

If $[a, b]$ commutes with a and b, then

(3) $[a^m, b^n] = [a, b]^{mn}$ *for all integers m and n*

and

(4) $(ab)^n = a^n b^n [b, a]^{C_{n,2}}$ *for positive n with $C_{n,2}$ the binomial coefficient $n(n-1)/2$.*

In particular (1), (2), (3), *and* (4) *hold in all class 2 groups.*

Proof.   To prove (1*) and (2*) we note that

$$[a, bc] = a^{-1}a^{bc} = a^{-1}a^c(a^{-1})^c a^{bc} = [a, c][a, b]^c$$

and that

$$[ac, b] = (b^{-1})^{ac}b = (b^{-1})^{ac}b^c(b^{-1})^cb = [a, b]^c[c, b].$$

Then (1) and (2) follow immediately from (1*) and (2*).

For $m=1$ and n positive, (3) follows by induction on n starting with $b=c$ in (1). Next an induction on m using (2) gives (3) for all positive m and n. Since for x, y in G, $1 = [x, yy^{-1}] = [x, y][x, y^{-1}]$, it follows that $[x, y]^{-1} = [x, y^{-1}]$, and similarly $[x, y] = [x^{-1}, y]$. Consequently (3) holds for all integral m and n.

To prove (4) we observe first that $ba = ab[b, a]$, and then that $(ab)^2 = a(ba)b = a^2b^2[b, a]$. Since for positive n, $C_{n,2} + C_{n,1} = C_{n+1,2}$, an induction on n gives (4); for

$$(ab)^{n+1} = aba^nb^n[b, a]^{C_{n,2}} = a^{n+1}b^{n+1}[b, a]^{C_{n,2}+n} = a^{n+1}b^{n+1}[b, a]^{C_{n+1,2}}$$

as was to be shown. Since the commutator subgroup of a class 2 group is in the center, the last assertion of the proposition follows and the proof is complete.

The following is an easy consequence of the first two equations of VI.1.k.

VI.1.l. Proposition. *If A, B, C, D are normal subgroups of a group G, then $[AB, C] = [A, C][B, C]$, and $[AB, CD] = [A, C][A, D][B, C][B, D]$; more generally if A_α and B_β are normal subgroups of G, α and β in some index sets M and N, respectively, then $[\mathfrak{S}(A_\alpha, \alpha \in M), \mathfrak{S}(B_\beta, \beta \in N)] = \mathfrak{S}([A_\alpha, B_\beta], \alpha \in M, \beta \in N)$. Furthermore, if $G = \prod_{\alpha \in M} A_\alpha$, then $G^k = \prod_{\alpha \in M} A_\alpha{}^k$ for each natural number k.*

Some of the basic theorems about abelian groups carry over to nilpotent groups. In particular, a nilpotent group has a unique Sylow p-subgroup for each prime p and, consequently, a periodic nilpotent group is a direct product of its Sylow p-subgroups. Our next major goal is a proof of the above facts; in order to do this we first introduce the notion of nilpotent products of groups and give some of the elementary facts about them as a means of studying in particular the most general nilpotent groups generated by two elements.

VI.1.m. Definition. Let F be the free product of two groups A and B; and let n be a natural number; then the **n-th nilpotent product**

of A and B is the factor group $F/(F^{n+1} \cap [A, B])$.   It will be denoted here by $A \circledn B$.

It is clear that the first nilpotent product $A \circled1 B$ is the direct product $A \times B$.

VI.1.n. Proposition.   *If A and B are groups, the subgroup $[A, B]$ of the free product $F = A * B$ is a normal subgroup of F; furthermore $F/[A, B]$ is isomorphic to the direct product $A \times B$.*

Proof.   If a, c are in A and $b \in B$, it follows from (2^*) of VI.1.k that $[a, b]^c$ is in $[A, B]$.   It follows that $[A, B]^A \le [A, B]$.   By a similar argument it follows that $[A, B]^B \le [A, B]$, and since A and B generate F it follows that $[A, B]$ is normal in F.   For the second statement of the proposition we observe that $[A, B]$ is in the kernel of the natural homomorphism from F onto $A \times B$, and that there is a natural homomorphism from $A \times B$ onto $F/[A, B]$.   Hence $F/[A, B]$ is isomorphic to $A \times B$, as was to be shown.

VI.1.o. Corollary.   *Let A and B be groups nilpotent of class at most n and let F denote $A * B$; then $A \circledn B$ is F/F^{n+1} and hence is nilpotent of class at most n.*

Proof. $F^{n+1} \le [A, B]$ and hence $F^{n+1} \cap [A, B] = F^{n+1}$.

We state the following proposition which is of interest in connection with nilpotent products; the reader may supply the proof directly or may consult [28] for a proof.

VI.1.p. Proposition.   *If A and B are abelian groups, then the commutator subgroup of $A \circled2 B$ is isomorphic to the tensor product of A and B.*

The facts which we shall need about the nilpotent product for the proof of our next theorem are as follows.

VI.1.q. Proposition.   *If k and m are relatively prime, then $C_k \circledn C_m = C_k \times C_m$ for each natural number n.*

Proof. Let G denote $C_k \circledn C_m$ and suppose that $n > 1$. If a is a generator of C_k and b a generator of C_m, then (since there are integers r and s so that $kr + ms = 1$) in G modulo G^3, $[a, b] = [a, b]^{kr+ms} \equiv [a^{kr}, b][a, b^{ms}]$ by (3) of VI.1.k; but the latter expression is 1 in view of the orders of a and b. It follows that $G^2 = G^3$. Now by VI.1.o, $G^{n+1} = 1$; and by (ii), $G^2 = G^{n+1}$. It follows that $G^2 = 1$ and hence that G is in fact the direct product $C_k \times C_m$, as was to be shown.

VI.1.r. Corollary. *In a nilpotent group elements of relatively prime orders commute.*

We list some further facts about nilpotent products which the interested reader will find instructive to prove.

VI.1.s. Proposition. *If Π and Σ are disjoint sets of primes and K is a Π-group and M a Σ-group, then $K \circledn M = K \times M$ for each natural number n.*

VI.1.t. Proposition. *A p-quasicyclic subgroup of a periodic nilpotent group is in the center of the group.*

VI.1.u. Proposition. *The set of triplets of rational numbers (k, m, n) can be made into a group with a product defined by the equation $(k, m, n)(r, s, t) = (k + r + ns, m + s, n + t)$ and with the inverse of (k, m, n) defined to be $(mn - k, -m, -n)$; it is isomorphic to the second nilpotent product of the group of additive rationals with itself.*

We now give a lemma which together with VI.1.r easily enables us to prove Theorem VI.1.w below.

VI.1.v. Lemma. *If G is a nilpotent group of class n and if G/G^2 has prime power exponent p^m, then for $k = 1, 2, \cdots, n$, G^k/G^{k+1} has exponent dividing p^m, and consequently G has exponent dividing p^{mn}.*

Proof. For $n = 1$, the lemma is trivially true; then let G be of class n, $n > 1$. We assume by induction on n that the lemma is true for

$\overline{G} = G/G^n$, noting that G^n is in the center of G. Since for $k = 1, 2, \cdots$, $n-1$, $\overline{G}^k/\overline{G}^{k+1} \cong G^k/G^{k+1}$, it is only necessary to prove that G^n (which is G^n/G^{n+1}) has exponent dividing p^m. We do this as follows.

If $g \in G$, $h \in G^{n-1}$, then $[g, h] \in G^n \leq \mathfrak{Z}(G)$, and hence, by Lemma VI.1.k, $[g, h^{p^m}] = [g, h^{p^m}] = 1$; for $\overline{h}^{p^m} = 1$ and hence $h^{p^m} \in \mathfrak{Z}(G)$. It follows that the abelian group $[G^{n-1}, G] = G^n$ has exponent dividing p^m, as was to be shown. From this and the induction assumption that G/G^n has exponent dividing $p^{m(n-1)}$, it follows that G has exponent dividing p^{mn} and this proves the lemma.

VI.1.w. Theorem. *A nilpotent group G has a unique Sylow p-subgroup for each prime p; and the subset of periodic elements of G is the direct product of these Sylow p-subgroups.*

Proof. If g and h are p-elements of G, then Lemma VI.1.v is applicable to $\mathfrak{S}(g, h)$; consequently $\mathfrak{S}(g, h)$ is a p-group and gh^{-1} is a p-element. Thus the set of p-elements S_p is a subgroup, the unique Sylow p-subgroup of G.

Now from Corollary VI.1.r, it follows that the p-elements commute with the q-elements if q is a p'-number and hence, if Λ denotes the set of all primes, $\mathfrak{S}(S_p, p \in \Lambda) = \prod_{p \in \Lambda} S_p$. It is clear that this subgroup contains all the periodic elements of G, so that the proof of the theorem is complete.

The following corollary is the converse of VI.1.j.

VI.1.x. Corollary. *A finite nilpotent group is a direct product of its Sylow p-subgroups.*

We conclude this section by proving that the Frattini subgroup of a nilpotent group contains the derived group; this is a fact which for finite groups is a characterization of nilpotent groups (cf. Theorem VI.3.o below).

VI.1.y. Theorem. *The Frattini subgroup of a nilpotent group contains the derived group.*

Proof.   Let G be a nilpotent group.   It will be sufficient to show that the elements of G^2 are non-generators of G or, equivalently, that if H is a subgroup of G with $G = G^2H$, then $G = H$.   We do this as follows.   Let G be any group and suppose that H is a subgroup such that $G = G^kH$ for some natural number k.   Then G^k/G^{k+1} is in the center of G/G^{k+1} so that $[G^kH/G^{k+1}, G^kH/G^{k+1}] = H^2G^{k+1}/G^{k+1}$; but this means that $[G^kH, G^kH] \leq H^2G^{k+1} \leq HG^{k+1}$.   Suppose now that $G = G^2H$.   The foregoing shows that $G^2 \leq HG^3$ so that $G = HG^2 \leq HG^3$ and $G = HG^3$; it follows that $G = G^tH$ for each natural number t, and hence when G is nilpotent it follows that $G = H$, as was to be shown.   This proves the theorem.

VI.1.z. Corollary.   *If G is a nilpotent group and G/G^2 is cyclic, then G is cyclic.*

In view of the above theorem, if G is a nilpotent group and G/G^2 is a direct sum of cyclic subgroups, then the cardinality of a minimal set of generators of G is equal to the cardinality of a minimal set of generators of G/G^2.

In view of I.3.t with VI.1.y, there is a one-one correspondence between the maximal subgroups of G and those of G/G^2, and hence from II.1.h we have the following extension of a part of VI.1.y.

VI.1.za. Theorem.   *If G is a periodic nilpotent group and Λ is the set of all primes, then $\Phi(G) = \bigcap_{p \in \lambda} G_{p,1}$ (the notation $G_{p,1}$ is explained in VI.2.f below).*

2. Residually nilpotent groups

An interesting extension of the notion of nilpotency may be obtained by requiring that $G^\omega = 1$ in place of the requirement that $G^n = 1$.   A group G such that $G^\omega = 1$ will be seen to be **residually nilpotent**. We shall consider some elementary properties of residually nilpotent groups in this section and show in particular that free groups are residually nilpotent.

VI.2.a. Definition. A group G has a property **residually** if for each non-identity element $g \in G$ there is a homomorphism θ_g of G such that $G\theta_g$ has the property and $g\theta_g \neq 1$. In particular, a group G is **residually nilpotent** if for each non-identity element $g \in G$ there is a homomorphism θ_g of G so that $G\theta_g$ is nilpotent and $g\theta_g \neq 1$.

Two obvious properties of residually nilpotent groups are as follows.

(i) *Subgroups of residually nilpotent groups are residually nilpotent.*
(ii) *Any cartesian product or direct product of nilpotent groups is residually nilpotent.*

On the other hand, a homomorphic image of a residually nilpotent group need not be residually nilpotent as will be seen by the example (VI.2.d below) of the infinite dihedral group.

First we give the characterization of residually nilpotent groups mentioned above.

VI.2.b. Proposition. *A group G is residually nilpotent if and only if $G^\omega = 1$.*

Proof. Let G be a group and for each α in an index set A let K_α range over the family $\mathscr{F}$ of normal subgroups of G such that G/K_α is nilpotent. Then it is clear that G is residually nilpotent if and only if $\bigcap_{\alpha \in A} K_\alpha = 1$. It is also clear that for each natural number n, G^n is in $\mathscr{F}$; and furthermore that each K_α of $\mathscr{F}$ contains some G^n Thus $G^\omega = \bigcap_{\alpha \in A} K_\alpha$, and the proposition follows.

VI.2.c. Corollary. *A finite group is residually nilpotent if and only if it is nilpotent.*

VI.2.d. Example. The infinite dihedral group $D_\infty = \mathfrak{G}(a, b \mid abab, b^2)$ (cf. I.5.m) has a sequence of normal subgroups $K_i = (a^{2^i})$ for $i = 1, 2, \cdots$ so that D_∞/K_i is a nilpotent dihedral group $D_{2^{i+1}}$ of order 2^{i+1}. Since $\bigcap_{i=1}^\infty K_i = 1$, D_∞ is residually nilpotent. On the other hand, the dihedral group D_{2n} of order not a power of 2 is a non-nilpotent (since it is not a direct product of p groups) image of D_∞.

Theorem VI.1.w carries over directly to periodic residually nilpotent groups as follows.

VI.2.e. Theorem.   *A periodic residually nilpotent group has a unique Sylow p-subgroup for each prime p and is a direct product of its Sylow p-subgroups.*

The proof is direct and is left to the reader.

In order to prove that free groups are residually nilpotent it will first be convenient to introduce the derived p-series.

VI.2.f. Definition.   If G is a group and p a prime, $G_{p,1}$ will denote the subgroup $\mathfrak{S}(G^2, pG)$, and for $i = 1, 2, \cdots, G_{p,i+1}$ will denote $(G_{p,i})_{p,1}$. The sequence of subgroups $G_{p,1}, G_{p,2}, \cdots$ is the **derived p-series of G,** and the intersection $\bigcap_{n=1}^{\infty} G_{p,n}$ of its members will be denoted by $G_{p,\omega}$.

We note the following immediately.

(iii) *If G is a group and p a prime, then for each natural number n, $G_{p,n}$ and also $G_{p,\omega}$ are fully invariant subgroups of G.*

(iv) *If G is a group and p a prime, then $G_{p,1}$ is the intersection of all the subgroups H such that G/H is an elementary abelian p-group.*

(v) *If G is a group, p a prime, and n a natural number, then $G/G_{p,n}$ is a locally finite p-group (by III.6.r) and hence is locally nilpotent (by VI.1.i).*

(vi) *If G is a finite group, then $G_{p,\omega}$ is the only member of its own derived p-series generated by p'-elements.*

(vii) *If F is a free group and p a prime, then $F > F_{p,1}$ (since F has a non-trivial elementary abelian p-group as homomorphic image), and consequently the derived p-series of F is infinite.*

VI.2.g. Theorem (*Magnus*).   *Every free group is residually nilpotent.*

Proof.   Let F be a free group $\mathfrak{G}(X)$ with $|X| > 1$ (since the infinite cyclic group is obviously residually nilpotent). By VI.2.b it will be sufficient to show that $F^\omega = 1$. Suppose then that $F^\omega \neq 1$ and that there is an $f \neq 1$ in F^ω. Since f is in F^n for each natural number n, there is a countable subset Y of X so that if H denotes $\mathfrak{S}(Y)$, then f is in H^ω. Since Y and consequently H are countable, it follows from

V.2.d that H is contained in a free group J generated by two elements and that $J^\omega \neq 1$.

On the other hand, if p is any prime and n any natural number, then $J/J_{p,n}$ is nilpotent by (v) (since J and $J/J_{p,n}$ are each generated by two elements). Hence there is a natural number m_n so that $J^{m_n} \leq J_{p,n}$. Thus $\bigcap_{n=1}^\infty J^{m_n} \leq \bigcap_{n=1}^\infty J_{p,n}$. But by (iii), (vii), and Theorem V.3.c, the latter intersection is 1. Accordingly we conclude that $J^\omega = \bigcap_{n=1}^\infty J^n$ is also 1, and hence that $F^\omega = 1$, as was to be shown.

We conclude this section by showing that the variety generated by the nilpotent groups contains all groups.

VI.2.h. Proposition.   *If G is a residually nilpotent group, then G is in the cartesian product of the nilpotent groups G/G^n for $n = 1, 2, \cdots$.*

Proof.   For each n let θ_n be the canonical homomorphism from G onto G/G^n, let P denote the cartesian product $\mathrm{P}_{n=1}^\infty G\theta_n$, and for $g \in G$ let $g\phi$ be the element $(g\theta_1, g\theta_2, \cdots)$ of P. Then ϕ is clearly a homomorphism from G into P; and the kernel of ϕ is 1, since G is residually nilpotent.

In view of VI.2.g and VI.2.h we see that free groups are in the variety generated by the nilpotent groups, and we have the following theorem.

VI.2.i. Theorem.   *The variety generated by the nilpotent groups contains all groups.*

3. Hypercentral groups

In this section we consider the idea that a group has a center, and modulo its center again a center, and so on.

VI.3.a. Definition.   *The **residual quotient** of a normal subgroup A of a group G is the complete inverse image of the center of G/A; it will be denoted by $(A:G)_1$.*

(i) *The center of a group G is the residual quotient $(1:G)_1$.*

(ii) *The residual quotient $(A:G)_1$ is a normal subgroup of G containing A, and consists of those elements b of G such that $[b, G] \leq A$; if B is a subgroup of G so that $[B, G] \leq A$, then $B \leq (A:G)_1$.*

(iii) *If A is a characteristic subgroup of a group G, then $(A:G)_1$ is also a characteristic subgroup.*

It will be convenient to use the notations $(A:G)_0$ for A, $(A:G)_{\alpha+1}$ for $((A:G)_\alpha : G)_1$ for any ordinal α, and $(A:G)_\alpha$ for $\bigcup_{\beta<\alpha} (A:G)_\beta$ when α is a limit ordinal. There is obviously a first ordinal δ so that $(A:G)_\delta = (A:G)_{\delta+1}$.

VI.3.b. Definitions. A **central system** of a group G (respectively, between subgroups H and K) is a normal system of G (respectively, with least member H and greatest member K), such that for each $G_{\alpha+1}$ in the system $[G_{\alpha+1}, G] \leq G_\alpha$; if the system is an ascending chain, it is an **ascending central series.**

VI.3.c. Proposition. *If G is a group with an ascending central series $\{G_\alpha\}$, then each subgroup and each homomorphic image of G also has an ascending central series.*

Proof. Let H be a subgroup of G, and let $H_1 = H \cap G_1$ (with G_1 denoting 1). Then define H_α inductively so that for each ordinal $\alpha+1$, $H_{\alpha+1}$ is $H \cap G_\beta$ where G_β is the least member containing H_α properly; whereas for a limit ordinal γ, H_γ is defined to be the union of all H_δ with $\delta < \gamma$. It is clear that $[H_{\alpha+1}, H] \leq H_\alpha$, and hence $\{H_\alpha\}$ is an ascending central series of G.

A similar argument shows that if θ is a homomorphism of G, then $G\theta$ has an ascending central series. Indeed let $\bar{G}_1 = G_1\theta$ and define $\bar{G}_\alpha$ inductively as follows. For each ordinal $\alpha+1$, $\bar{G}_{\alpha+1}$ is $G_\beta\theta$ where G_β is the least member so that $G_\beta\theta$ properly contains $\bar{G}_\alpha$. For a limit ordinal γ, $\bar{G}_\gamma$ is the union of all $\bar{G}_\delta$ with $\delta < \gamma$. Again it is clear that $[\bar{G}_{\alpha+1}, \bar{G}] \leq \bar{G}_\alpha$, and hence that $\{\bar{G}_\alpha\}$ is an ascending central series of $\bar{G}$.

VI.3.d. Definitions. If G is a group, the chain of subgroups consisting of 1 and all subgroups $(1:G)_\alpha$ is the **upper central series** of G. The last member of the upper central series is the **hypercenter**; any subgroup of the hypercenter is a **hypercentral** subgroup.   A group equal to its hypercenter is a **hypercentral group**.

(iv) *The upper central series of a group is an ascending central series between* 1 *and the hypercenter of the group.*

(v) *Each member of the upper central series of a group is a characteristic subgroup.   The terminology "upper central series" comes from the following proposition.*

VI.3.e. Proposition.   *If G is a group and $\{G_\alpha\}$ is an ascending central series between* 1 *and some subgroup G_δ, then for each ordinal $\alpha \leq \delta$,* $G_\alpha \leq (1:G)_\alpha$.

Proof.   Suppose the assertion is true for all $\beta < \alpha$ that $G_\beta \leq (1:G)_\beta$. If α is of the form $\gamma + 1$, then $G_\gamma \leq (1:G)_\gamma$ and, since $[G_\alpha, G] \leq G_\gamma$, it follows that $[G_\alpha, G] \leq (1:G)_\gamma$; consequently $G_\alpha \leq (1:G)_{\gamma+1} = (1:G)_\alpha$. If α is a limit ordinal, then $G_\alpha = \bigcup_{\beta < \alpha} G_\beta \leq \bigcup_{\beta < \alpha}(1:G)_\beta = (1:G)_\alpha$ and the proposition follows.

VI.3.f. Corollary.   *A group has an ascending central series if and only if it is hypercentral.*

VI.3.g. Corollary.   *Subgroups and homomorphic images of hypercentral groups are hypercentral.*

It is worth pointing out here that a **descending central series** may be defined as a central system which is well-ordered "downwards" (i.e., under $\geq$ instead of $\leq$).   The terminology "lower central series" (cf. VI.1.a) comes from a proposition analogous to Proposition VI.3.e; and the Corollary VI.3.f has the analogue that a group is residually nilpotent if and only if it has a descending central series whose last member is indexed by the first limit ordinal.   We give an example of a group with a descending central series such that the $\omega +$ first term is the first member equal to 1.

VI.3.h. Example.   For each natural number n let G_n be a nilpotent group of class n with an element a_n of infinite order in $G_n^{\ n}$ (a free group modulo the $n+$first member of its lower central series is such a group), and let $\bar{G}_n$ denote $G_n/(a_n)$. Then both $G = \prod_{n=1}^{\infty} G_n$ and $\bar{G} = \prod_{n=1}^{\infty} \bar{G}_n$ are residually nilpotent. If

$$H = \mathfrak{S}(a_n a_{n+1}^{-1}, n = 1, 2, \cdots),$$

let $R = G/H$. Then $a_n H \in R^{\omega}$ and $R^{\omega} \leq (a_n H)$ since $R/(a_n H) \cong \bar{G}$. Thus $R^{\omega} \neq 1$, $R^{\omega+1} = 1$.

We remind the reader that the **normalizer condition** was introduced in connection with Theorem III.1.t, where it was shown that each finite p-group satisfies the normalizer condition. Here we show that the normalizer condition is also satisfied by each hypercentral group.

VI.3.i. Theorem. *A hypercentral group satisfies the normalizer condition.*

Proof. Let G be a hypercentral group and let H be a proper subgroup of G. We must show that $H < \mathfrak{N}(H)$. Let α be the least ordinal so that $(1:G)_\alpha$ is not in H. Then α is not a limit ordinal and hence $\alpha = \beta + 1$ for some β. Since $[G, (1:G)_\alpha] \leq (1:G)_\beta \leq H$, it follows that $[H, (1:G)_\alpha] \leq H$ and hence that $(1:G)_\alpha \leq \mathfrak{N}(H)$. Thus $H < \mathfrak{N}(H)$, as the theorem asserts.

VI.3.j. Proposition. *In a hypercentral group, or more generally in a group with a central system, two elements commute if their orders are relatively prime. If furthermore the group is periodic, it is the direct product of its Sylow p-subgroups.*

We give a hint and leave the proof of VI.3.j to the reader.
Hint: To study the properties of a commutator $[a, b]$, factor the union of all the members of the central system not containing $[a, b]$ (cf. (ii) of Section III.6).

VI.3.k. Theorem (*Grün*). *A non-trivial hypercentral group contains its derived group properly.*

Proof.   Let G be a hypercentral group.   If $G=(1:G)_1$, the statement is obvious.   If $G>(1:G)_1$, let h be in $(1:G)_2$ but not in $(1:G)_1$ and define the map ϕ_h on G by the equation $g\phi_h=[g, h]$ for g in G. Then ϕ_h maps G onto a non-trivial subset of the centre of G, and, by VI.1.k, ϕ_h is a homomorphism.   If K is the kernel of ϕ_h, then $G' \leq K < G$ and the theorem is proved.

It is easy to check that the infinite dihedral group D_∞ (cf. VI.2.d) has center 1.   It follows directly that a residually nilpotent group need not be hypercentral.   We now give an example of a hypercentral group which is not residually nilpotent.

VI.3.1. Example.   Let Q be a 2-quasicyclic group and let σ be an automorphism of Q so that $q\sigma=q^{-1}$ for $q \in Q$.   The holomorph G of Q with the group generated by σ may be defined thus:

$$G=\mathfrak{G}(b, a_n, n=1, 2, \cdots \mid a_1{}^2=1, \ a_{n+1}{}^2=a_n, \ b^2=1, \ a_n{}^b=a_n{}^{-1}).$$

Then $(1:G)_1=(a_1), \cdots, (1:G)_n=(a_n), \cdots$, and hence G is hypercentral.   In fact $(1:G)_{\omega+1}=G$ but $(1:G)_\omega=Q<G$.   On the other hand, since $[a_n, b]=a_n{}^{-2}=a_{n-1}{}^{-1}$, it is easy to check that $\mathfrak{G}(a_1, a_2, \cdots)$ $=G^2=G^3$, and hence that G and G^2 are the only two members of the lower central series.

By way of contrast to the above facts, the following theorem shows that a group is nilpotent if and only if it is hypercentral with a finite upper central series.

VI.3.m. Theorem.   *The non-trivial group G is nilpotent of class n if and only if $G=(1:G)_n$ and $G\neq(1:G)_{n-1}$.*

Proof.   For $n=1$ the theorem is obvious.   For $n>1$, we proceed by induction on n, observing that G is nilpotent of class n if $G^n\neq 1$, $G^{n+1}=1$; but this in turn means that $G^n \leq (1:G)_1$ while $G^{n-1} \nleq (1:G)_1$. Then if G is nilpotent of class n, $G/(1:G)_1$ is nilpotent of class $n-1$; hence by the induction assumption, the upper central series of $G/(1:G)_1$ has $n-1$ non-trivial distinct members corresponding to the distinct subgroups $(1:G)_2, (1:G)_3, \cdots, (1:G)_n$.   It follows that the upper central series of G contains the above $n-1$ subgroups and $(1:G)_1$, and hence has n members so that $G = (1:G)_n$, $G \neq (1:G)_{n-1}$, as the theorem asserts.

Conversely, if $(1:G)_n = G$, $(1:G)_{n-1} \neq G$, then $G/(1:G)_1$ is nilpotent of class $n-1$ so that $G^n \leq (1:G)_1$, $G^{n-1} \nleq (1:G)_1$ and G is nilpotent of class n. This proves the theorem.

VI.3.n. Corollary. *A hypercentral group satisfying the maximum condition for subgroups is nilpotent.*

The situation for finite groups may be summarized as follows.

VI.3.o. Theorem. *The following statements are equivalent for a finite group.*

(1) *G is nilpotent.*
(2) *G is hypercentral.*
(3) *G satisfies the normalizer condition.*
(4) *G is a direct product of Sylow p-subgroups.*
(5) *The Frattini subgroup of G contains the derived group of G.*

Proof. Theorem VI.3.m gives the equivalence of (1) and (2). Corollaries VI.1.j and VI.1.x give the equivalence of (1) and (4). Theorems VI.1.y and VI.3.i give the implications $(1) \rightarrow (5)$ and $(2) \rightarrow (3)$, respectively. Since any subgroup containing the normalizer of a Sylow p-subgroup is its own normalizer by IV.2.a, it follows that either (3) or (5) implies that each Sylow p-subgroup is normal in the group and hence $(3) \rightarrow (4)$ and $(5) \rightarrow (4)$. This completes the proof of the theorem.

4. Nilpotent extensions of cyclic groups by cyclic groups

In this section we continue the study of the extensions of cyclic groups by cyclic groups, begun in Section III.4 in connection with the classification of groups of order p^3. We introduce the general quaternion groups and give some of their interesting properties. Finally, we give a characterization of groups, all of whose subgroups are normal.

VI.4.a. Proposition.   *For an odd prime p a group of the form $[C_{p^n}]C_p$ has at least two cyclic subgroups of order p^m for each integer m with $1 \le m \le n$.*

Proof.   Suppose that G has the form $[C_{p^n}]C_p$, let $a \in G$ be of order p^n, and let $b \in G$, $b \notin (a)$ be of order p.   We shall prove the proposition by showing that $a^{p^{n-m}}b$ has order p^m.   If $ab = ba$, this is obvious since $(a^{p^{n-m}})^{p^m} = a^{p^n}b^{p^m} = 1$ and $(a^{p^{n-m}}b)^{p^{m-1}} = a^{p^{n-1}}b^{p^{m-1}} \ne 1$.   If $ab \ne ba$, then $n \ge 2$ by III.1.s and $(a) \lhd G$ by the normalizer condition (or the form of G if a is chosen properly).   It follows (cf. Section III.2) that $a^b = a^{1+kp^{n-1}}$ with k prime to p, that $\mathfrak{S}[(a, b)] = (a^{p^{n-1}})$ is of order p, and hence that G is nilpotent of class 2.   By (4) of VI.1.k,

$$(a^{p^{n-m}}b)^{p^m} = a^{p^n}b^{p^m}[b, a^{p^{n-m}}]^{p^m(p^m-1)/2} = 1,$$

while $(a^{p^{n-m}}b)^{p^{m-1}} = a^{p^{n-1}}b^{p^{m-1}}[b, a^{p^{n-m}}]^{p^{m-1}(p^{m-1}-1)/2} \ne 1$, since p is odd and $(p^{m-1}-1)/2$ is integral.   This proves the proposition.

The statement of VI.4.a fails to be true for $p = 2$ as a study of the dihedral groups $D_{2^{k+1}}$ for $k \ge 2$ (cf. III.4.d) reveals; for if $D_{2^{k+1}} = [(a)](b)$ with b of order 2, then $(a^s b)^2 = 1$ for each integer s.

VI.4.b. Definition.   If n is a natural number greater than 1, the group $\mathfrak{G}(a_n, b \mid a_n{}^{2^n} = 1, b^{-1}a_n b = a_n{}^{-1}, b^2 = a_n{}^{2^{n-1}})$ is the **quaternion group** $Q_{2^{n+1}}$ (cf. III.4.h for the case $n = 2$).   The group

$$\mathfrak{G}(b, a_n, n = 1, 2, \cdots \mid b^2 = a_1, a_n{}^b = a_n{}^{-1}, a_{n+1}{}^2 = a_n, a_1{}^2 = 1)$$

is the **infinite quaternion group** Q_{2^∞}.
   We list some facts about quaternion groups; the proofs are good exercises for the reader.

   (i) *The order of $Q_{2^{n+1}}$ is 2^{n+1}.*
   (ii) *The group Q_{2^∞} contains a copy of Q_{2^n} for each $n \ge 3$, and in fact is the ascending union $\bigcup_{n=3}^\infty Q_{2^n}$.*
   (iii) *Let A be a subgroup of a 2-quasicyclic group with $|A| > 2$, let θ be the automorphism of A defined by the equation $a\theta = a^{-1}$ for $a \in A$, and let $B = \mathfrak{G}(b \mid b^4 = 1)$.   If G is the semi-direct product $[A]B$ with b inducing the automorphism θ on A, and if u is the*

unique element of order 2 of A, then $G/(ub^2)$ is isomorphic to a quaternion group $Q_{2^{n+1}}$ or Q_{2^∞} according as $|A| = 2^n$ or $|A| = \infty$.

(iv) *$Q_{2^{n+1}}$ has $2^{n-1} + 1$ cyclic subgroups of order 4 and only one cyclic subgroup of order 2^m for $m \neq 2$ with $1 \leq m \leq n$.*

(v) *Each subgroup of Q_8 is normal in Q_8.*

(vi) *$Q_{2^{n+1}}$ has no non-cyclic abelian subgroups and hence is not a semi-direct product of a non-trivial subgroup.*

(vii) *If $n > 2$, $Q_{2^{n+1}}$ has two subgroups isomorphic to Q_{2^n}.*

(viii) *The center of any quaternion group has order 2.*

(ix) *$Q_{2^{n+1}}$ is nilpotent of class n; Q_{2^∞} is hypercentral but not nilpotent. In fact, $Q_{2^{n+1}}$ modulo its center is isomorphic to the dihedral group D_{2^n}, while Q_{2^∞} modulo its center is isomorphic to the group G of Example VI.3.1; there are only two members in the lower central series of Q_{2^∞}.*

VI.4.c. Proposition.   *If G is a nilpotent non-abelian group, generated by elements a and b with $(a) \lhd G$ and $|a| \geq |b|$, then G is finite. If, in addition, G is a class 2 p-group for some prime p, then there is a $c \in G$ so that $G = [(a)](c)$ or else G is a quaternion group of order 8.*

Proof. If $|a| = \infty$, then the group of automorphisms of (a) has order 2 so that either $a^b = a$ (contrary to the fact that G is non-abelian) or $a^b = a^{-1}$. But if $a^b = a^{-1}$, then $[b, a] = a^2$, and for each natural number n, $[b, a^{2^n}] = a^{2^{n+1}}$ contrary to the nilpotency of G. Thus G is finite.

Now suppose that G is a finite class 2 p-group. Let $|a| = p^n$, $|b| = p^m$, $|G:(a)| = p^t$, and let $[b, a] = a^{kp^r}$ (since $(a) \lhd G$) with k prime to p and $r > 0$ since G is a class 2 group and a is not in the center of G. Then if $m = t$, $G = [(a)](b)$ and the theorem follows. Accordingly, we assume that $m > t$. Then $b^{p^t} \in (a)$ and hence $b^{p^t} = a^{sp^q}$ with s prime to p and $q = n - m + t$ since p^{n-q} is the order of a^{p^q} and p^{m-t} the order of b^{p^t}. If $c = a^{vp^{n-m}}b$, then by Lemma VI.1.k,

$$c^{p^t} = a^{vp^{n-m+t}}b^{p^t}[b, a^{vp^{n-m}}]^{p^t(p^t-1)/2}$$
$$= a^{(v+s)p^q}a^{kp^r vp^{n-m}p^t(p^t-1)/2} = a^{p^q(v+s+kp^r v(p^t-1)/2)}.$$

Hence c has order p^t if $v + s + kp^r v(p^t - 1)/2 \equiv 0 \bmod p^{m-t}$, or if $v(1 + kp^r(p^t - 1)/2) \equiv -s \bmod p^{m-t}$. Since this congruence can always be solved for v if p is odd or if $r > 1$ when $p = 2$, it follows that c can be chosen of order p^t in these cases; and then since $|G| = p^{n+t}$, $|a| = p^n$, $|c| = p^t$, and $G = \mathfrak{S}(a, b) = \mathfrak{S}(a, c)$, it follows that $G = [(a)](c)$ as the theorem asserts, except possibly when $p = 2$, $r = 1$.

In case $p = 2$ and $r = 1$, $[b, a] = a^{2k}$, k odd, so that $a^b = a^{1-2k}$. Since $[b, a]$ is in the center of G, a^{2k} and hence a^2 is in the center of G and $a^2 = (a^2)^b = (a^b)^2 = a^{2-4k}$; thus $a^{4k} = 1$ and hence $a^4 = 1$. If $(b) \cap (a) = 1$, then $G = [(a)](b)$; otherwise $b^2 = a^2 \neq 1$, $G = Q_8$, and the theorem follows.

VI.4.d. Proposition. *If G is a finite non-abelian p-group, p a prime, with a cyclic subgroup of index p, then G is either a split extension of the cyclic subgroup or else a quaternion group.*

Proof. Let (a) be a cyclic subgroup of order p^n and index p in G, and let $b \in G$, $b \notin (a)$. Since $(a) \lhd G$, conjugation by b induces an automorphism in (a) which is of order p; then for odd p, $a^b = a^{kp^{n-1}+1}$ with k prime to p, whereas for $p = 2$, a^b is either $a^{2^{n-1}+1}$, $a^{2^{n-1}-1}$, or a^{-1} (cf. Section III.2). If $|b| = 2$, $G = [(a)](b)$. If $a^b = a^{-1}$ or $a^b = a^{2^{n-1}-1}$, and $|b| \neq 2$, then $b^2 = a^{2^{n-1}}$ since $(a^{2^{n-1}})$ is the centralizer of b in (a); hence if $a^b = a^{-1}$, $G = Q_{2^{n+1}}$, whereas if $a^b = a^{2^{n-1}-1}$, $(ab)^2 = ba^b ab = ba^{2^{n-1}} b = 1$ and $G = [(a)](ab)$. In all other cases, $[a, b]$ commutes with b as well as a so that G is nilpotent of class 2; the proposition then follows from VI.4.c and the proof is complete.

VI.4.e. Proposition. *If for an odd prime p, the p-group G satisfies the normalizer condition and has exactly one cyclic subgroup of order p^m for some $m > 0$, then G is locally cyclic. If a 2-group satisfies the normalizer condition and has exactly one subgroup of order 2, then it is locally cyclic or a quaternion group.*

Proof. Whether p is 2 or an odd prime, suppose the cyclic subgroup (c) of order p^m is embedded in a locally cyclic subgroup A of the group G so that A is contained in no larger locally cyclic subgroup of G. We first show that $A = \mathfrak{C}(A)$. If not, there is a $g \in \mathfrak{C}(A)$, $g \notin A$, with $g^p \in A$ since $A < \mathfrak{C}(A)$.   Then by the maximality of A there is a $d \in A$ so that $d^p = g^p$.   But then cdg^{-1} generates a cyclic subgroup of order p^m which is different from (c) (since $cdg^{-1} \notin A$).   This is contrary to hypothesis and we conclude that $A = \mathfrak{C}(A)$.

Now if $G \neq A$, then $A < \mathfrak{N}(A)$ by the normalizer condition, and there is a $b \in \mathfrak{N}(A)$, $b \notin A = \mathfrak{C}(A)$ so that $b^p \in A$.   By III.2.s, A cannot be infinite when p is odd, and hence, by VI.4.d, $\mathfrak{S}(a, b)$ is a split extension of a non-trivial subgroup; thus by VI.4.a, $\mathfrak{S}(a, b)$ has two cyclic subgroups of order p^m contrary to hypothesis.   We conclude that $A = G$ and that G is locally cyclic when p is odd, as the proposition asserts.

When $p = 2$, if $A \neq G$ and A is infinite, then it follows easily from III.2.t that $\mathfrak{S}(A, b)$ is either isomorphic to Q_{2^∞} or to a split extension $[C_{2^\infty}]C_2$.   The latter possibility is excluded by the hypothesis since any p-group which is a split extension of a proper non-trivial subgroup has two subgroups of order p^m.   It also follows from the above remark and VI.4.d that, if A is finite, then $\mathfrak{S}(A, b)$ is isomorphic to a quaternion group $Q_{2^{n+1}}$.   Thus, whether A is finite or not, if $A \neq G$, $\mathfrak{S}(A, b)$ is a quaternion group Q.   If $Q \neq G$ there is an element $c \in \mathfrak{N}(Q)$, $c \notin Q$, so that $c^2 \in Q$ and hence $c^4 \in A$.   If $c^2 \in A$, then, as above, c induces the same automorphism in A as was induced by b.   Thus $cb^{-1} \in \mathfrak{C}(A) = A$ contrary to the fact that $c \notin \mathfrak{S}(A, b) = Q$.   We conclude that $c^2 \notin A = \mathfrak{C}(A)$ and hence that c induces an automorphism of order 4 on A (since A is characteristic in Q by (iv)).   Thus the automorphism induced by b on A is the square of that induced by c.   On the other hand, the automorphism induced by b on a finite cyclic characteristic subgroup A_n of A of order 2^n corresponds to the element -1 in the group of units of the ring of integers mod 2^n; and the element -1 is not a square by the proof of III.2.m.   We conclude from this contradiction that $Q = G$ and the proposition is proved.

The proof of the next proposition is left for an exercise; it is similar to the proof of VI.4.e.

VI.4.f. Proposition.   *Let G be a p-group whose order is greater than some prime power p^m with $m \geq 2$ (with $m \geq 3$ when $p = 2$), and suppose that G satisfies the normalizer condition.   If each subgroup of order p^m of G is cyclic, then G is locally cyclic.*

We conclude this section with a characterization of the hamiltonian groups which are defined as follows.   A group is **hamiltonian** (after W. R. Hamilton) if it is not abelian and each of its subgroups is normal. The following facts are immediate consequences of the definition.

(x) *Subgroups and factor groups of hamiltonian groups are hamiltonian.*

(xi) *If a subgroup of a hamiltonian group is a semi-direct product $[A]B$, then it is the direct product $A \times B$.*

VI.4.g. Theorem.   *A group is hamiltonian if and only if it is a direct product of a quaternion group of order 8 with a periodic abelian group containing no element of order 4.*

Proof.   Let G be a direct product of a quaternion group

$$Q = \mathfrak{G}(a, b \mid a^2 = b^2 = [a, b], a^4 = 1)$$

of order 8 with a periodic abelian group C containing no element of order 4.   We shall show that each subgroup of G is normal by showing that each cyclic subgroup of G is normal.   Since each cyclic subgroup of odd order or of order 2 is central and since G has no element of order 8, it is sufficient to show that each subgroup of order 4 is normal. If $x \in G$ has order 4, then without loss of generality we can take x to be ac with $c \in C$ of order 1 or 2.   Now $\mathfrak{S}(C, a)$ centralizes x, while $(ac)^b = a^{-1}c = (ac)^3$; since $G = \mathfrak{S}(C, a, b)$, it follows that (x) is normal in G, as was to be shown.

Conversely, we suppose that G is a hamiltonian group and that a and b are elements of infinite or prime power order so that $ab \neq ba$. Since (a) and (b) are normal in G, both (a) and (b) contain $[b, a]$ and therefore $\mathfrak{S}(a, b)$ is nilpotent of class 2.   It follows from VI.4.c and (xi) that $\mathfrak{S}(a, b)$ is a quaternion group Q of order 8, with $a^2 = b^2 = [a, b]$ of order 2.

Since (a) is normal in G and has automorphism group of order 2, it follows that for any $g \in G$ either g or gb commutes with a; and then one element of the pair g, ga, or of the pair gb, gba commutes with both a and b so that if C is the centralizer of Q in G, then $G = QC$. Then if $c \in C$, $(cb)^a$ is a power, for definiteness the kth power of cb, so that $(cb)^a = c^a b^a = cb^{-1} = (cb)^k = c^k b^k$ and $c^{k-1} = b^{-1-k}$.   It follows that $|c| \neq \infty$ and, since $b \notin C$, it follows that k is odd.   Now if $|c|$ were

4 and k were 1 or 3 mod 4, we would have the contradiction $1 = b^{-2}$ or $c^2 = 1$, respectively.   We conclude that C has no elements of order 4 or of infinite order.   Therefore, by the argument at the beginning of the proof, C is abelian and periodic, and hence the direct product of its Sylow p-subgroups, with the Sylow 2-subgroup elementary abelian.

Now $[a, b] \in C$ and hence $([a, b])$ is a direct factor of C so that for some subgroup D, $C = D \times ([a, b])$.   But then $G = QC = Q \times D$ and the proof of the theorem is complete.

5. The classification of groups of order p^4 when p is a prime

If p is a prime, the groups of order p^2 are described in III.1.s; those of order p^3 are described in III.4.j and III.4.k.   In §§117 and 118 of Burnside's Theory of Groups [B] it is seen that there are fifteen isomorphism classes of groups of order p^4 when p is an odd prime, fourteen classes of order p^4 when $p = 2$.   We shall exhibit these groups here.   It is a little more tedious to show that a group of order p^4 is isomorphic to one of the groups of this section; the reader is referred to Burnside's book for this.

An abelian group of order p^4 has one of the following five types: (4), (3, 1), (2, 2), (2, 1, 1), (1, 1, 1, 1), and thus there are five isomorphism classes of abelian groups of order p^4.   The classes of non-abelian groups will be classified by means of two tables according as the derived group has order p or p^2 (a group with derived group of order p^3 does not occur in view of VI.1.z).   In view of VI.1.g it follows that a p-group has class 2 if its derived group has order p; thus the groups in the first table have class 2.   We now show that the groups in the second table have class 3.   Since the derived group has order p^2, a minimal set of generators (cf. VI.1.y and VI.1.z) has two elements, say a and b, and these are of order p modulo the derived group.   If now $G^3 = 1$, then by VI.1.v, $[a, b]$ would have order p and the group would have order p^3 contrary to hypothesis.   We conclude that the groups in the two tables have classes 2 and 3 according as the derived groups have order p or p^2.

Each of the groups except for the last in Table I is constructed by means of a semi-direct product of a group of order less than p^4.   Since the automorphism group of $C_p \times C_p$, as well as that of C_{p^2}, has order whose p-share is p (cf. III.2.m and III.3.m), each semi-direct product indicated is determined up to automorphism.   It is easy to verify the entries in the first table under the headings "minimal number of generators," "type of center," and "types of maximal abelian sub-groups"; and the reader is advised to do so.   A glance at the table then reveals that there are 6 isomorphism classes of groups of order p^4 with derived group p both for p odd as well as for $p=2$.

We have already mentioned three groups of order 16 with derived group of order 4, namely, the quaternion group of order 16 and two split extensions $[C_8]C_2$ (cf. footnote ‡ of Table I).   Since there are only 14 isomorphism classes of groups of order 16, they have now all been listed here; 5 are abelian, 6 have derived group of order 2, and 3 have derived group of order 4.

When p is odd, a group of order p^4 with a cyclic subgroup of order p^3 is a split extension by VI.4.d.   Then since the automorphism group of a cyclic group of order p^3 is cyclic (cf. III.2.m), it follows that such a group of order p^4 is isomorphic to the group described in row 5 of Table I.

TABLE I

CLASS 2 GROUPS OF ORDER p^4 (WITH DERIVED GROUP OF ORDER p)

Group	Form as Split Extension or Factor Thereof	Minimal Number of Generators	Type of Center	Types of Maximal Abelian Subgroups
1	$[C_p \times C_p]C_{p^2}$	2	(1, 1)	(1, 1, 1), (2, 1)
2	$[C_{p^2}]C_{p^2}$	2	(1, 1)	(2, 1)
3*	Factor group of $[C_p \times C_p]C_p \times C_{p^2}$	3	(2)	(2, 1)
4†	$[C_{p^2}]C_p \times C_p$	3	(1, 1)	(1, 1, 1), (2, 1)
5‡	$[C_p{}^3]C_p$	2	(2)	(2, 1), (3)
6†	$[C_p \times C_p]C_p \times C_p$	3	(1, 1)	(1, 1, 1) (also (2, 1) when $p=2$)
7	$Q_8 \times C_2$	3	(1, 1)	(2, 1)

* If a is a center element of order p of $[C_p \times C_p]C_p$ and b is an element of order p in C_{p^2}, then (ab) is the normal subgroup to be factored.
† For $p=2$, groups of rows 4 and 6 are isomorphic (cf. III.4.j).
‡ For $p=2$, there are three non-isomorphic such groups (cf. III.4.1) but only one such group with commutator subgroup of order 2.

Whether p is odd or not, let G be a group of order p^4 with G^2 of order p^2.   Since the Sylow p-subgroup of the automorphism group of a group of order p^2 has order p and since $G^2 \triangleleft G$, it follows that $\mathfrak{C}(G^2)$ is of order p^3 and is abelian.   For $p = 2$, it can easily be checked in each case that $\mathfrak{C}(G^2)$ is cyclic of order 8.   For odd p, on the other hand, $\mathfrak{C}(G^2)$ cannot be cyclic by the remark above, and hence must be of type (2, 1) or (1, 1, 1).   Now G has two generators a and b where, without loss of generality, b may be chosen in $\mathfrak{C}(G^2)$ and a not in $\mathfrak{C}(G^2)$. Then since $\mathfrak{C}(G^2) \triangleleft G$, $[a, b]$ is in the abelian subgroup $\mathfrak{C}(G^2)$ and hence $[a, 2b] = 1$.   Thus since G has class 3, $[b, 2a] \neq 1$.   In summary, a induces an automorphism of order p in $\mathfrak{C}(G^2)$, and $\mathfrak{C}(G^2)$ is either $(b) \times ([b, a]) \times ([b, 2a])$ of type (1, 1, 1) or else $(b) \times [b, a]$ of type (2, 1) with $(b^p) = ([b, 2a])$.   It is clear that the center $([b, 2a])$ has order p, that $\mathfrak{C}(G^2)$ is the only abelian subgroup of order p^3 (since any element not in $(\mathfrak{C}(G^2)$ fails to commute with $[b, a]$), and that 2 is the minimal number of generators.   For $p \neq 3$, there are two isomorphism classes for each of the two types of $\mathfrak{C}(G^2)$ listed in Table II; for $p = 3$ there is only one class when $\mathfrak{C}(G^2)$ has type (1, 1, 1).

TABLE II

Class 3 Groups of Order p^4, p an Odd Prime, with Derived Group of Order p^2 and Generated by $b \in \mathfrak{C}(G^2)$, $a \notin \mathfrak{C}(G^2)$.

Group	Relations Besides Those in the Text Needed to Specify the Group	Exponent	Type of $\mathfrak{C}(G^2)$
1	$a^p = b^p = 1$, $p \neq 3$	p	(1, 1, 1)
2	$a^p = [b, 2a]$, $b^p = 1$	p^2	(1, 1, 1)
3	$a^p = 1$, $b^{ps} = [b, 2a]$,	p^2	(2, 1)
	s a quadratic residue modulo p		
4	$a^p = 1$, $b^{mp} = [b, 2a]$,	p^2	(2, 1)
	m a quadratic non-residue modulo p		
5	$a^3 = [b, 2a] = b^{-3}$	3^2	(2, 1)

In order to verify the statements listed in Table II, we first give a lemma which facilitates computation in an extension of an abelian group by a cyclic group.

VI.5.a. Lemma.   *Let G be a group with an abelian normal subgroup B. Suppose that $b \in B$, $a \in G$, $a \notin B$, and that n and r are natural numbers; then*

(1) $(ba)^n = a^n \prod_{k=0}^{n} [b, ka]^{C_{n,k}}$

and more generally

(1*) $(\prod_{i=1}^{m} b_i)a^n = a^n \prod_{i=1}^{m} \prod_{k=0}^{n} [b_i, ka]^{C_{n,k}}$ with $C_{n,k}$ the binomial coefficients.

(2) $(a^n b)^r = a^{rn} \prod_{m=0}^{r-1} \prod_{k=0}^{mn} [b, ka]^{C_{mn,k}}$

and more generally

(3) $[b, a^n] = \prod_{k=1}^{n} [b, ka]^{C_{n,k}}$;

and

(3*) $[\prod_{i=1}^{m} b_i, a^n] = \prod_{i=1}^{m} \prod_{k=1}^{m} [b_i, ka]^{C_{n,k}}$.

(4) $[b, 2a^n] = \prod_{r=2}^{2n} [b, ra]^{\sum_{k=1}^{r} C_{n,k} C_{n,r-k}}$;

in particular in a class 3 group, (4) reduces to

(4*) $[b, 2a^n] = [b, 2a]^{n^2}$.

Proof. Equation (1) follows by induction on n from the fact that $ba = ab[b, a]$. The detail of the proof is left to the reader; it uses (2*) of VI.1.k together with the fact that B is abelian as well as the formula $C_{n+1,k+1} = C_{n,k+1} + C_{n,k}$. Then (1*) is an immediate consequence of (1). The proof of (2) follows by induction on r using (1) and the fact that $(a^n b)^{r+1} = a^n b a^{rn} \prod_{m=0}^{r-1} \prod_{k=0}^{mn} [b, ka]^{C_{mn,k}}$. Equation (3) follows from the general fact that $c^a = c[c, a]$ together with the fact that $[b, a^{n+1}] = [b, a][b, a^n]^a$. The detail of the proof is left to the reader; it is based on the same facts as the proof of (1) above. Equation (3*) follows from (3) and the fact that $[b_1 b_2, a] = [b_1, a][b_2, a]$ when $b_1, b_2 \in B$ (so that $[b_1 b_2, ka] = [b_1, ka][b_2, ka]$). Finally, (4) follows from (3) and (3*); for $[b, 2a^n] = [\prod_{k=1}^{n} [b, ka]^{C_{n,k}}, a^n]$ $= \prod_{k=1}^{n} \prod_{m=1}^{n} [b, (k+m)a]^{C_{n,m}C_{n,k}}$. This completes the proof of the lemma.

We see immediately from (2) and (1*) of Lemma VI.5.a that a group defined by the relations of row 1 of Table II has exponent p when $p \neq 3$, and hence cannot be isomorphic to a group of row 2; whereas when $p = 3$, such a group is in fact isomorphic to the group of row 2.

We next use (4*) and (3*) of the lemma to show that the groups of rows 3 and 4 of Table II are not isomorphic. To do this we suppose that a and b generate a group G as in row 3 of Table II, and that there is an isomorphism ϕ onto G from a group generated by a', b' as in row 4.   Then $b'\phi = b^r d$ with $d \in G^2$ and $1 \leq r < p$, and $a'\phi = ca^n$ with $1 \leq n < p$ and $c \in \mathfrak{C}(G^2)$.   Since ϕ is an isomorphism from a group as in row 4, $[b^r d, 2(ca^n)] = (b^r d)^{mp}$ with m a non-residue.   On the other hand, $[b^r d, 2(ca^n)] = [b^r d, 2a^n]$ since $\mathfrak{C}(G^2)$ is abelian; and this is equal to $[b^r d, 2a]^{n^2}$ by (4*) and the fact that $G^4 = 1$.   This latter is $[b, 2a]^{n^2 r}$ by (3*) and the fact that $G^4 = 1$.   Finally, this is $b^{spr n^2}$, since G is a group from row 3; and the latter is $(b^r d)^{sp n^2}$, since G^2 has exponent p, with sn^2 a residue.   We have a contradiction on the assumption that a group of row 4 is isomorphic to one of row 3.

To finish the discussion on the groups of order p^4, we need only show that each element of the group of row 5 not in $\mathfrak{C}(G^2)$ has order 9 and hence cannot be isomorphic to a group of row 3 or of row 4.   This follows easily from Lemma VI.5.a and we leave the verification to the reader.   It follows also from this that a group of row 5 is the only group of Table II which is not a split extension of one of its non-trivial subgroups.

6. More about nilpotent groups

We begin with a generalization of Theorem II.3.1 to nilpotent groups.

VI.6.a. Theorem.   *A nilpotent group satisfies the maximum condition for subgroups if and only if it is finitely generated.*

Proof.   In view of I.7.f, we need only prove that if the group G is finitely generated, then it satisfies the maximum condition.   Let n be the class of nilpotency of G; then $G^{n+1} = 1$ and $G^n \neq 1$.   If $n = 1$, G is abelian and the theorem follows from II.3.1.   Accordingly we assume that $n > 1$ and by an induction argument we assume that G^{n-1}/G^n is finitely generated.   Thus there are a finite number of elements b_i of G^{n-1} so that each element of G^{n-1} is a product of some of the b_i, perhaps repeated, times an element of G^n.   Since G is finitely generated, a finite set of elements a_j generates G; then in view of VI.1.k, since G^n is in the center of G, the finite set of elements

$[a_j, b_i]$ generates G^n which is $[G^{n-1}, G]$. Thus G^n satisfies the maximum condition by II.3.1. The theorem then follows from (iii) of Section I.7 since G/G^n and G^n both satisfy the maximum condition.

Our next theorems on nilpotent groups are of fundamental importance; they are consequences of the following general theorem.

VI.6.b. Theorem.   (*P. Hall.*)   *If A, B, C are subgroups of a group G, then the normal closure of $\{[A, B, C], [B, C, A]\}$ contains $[C, A, B]$. In particular, if $[A, B, C]$ and $[B, C, A]$ are normal in G, then $[A, B, C][B, C, A] \geq [C, A, B]$.*

Proof. If $x, y, z \in G$, then a direct verification shows that $(xzy^x)^{-1}(yxz^y) = [x, y^{-1}, z]^y$. If x, y, z are permuted cyclically, two similar equations are obtained. If the three equations are multiplied together so that the left side is 1, then we have the following equation known as the Witt identity:

$$(*) \qquad 1 = [x, y^{-1}, z]^y[y, z^{-1}, x]^z[z, x^{-1}, y]^x.$$

It follows that the normal closure of $\{[A, B, C], [B, C, A]\}$ contains all the elements $[c, a, b]$, $c \in C$, $b \in B$, $a \in A$, and their conjugates in G. But the subgroup $[C, A, B]$ is generated by conjugates of such elements as a straightforward application of (2*) of VI.1.k shows. This proves the first statement of the theorem; the second statement follows immediately from the first and the proof of the theorem is complete.

VI.6.c. Corollary.   *In any group G, $[G^m, G^n] \leq G^{m+n}$.*

Proof. This is true by definition for $m = 1$. We proceed by induction on m. By definition of G^m we have $[G^m, G^n] = [G^{m-1}, G, G^n]$. From VI.6.b, we get $[G^{m-1}, G, G^n] \leq [G^{n+1}, G^{m-1}][G^{n+m-1}, G]$ which is contained in G^{n+m} by the induction assumption.

VI.6.d. Corollary.   *If A, B, C are normal subgroups of a group G, then for each natural number n, $[A, B, nC] \leq \prod_{i+j=n} [A, iC, [B, jC]]$.*

Proof. This is clear from VI.6.b for $n=1$. An induction on n using VI.6.b again readily gives the general case.

VI.6.e. Corollary (*P. Hall*). *If N is a normal subgroup of a group G and if $N \leq (N^2:G)_n$, then for each natural number r, $N^r \leq (N^{r+1}:G)_{k_r}$ with $k_r = r(n-1) + 1$.*

Proof. The hypothesis is equivalent to the fact that $[N, nG] \leq N^2$, the conclusion to the fact that $[N^r, k_r G] \leq N^{r+1}$. For $r=1$ the conclusion is the hypothesis. We proceed by induction on r, assuming that $[N^{r-1}, k_{r-1}G] \leq N^r$. Then

$$[N^r, k_r G] = [N^{r-1}, N, k_r G] = \prod_{i+j=k_r} [N^{r-1}, iG, [N, jG]]$$

by VI.6.d. In this product either $i \geq k_{r-1}$ or $j \geq n$ so that each factor is in N^{r+1} and the corollary follows.

VI.6.f. Corollary. *If N is a nilpotent normal subgroup of a group G and if $N \leq (N^2:G)_n$, then N is in the hypercenter of G.*

Proof. Let s be the class of nilpotency of N; then for $r = 1, 2, \cdots, s$, $[N^r, k_r G] \leq N^{r+1}$ by VI.6.e. If $c = \sum_{r=1}^s k_r$, then $[N, cG] = 1$, and hence N is in the hypercenter of G.

VI.6.g. Corollary (*P. Hall*). *If G is a group with a normal nilpotent subgroup N of class s such that G/N^2 is nilpotent of class n, then G is also nilpotent, and its class is not more than $n C_{s+1,2} - C_{s,2}$ (here $C_{r,2}$ denotes the binomial coefficient $r(r-1)/2$).*

Proof. By hypothesis $G^{n+1} \leq N^2$ and hence $[N, nG] \leq N^2$. It follows from VI.6.e that for each r, $[N^r, k_r G] \leq N^{r+1}$. If $c = \sum_{r=1}^s k_r$, then $[G, cG] = 1$ so that G has class at most c. But

$$c = 1 + (n-1) + 1 + 2(n-1) + \cdots + 1 + s(n-1)$$
$$= s(s+1)(n-1)/2 + s = ns(s+1)/2 - s(s-1)/2,$$

and the corollary follows.

VI.6.h. Corollary.   *If N is a nilpotent p-group, p a prime, and if σ is a non-trivial automorphism of N of prime power order q^k such that σ induces the trivial automorphism in N/N^2, then $q = p$.*

Proof.   By VI.6.e, the holomorph of N with σ is nilpotent, and hence if $q \neq p$, then σ commutes (by VI.1.w) with all the elements of N, contrary to hypothesis.

In the last theorem and its corollaries the hypothesis is that N is hypercentral modulo N^2. That in some cases it is only necessary to assume that N be hypercentral modulo $\Phi(N)$ follows from the next lemma.

VI.6.i. Lemma.   *Suppose that A is an abelian normal subgroup of a group G and that A is a direct product of cyclic groups, each having at most m proper subgroups for some natural number m; if for some natural number k, $(\phi(A):G)_k \geq A$, then $(1:G)_{km} \geq A$.*

Proof.   The fact that $(\Phi(A):G)_k \geq A$ is equivalent to the fact that $[A, kG] \leq \phi(A)$. Now in view of the hypothesis, A is the direct product of Sylow p-groups P of exponent at most p^m. Then since $\Phi(A)$ is the direct product of the subgroups pP and since each P is characteristic in A, we have $[P, kG] \leq pP$. It follows readily from this with VI.1.k that $[pP, kG] \leq p^2 P$ and then (inductively) that $[P, mkG] \leq p^m P = 1$; or equivalently that $(1:G)_{km} \geq P$. Since this is true for each P, $(1:G)_{km} \geq A$, as the lemma asserts.

In view of VI.6.i, VI.6.e, and VI.6.g we have the following theorem.

VI.6.j. Theorem.   *Let N be a nilpotent normal subgroup (of class s) of a group G such that N/N^2 is a direct product of cyclic subgroups, each having at most m proper subgroups for some given natural number m. If there is a natural number v so that $(\Phi(N):G)_v \geq N$, then there is a natural number t so that $(1:G)_t \geq N$. If $G/\Phi(N)$ is nilpotent of class n, then G is nilpotent of class at most $mnC_{s+1,2} - C_{s,2}$.*

7. Locally nilpotent groups, the Hirsch-Plotkin radical, and N-groups

In view of VI.1.1 it is easy to show that if, for $i = 1, 2$, H_i is a nilpotent normal subgroup of class m_i of a group, then $H_1 H_2$ is nilpotent of class at most $m_1 + m_2$. It follows that in particular a finite group (or more generally a group satisfying the maximum condition for nilpotent normal subgroups) has a unique maximal nilpotent normal subgroup—the **nil radical.**

On the other hand, if, for each natural number n, G_n is a nilpotent group of class n, then the direct product $\prod_{n=1}^{\infty} G_n$ is not nilpotent and does not have any maximal nilpotent normal subgroup. The situation is different for locally nilpotent normal subgroups, and we shall show here, following Plotkin [23] that every group has a unique maximal locally nilpotent normal subgroup—the **Hirsch-Plotkin radical** of the group. We shall also show in this section that a group satisfying the normalizer condition is locally nilpotent.

We begin with some elementary properties.

   (i) *Subgroups and homomorphic images of locally nilpotent groups are locally nilpotent.*

  (ii) *Any locally nilpotent subgroup of a group (and in particular, any element) is contained in a maximal locally nilpotent subgroup.*

 (iii) *A locally nilpotent periodic group is a direct product of its Sylow p-subgroups, one for each prime p.*

VI.7.a. Lemma (*Plotkin*).   *Let G be a group generated by one of its elements g and a normal locally nilpotent subgroup H, and suppose that for each h in H there is a natural number n_h so that $[h, n_h g] = 1$.   Then G is locally nilpotent.*

Proof.   Since each element of G is a power of g times an element of H, it will be sufficient to show that if $h_1, \cdots, h_k$ are elements of H, then $\mathfrak{S}(g, h_1, \cdots, h_k)$ is nilpotent.   We look at the set B of elements of the form $[h_i, ng]$ as n ranges over the non-negative integers.   In view of the hypotheses, B is finite and hence generates a nilpotent subgroup F of H.   Furthermore $[B, g] \le B$, and hence $F \triangleleft \mathfrak{S}(F, g)$.

Now if $z \ne 1$ is in the center of F, then for some non-negative integer r, $[z, rg] \neq 1$ and $[z, (r+1)g] = 1$, so that $\mathfrak{S}(F, g)$ has a non-trivial center.   By repetition of this argument we see that $\mathfrak{S}(F, g)$ is hypercentral.   Since F is finitely generated and nilpotent, it follows from VI.6.a that F satisfies the maximum condition for subgroups, and hence, by (iii) of Section I.7, so does $\mathfrak{S}(F, g)$.   Finally, it follows from VI.3.n that $\mathfrak{S}(F, g)$ is nilpotent, and since $\mathfrak{S}(F, g) = \mathfrak{S}(g, h_1, \cdots h_k)$, the lemma follows.

VI.7.b. Theorem (*Hirsch-Plotkin*).   *Every group has a unique maximal locally nilpotent normal subgroup.*

Proof.   Since an ascending union of locally nilpotent normal subgroups is locally nilpotent and normal, it is only necessary to show that if H and K are locally nilpotent normal subgroups, then so also is HK.   Suppose then that for $i = 1, \cdots, n$ $\{g_i = h_i k_i\}$ is a finite set of elements of HK with $h_i \in H$, $k_i \in K$.   We shall show that $\mathfrak{S}(g_1, \cdots, g_n)$ is nilpotent by showing that $\mathfrak{S}(K, h_1, \cdots, h_n)$ is locally nilpotent.   But this latter fact follows easily by an induction using VI.7.a; for $\mathfrak{S}(h_1, \cdots, h_n)$ is nilpotent and hence satisfies the maximum condition for subgroups so that there is a finite chain of subgroups $1 = R_0 \lhd R_1 \lhd \cdots \lhd R_m = \mathfrak{S}(h_1, \cdots, h_n)$ with cyclic factors between 1 and $\mathfrak{S}(h_1, \cdots, h_n)$.   It follows that there is a finite chain of subgroups $K = KR_0 \lhd KR_1 \lhd \cdots \lhd KR_m = \mathfrak{S}(K, h_1, \cdots, h_n)$ with cyclic factors.   Furthermore, if $k \in K$, $h \in H$, then there is an integer n (depending on h and k) so that $[k, nh] = 1$; for $[h, k]$ and h are in H and generate a nilpotent subgroup of H.   Thus KR_1 is locally nilpotent by VI.7.a, and inductively we find that $KR_m = \mathfrak{S}(K, h_1, \cdots, h_n)$ is locally nilpotent, as was to be shown.   This proves the theorem.

VI.7.c. Definition.   The unique maximal normal locally nilpotent subgroup of a group is its **Hirsch-Plotkin radical.**

We conclude this section with a study of groups satisfying the normalizer condition (cf. Section III.1), and show that such groups are locally nilpotent.

VI.7.d. Definition.   A group **satisfies the normalizer condition** if each of its proper subgroups is distinct from its normalizer. Following Kurosh we shall call such a group an **N-group.**

The following properties of N-groups are easy to verify (cf. [K]); the verification is left to the reader.

  (iv) *A group is an N-group if and only if each of its subgroups is a member of an ascending normal series of the group.*
  (v) *Subgroups and homomorphic images of N-groups are N-groups.*
  (vi) *An N-group has a unique Sylow p-subgroup for each prime p (cf. IV.1.d).*

VI.7.e. Theorem (*Plotkin*).   *A group satisfying the normalizer condition is locally nilpotent.*

Proof.   We first show that a maximal locally nilpotent subgroup H is normal in the group G. Indeed $\mathfrak{N}(\mathfrak{N}(H)) = \mathfrak{N}(H)$; for if $x \in \mathfrak{N}(\mathfrak{N}(H))$, then $\mathfrak{S}(H, H^x)$ is locally nilpotent by VI.7.b, and hence is H by the maximality of H, so that $H^x \leq H$ (similarly $H^{x^{-1}} \leq H$) and $x \in \mathfrak{N}(H)$. In view of the normalizer condition we conclude that $\mathfrak{N}(H) = G$ and H is normal in G, as was to be shown.

Now from (ii) we know that G is covered by maximal locally nilpotent subgroups; since each of these is normal, we conclude from VI.7.b that G is locally nilpotent and the theorem is proved. As a corollary of VI.3.i and VI.7.e we have the following.

VI.7.f. Theorem.   *A hypercentral group is locally nilpotent.*

Theorem VI.7.e can also be obtained as a consequence of the following.

VI.7.g. Theorem (*Gruenberg*).   *Suppose that A is a locally nilpotent subgroup of a group G and that A is a member of an ascending normal series of G, $A = A_1 \lhd A_2 \lhd \cdots \lhd A_\alpha = G$. Then A is in the Hirsch-Plotkin radical of G.*

Proof. For each λ let M_λ be the normal-closure of A in A_λ; then $A = M_1$ and we have the ascending normal series $A = M_1 \lhd M_2 \lhd \cdots \lhd M_\alpha \lhd G$. We must show that M_α is locally nilpotent. Suppose it is not, and let M_β be the first member of the series which is not locally nilpotent. Then either M_β has an immediate predecessor $M_{\beta-1}$ or else $M_\beta = \bigcup_{\gamma < \beta} M_\gamma$. In the first case, M_β is $\mathfrak{S}(M_{\beta-1}^x, x \in A_\beta)$ and M_β is locally nilpotent in view of VI.7.b, since $M_{\beta-1}^x$ is normal in A_β. In the second case, M_β is locally nilpotent since it is a union of locally nilpotent subgroups. Thus we have a contradiction unless the theorem is true.

In view of (ii) and (iv), Theorem VI.7.e is an immediate corollary of VI.7.g.

8. Engel elements

VI.8.a. Definition. An element g of a group G is a **left Engel element (with respect to a subset H of G)** if, to each $x \in G$ (or H), there is a natural number n depending on x so that $[x, ng] = 1$; g is a **bounded left Engel element (with respect to H)** if, in the above, n is independent of x. The element g is a **right Engel element** (with respect to H) if, for each $x \in G$ (or H), there is a natural number n depending on x so that $[g, nx] = 1$; if, in the above, n is independent of x, g is a **bounded right Engel element.**

(i) *The homomorphic images of left Engel elements, bounded left Engel elements, right Engel elements, and bounded right Engel elements, are respectively left Engel elements, bounded left Engel elements, right Engel elements and bounded right Engel elements. In particular, the sets of left Engel elements, bounded left Engel elements, right Engel elements, bounded right Engel elements are fully invariant subsets.*

(ii) *The elements of a nilpotent normal subgroup of a group are bounded left Engel elements; the elements of the Hirsch-Plotkin radical are left Engel elements. The elements of the hypercenter of a group G are right Engel elements; the elements of the subgroup $\bigcup_{n=1}^{\infty} (1:G)_n$ are bounded right Engel elements.*

We begin with an interesting proposition to show that if M is a subgroup and x an element of a group G such that $M^x \leq M$ and such that x is a left Engel element with respect to M, then $M^x = M$.   This is by way of contrast to the Example of III.1.1.

VI.8.b. Proposition (*Gruenberg*).   *Let M be a subgroup and x an element of a group G such that $M^x \leq M$, and suppose that x is a left Engel element with respect to a set Y of generators of M; then $M^x = M$, that is, x is in the normalizer of M.*

Proof.   Since $[y, (r+1)x] = [y, rx]^{-1} [y, rx]^x$ for each natural number r, it follows by induction on r (the case $r = 0$ following from the hypothesis) that if y is in Y, then for all r $[y, rx]$ is in M.   From this and the fact that there is an integer n_y so that $[y, n_y x] = 1$, it follows by induction on j from the relation

$$[y, (n_y - j)x]^{x^{-1}} = ([y, (n_j - j - 1)x]^{-1})^{x^{-1}}[y, (n_y - j - 1)x]$$

that $[y, rx]^{x^{-1}}$ is in M for all non-negative integers r.   Consequently $Y^{x^{-1}}$ is in M, $M^{x^{-1}} \leq M$, so that $M \leq M^x$, and $M^x = M$, as was to be shown.

VI.8.c. Exercise.   *Show that in a group of exponent 3, $[x, 2y] = 1$ for all x, y in the group.*

VI.8.d. Theorem (*Levi*).   *If for all elements x, y of the group G, $[x, 2y] = 1$, then G is nilpotent of class at most 3 and G^3 has exponent dividing 3.*

Proof.   If a, b, c are in G, then by (2*) of VI.1.k,

(1) $1 = [ac, b, b] = [[a, b]^c[c, b], b] = [[a, b]^c, b]$.

Also by (1*) of VI.1.k,

$1 = [a, bc, bc] = [[a, c][a, b]^c, bc] = [[a, c][a, b]^c, c][[a, c][a, b]^c, b]^c$.

By transforming this last expression by c^{-1} and using the hypothesis and (1), $1 = [a, b, c][a, c, b]^{[a,b]^c}$; and transforming this by $[b, a]^c$, we get $1 = [c, [b, a]][[a, c], b]$ or

(2) $[b, a, c] = [a, c, b]$.

Hence $[a, b, c]$ is unchanged by cyclically permuting a, b, and c.

It follows from this that $[a, b, [c, d]] = [c, d, a, b]$ and hence $[a, b, [c, d]]$ is unchanged by cyclic permutation of the symbols excluding the second one. Thus $[a, b, [c, d]] = [c, b, [d, a]]$. But $[a, b, [c, d]]$ is also equal to $[b, a, [d, c]]$ (since $[g, h] = [g^{-1}, h^{-1}]$ in view of (3) of VI.1.k) and hence by cyclic permutation of b, d, and c, $[b, a, [d, c]] = [d, a, [c, b]]$ which is the inverse of $[c, b, [d, a]]$. We have shown that $[a, b, [c, d]]$ is its own inverse and therefore has order dividing 2.

Now we consider the group K generated by three elements a, b, and c. From the above arguments we get (by cyclically permuting the first three symbols) that $[a, b, c, a] = 1 = [a, b, c, c] = [a, b, c, b]$. Thus $[a, b, c]$ is in the center of K and hence $[a, b, c]^{-1} = [a, b, c^{-1}]$ and $[a, b^{-1}, c] = [a, b, c]^{-1}$. It follows from the Witt identity ((*) of Section VI.6) that $[a, b, c][b, c, a][c, a, b] = 1$ and then by (2) above that $[a, b, c]$ has order 3.

Now $[x^3, y] = [x, y]^3$ in G and hence in $\mathfrak{S}([a, b], c, d)$, $[a, b, c, d]^3 = [[a, b, c]^3, d] = 1$ and therefore $[a, b, c, d]$ has order dividing 3. On the other hand, $[a, b, c, d] = [c, d, [a, b]]$ must be of order dividing 2 and hence $[a, b, c, d] = 1$ so that G has class at most 3 as the theorem asserts. Since $[a, b, c]^3 = 1$, G^3 has exponent dividing 3 and the theorem is proved.

In view of VI.8.c we have the immediate corollary that a group of exponent 3 is nilpotent. It is also known that a group of exponent 2 is abelian (cf. I.8.e) and that finitely generated groups of exponent 4 and of exponent 6 are also nilpotent (cf. [H]). These results are of interest in connection with the Burnside conjecture that a group of finite exponent is locally finite. This conjecture has been a problem for many years, and to date there are proofs only for special cases, the above results being equivalent to a proof of the conjecture in the case of a group of exponent 2, 3, 4, or 6. On the other hand, Novikov [22] claimed to have disproved the conjecture for prime exponent greater than 72, but his proof of this has not yet appeared.

Also of interest in this connection is the so-called restricted Burnside conjecture that for integers k and n there is a bound on the orders of the finite groups of exponent n which are generated by k elements. This conjecture has been proved by Kostrikhin [16] for prime exponent p, and in view of [12] for exponent of the forms $4p$ or pq with p and q primes.

Finally it is of interest to note that if G is a group on two generators such that for all x, $y \in G$, $[x, 3y] = 1$, then G is nilpotent (cf. [14]).

We conclude this section with some results relating to nil radical, the hypercenter, and the sets of left and right Engel elements.

VI.8.e. Theorem (*Heineken*).   *The inverse of a right Engel element is a left Engel element.   Thus if either the set L of left Engel elements or the set R of right Engel elements is a subgroup, then $L \supseteq R$.*

Proof.   Let g^{-1} be a right Engel element and x any element of G. Then $(g^{-1})^x$ is also a right Engel element so that for a suitable natural number n,

$$[(g^{-1})^x, ng] = 1.$$

But $[(g^{-1})^x, g] = [g^{-1}, x, g]$, and hence $[g^{-1}, x, ng] = 1$.   Transforming by g, this becomes

$$1 = [[g^{-1}, x]^g, ng] = [x, g, ng] = [x, (n+1)g],$$

so that in fact g is a left Engel element since x was arbitrary.   The second statement of the theorem follows immediately from the first.

Before the next theorem it is convenient to give some definitions.

VI.8.f. Definitions.   A group is **hyperabelian** if it has an ascending invariant series with abelian factors.   A group is **solvable** if it has a finite invariant series with abelian factors; **it is solvable of length n** if n is the length of the shortest such series of the group.

(iii) *A solvable group is hyperabelian.*
(iv) *A group is hyperabelian if and only if it has a non-trivial abelian normal subgroup and modulo this is again hyperabelian.*

VI.8.g. Theorem (*Gruenberg*).   *The Hirsch-Plotkin radical of a hyperabelian group is precisely the set of left Engel elements and contains the set of right Engel elements.*

Proof.   In view of (ii) and VI.8.e it is only necessary to show that an arbitrary left Engel element g is in the Hirsch-Plotkin radical, and to show this, in view of VI.7.g, we need only show that (g) is a member of an ascending normal series of the group G.   We do this as follows. Since G is hyperabelian, let $1 = A_0, A_1, \cdots, A_\lambda, \cdots, A_\alpha = G$ be an ascending invariant series of G with abelian factors.   For each λ let $A_{\lambda 0}$ denote A_λ, and for each natural number n let $A_{\lambda n}$ denote the subgroup generated by $A_{\lambda(n-1)}$ with those x of $A_{\lambda+1}$ such that $[x, g]$ is in $A_{\lambda(n-1)}$.   Then $A_{\lambda(n-1)}$ is normal in $A_{\lambda n}$ since $A_{\lambda+1}/A_\lambda$ is abelian; and $\bigcup_{n=0}^{\infty} A_{\lambda n}$ is $A_{\lambda+1}$ since g is a left Engel element.   Thus the set of subgroups $A_{\lambda n}$ is an ascending normal series of G.   Furthermore, if $B_{\lambda,n}$ denotes the subgroup generated by $A_{\lambda n}$ and g, then $B_{\lambda(n-1)}$ is normal in $B_{\lambda n}$, and hence the set of subgroups $B_{\lambda n}$ is also an ascending normal series of G.   This series begins with $B_{00} = (g)$, as we wished to show, and the theorem is proved.

VI.8.h.   Corollary.   *A hyperabelian p-group is locally nilpotent.*

Proof.   Let G be a p-group with an ascending invariant series A_λ with abelian factors.   If a and b are elements of G, then the element $[a, b]$ determines a jump (cf. (ii) of Section III.6) in the series of A_λ. Let B_1 be the first member of the series containing $[a, b]$, and B_2 be the last member of the series not containing $[a, b]$ and B_2 be the last member of the series not containing $[a, b]$.   Then modulo B_2, a and $[a, b]$ generate a finite p-group; for a has finite order, and hence there are only a finite number of conjugates of $[a, b]$ by the powers of a, and these generate a finite normal subgroup of $\mathfrak{S}(a, [a, b])B_2/B_2$ since B_1/B_2 is abelian.   Thus there is an integer n_1 so that $[a, n_1 b]$ is in B_2. We repeat the above argument with $[a, n_1 b]$ in place of $[a, b]$; that is, we let B_3 be the last member of the series not containing $[a, n_1 b]$ noting that $B_3 < B_2$ and then that as before there is an integer n_2 so that $[a, n_2 b]$ is in B_3.   Continuing in this way we obtain a properly descending series $B_1 > B_2 > B_3 > \cdots$ of the ascending series: hence this series must be finite and consequently there is an integer n so that $[a, nb] = 1$.   Thus b is a left Engel element.   Since b was arbitrary, G is its own Hirsch-Plotkin radical by VI.8.g, so that G is locally nilpotent as was to be shown.

The next theorem concerns groups satisfying the maximum condition for subgroups. First we need some basic facts about such groups; the proofs are straightforward (in view of VI.8.g) and are left to the reader.

VI.8.i. Proposition. *In a group G satisfying the maximum condition for subgroups, any locally nilpotent subgroup is nilpotent and in particular the Hirsch-Plotkin radical is nilpotent; the hypercenter is nilpotent and is in fact $(1:G)_n$ for some natural number n; finally any solvable or hyperabelian subgroup generated by Engel elements is nilpotent.*

VI.8.j. Theorem (*Baer*). *In a group G satisfying the maximum condition for subgroups, the set of left Engel elements is the Hirsch-Plotkin radical and the set of right Engel elements is the hypercenter.*

Proof. To prove that the set L of left Engel elements is the Hirsch-Plotkin radical of G, it is only necessary in view of (i), (ii), and VI.8.i to show that the subgroup generated by L is solvable. We do this as follows. We let $\mathcal{F}$ be the family of subsets H of L such that H is the intersection of a solvable subgroup of G with L. Then $\mathcal{F}$ is non-empty since $1 \in L$; and if $s \in L$, $(s) \cap L$ is in $\mathcal{F}$. Furthermore there is a one-one map between $\mathcal{F}$ and the family of subgroups generated by the elements of $\mathcal{F}$; and hence every chain in $\mathcal{F}$ has a maximal element. In view of the first sentence of the proof, it is only necessary to show that $L \in \mathcal{F}$. Accordingly we assume that $L \notin \mathcal{F}$ and hence that there is a maximal element H of $\mathcal{F}$ different from L. Accordingly there is an element s of L, $s \notin H$, and since $(s) \cap L \in \mathcal{F}$, $(s) \cap L$ is contained in a maximal element of $\mathcal{F}$ different from H. Thus $\mathcal{F}$ must contain at least two maximal elements, and we let D be maximal in that it is the intersection of two maximal elements H_i, $i = 1, 2$, of $\mathcal{F}$. Since $\mathfrak{S}(H_i)$ is solvable, it is nilpotent by VI.8.i, and hence has a normal series containing $\mathfrak{S}(D)$. If M_i is the first member of this series so that $M_i \cap L \supset D$, and if J_i is the last member of the series so that $J_i \cap L = D$, then $\mathfrak{S}(D) \lhd \mathfrak{S}(M_i \cap L)$; for if $m \in M_i \cap L$, then $D^m \subseteq J_i \cap L = D$.

Now let N denote $\mathfrak{N}(\mathfrak{S}(D))$ and let $\mathscr{E}$ be the subfamily of those H of $\mathcal{F}$ so that $D \subset H \subseteq N$. Since $\mathscr{E}$ contains $M_i \cap L$, $\mathscr{E}$ has at least two elements and hence two maximal elements K and M; further-more, in view of the maximality of D, the intersection of any two elements of $\mathscr{E}$ is D. We choose $k \in K$, $k \notin D$ and $m \in M$, $m \notin D$. If m were in $\mathfrak{N}(\mathfrak{S}(K))$, then $\mathfrak{S}(K,m)$ would be solvable and $\mathfrak{S}(K, m) \cap L$ would be an element of $\mathscr{E}$ properly containing K contrary to the maximality of K. Accordingly, we conclude that m is not in $\mathfrak{N}(\mathfrak{S}(K))$. On the other hand, there is a natural number r so that $[m, rk] = 1$ since k is a left Engel element; and there is a number s so that $a = [m, sk] \notin \mathfrak{N}(\mathfrak{S}(K))$ and $[a, k] \in \mathfrak{N}(\mathfrak{S}(K))$. Since $a \in N$ and $a \notin \mathfrak{N}(\mathfrak{S}(K))$, it follows that $K^{a^{-1}}$ is an element of $\mathscr{E}$ distinct from K, and hence in view of a remark above, that $K^{a^{-1}} \cap K = D$. On the other hand, $[a, k] = (k^{-1})^a k$ is in $\mathfrak{N}(\mathfrak{S}(K))$ and hence $\mathfrak{S}(K, [a, k])$ is solvable, so that by the maximality of K since k^a is in L, k^a is in K. Consequently, k is in $K^{a^{-1}}$ and since $K^{a^{-1}} \cap K = D$, $k \in D$ contrary to the choice of k. We arrived at this contradiction by assuming that $L \notin \mathscr{F}$; accordingly we conclude that $L \in \mathscr{F}$ and have completed the proof of the first assertion of the theorem.

We shall now show that the set R of right Engel elements is the hypercenter. If T is the subgroup generated by R, then by VI.8.e and (i) we know that T is a nilpotent normal subgroup of G. In view of VI.6.f, it is only necessary to prove the theorem for T abelian. Accordingly we assume that T is abelian and shall then show that T is hypercentral.

We let M denote a normal subgroup of G maximal in that it is properly contained in T and use bars to denote subgroups of G modulo M. Then $\bar{T}$ is a minimal normal subgroup of $\bar{G}$ and hence $[\bar{G}, \bar{T}]$ is either 1 or $\bar{T}$. Now T is finitely generated and, by the minimality of $\bar{T}$, $\bar{T}$ is a finite elementary p-group for some prime p. It follows from VI.7.a that for each $g \in G$, $\mathfrak{S}(\bar{T}, \bar{g})$ is nilpotent; consequently the automorphism induced in $\bar{T}$ by $\bar{g}$ has order a power of p. It follows from this and the finiteness of $\bar{T}$ that the group B of automorphisms induced by $\bar{G}$ and acting in $\bar{T}$ is a finite p-group. Consequently, the semi-direct product of $\bar{T}$ with B is a finite p group, and hence the intersection of its center with $\bar{T}$ is non-trivial; it follows from the minimality of $\bar{T}$ that this intersection is $\bar{T}$. We conclude therefore that $[\bar{G}, \bar{T}] = 1$ or, going back to G, that $[G, T] \leq M$.

Now M was an arbitrary normal subgroup of G, maximal in that it was properly contained in T. If T has positive torsion free rank, then there is such an M for every prime p (for pT is normal in G and is properly contained in T), and hence $[G, T]$ has torsion-free rank less than T. If T has a non-trivial periodic subgroup, then $[G, T]$ has a periodic subgroup of lower order than that of T. Thus by induction on the torsion-free rank plus the order of the torsion subgroup of T, there is an integer n so that $[G, nT] = 1$, and hence T is hypercentral, as was to be shown.

Chapter *VII*

SOLVABLE AND SUPERSOLVABLE GROUPS

In this chapter it is seen that much of the theory of solvable groups depends on exploiting the fact that a non-trivial solvable group has a non-trivial abelian normal subgroup. A general theorem of P. Hall is proved, from which it follows (among other things) that a finite solvable group satisfies the Sylow Π-theorem for every set of primes Π.

Various notions of supersolvability are introduced and it is seen how the study of supersolvable groups depends essentially on the study of the automorphism groups of cyclic groups. Two theorems of Huppert are proved; first, that a finite group is supersolvable if and only if its maximal subgroups are of prime index; and second, that a finite group is solvable if each of its proper subgroups is supersolvable. As an interesting consequence of these theorems it is easy to deduce Iwasawa's theorem that a finite group is supersolvable if and only if all maximal chains of subgroups have the same length. Also given is Baer's theorem that a finitely generated hypercyclic group is supersolvable. Finally, the hypothesis that abelian subgroups are cyclic is considered for solvable periodic groups, and some of its consequence are derived.

1. Solvable groups

VII.1.a. Definition. The **derived series** or **commutator series** of a group G is the chain of subgroups $G^{(0)} = G$, $G^{(1)} = [G, G], \cdots, G^{(n)} = [G^{(n-1)}, G^{(n-1)}], \cdots, G^{(\omega)} = \bigcap_{n=0}^{\infty} G^{(n)}$, $G^{(\omega+1)}, \cdots,$ continued transfinitely if necessary. Usually $G^{(1)}$, $G^{(2)}$, and $G^{(3)}$ will be written G', G'', and G''', respectively, as in III.1.c.

The following facts are left to the reader to verify; they are for the most part easy consequences of the definitions.

(i) *The members of the derived series of a group are fully invariant subgroups.*

(ii) *There is an ordinal α so that $G^{(\alpha)} = G^{(\alpha+1)}$. If for some natural number n, $G^{(n)} = G^{(n+1)}$, then $G^{(n)} = G^{(n+r)}$ for each natural number r, $G^{(n)} = G^{(\omega)}$, and the derived series has only a finite number of distinct terms; in particular, if G is a finite group, there is an n so that $G^{(n)} = G^{(\omega)}$.*

(iii) *A group G is solvable (cf. VI.8.f) if and only if $G^{(n)} = 1$ for some natural number n; it is solvable of length n if n is the least integer so that $G^{(n)} = 1$.*

(iv) *A group is solvable if and only if it has a finite normal series with abelian factors.*

(v) *Non-trivial abelian groups are solvable of length 1; nilpotent groups of class n are solvable of length at most n (in fact, in view of VI.6.c), of length at most $\log_2 n$.*

(vi) *A non-trivial solvable group has a non-trivial abelian characteristic subgroup; a non-trivial solvable periodic group has a non-trivial characteristic abelian p-subgroup for some prime p, in fact, a non-trivial characteristic elementary abelian p-subgroup.*

(vii) *A subgroup of a group solvable of length at most n is itself solvable of length at most n.*

(viii) *A cartesian product of groups each solvable of length at most n is itself solvable of length at most n.*

As a corollary of VI.1.c, we have the following two facts:

(ix) *If G is a group and k and n integers with $1 \le k \le n$, then $(G/G^{(n)})^{(k)} = G^{(k)}/G^{(n)}$.*

(x) *If G is a group solvable of length n and θ is a homomorphism of G, then $G\theta$ is solvable of length at most n.*

In view of (vii), (viii), and (x), we have the following immediate consequence of I.8.u.

VII.1.b. Theorem.   *The groups solvable of length at most n constitute a variety.*

The reader will find it an easy exercise to check that the single word $[\cdots[[[x_1, x_2], [x_3, x_4]], [[x_5, x_6], [x_7, x_8]]], \cdots]$ of $\mathfrak{G}(x_1, x_2, \cdots, x_{2^n})$. defines the variety of VII.1.b.

VII.1.c. Examples.   The non-abelian group of lowest order is D_6 (or S_3, cf. III.4.e); it is solvable but not nilpotent. The dihedral groups and, more generally, the holomorphs of locally cyclic groups, are solvable of length at most 2.

We conclude this section with some results of Fitting which lead to the notion of a radical and semi-simplicity for certain groups.

VII.1.d. Proposition.   *If the group G has a normal subgroup K, solvable of length m, and if the factor group G/K is solvable of length n, then G is solvable of length not more than $m + n$; furthermore, the bound $m + n$ is attained for all values of m and n.*

Proof.   Since G/K is solvable of length n, $G^{(n)} \leq K$ and, since $K^{(m)} = 1$, $G^{(n+m)} = 1$, as is asserted in the first statement of the theorem. To prove the second assertion we observe that any non-trivial subgroup of a non-abelian free group F is a non-abelian free group and hence for all natural numbers $m > t$, $1 < F^{(m)} < F^{(t)}$. Thus $F/F^{(m+n)}$ is solvable of length $m + n$, and hence the bound $m + n$ is obtained for the group $G = F/F^{(m+n)}$ with the normal subgroup $F^{(n)}/F^{(m+n)}$.

VII.1.e. Corollary.   *If H and K are solvable normal subgroups of a group G, then HK is also a solvable normal subgroup.*

As a consequence of VII.1.e, it follows that if the lengths of the solvable normal subgroups of a group are bounded—in particular, if the group is finite—then the group has a unique maximal solvable normal subgroup, called the **radical** of the group. A group with trivial radical is said to be **semi-simple**. It follows directly from VII.1.d that a group modulo its radical is semi-simple; and thus, in particular, every finite group is an extension of a solvable group (the radical) by a semi-simple group.

VII.1.f. Exercise. *Prove that a periodic solvable group is locally finite.*

2. More on Sylow Theory

We have already seen that a finite group satisfies the Sylow p-theorem for a single prime p and that a nilpotent group has a unique Sylow Π-subgroup for any set of primes Π. In this section and the next we give further results on Sylow theory and show in particular that a finite solvable group satisfies the Sylow Π-theorem for any Π. The ambitious reader will find it a profitable exercise (using (vi) of Section 1 and IV.2.f) to prove the Sylow Π-theorem for finite solvable groups at this stage. Our argument here is rather complicated and is given in a series of steps. We prove a much more general theorem of P. Hall and then deduce the Sylow Π-theorem for finite solvable groups as a corollary.

VII.2.a. Proposition. *Let A be an abelian normal subgroup of a group G and let the exponent of A be a finite Π-number for some set of primes Π. If G has a normal Sylow Π-subgroup of finite index in G, then for any $\Delta \subseteq \Pi'$, G has only one class of Sylow Δ-subgroups if and only if G/A does, and G satisfies the Sylow Δ-theorem if and only if G/A does.*

Proof. In view of the hypothesis every Δ-subgroup of G is finite. Hence, TA/A is a Sylow Δ-subgroup of G/A if and only if T when properly chosen, as in IV.7.b, is a Sylow Δ-subgroup of G; since $|G/A:TA/A| = |G:T|$, we have only to consider the conjugate classes of Sylow Δ-subgroups. In the first place it is clear that if G has only one class of Sylow Δ-subgroups, then the same is true of G/A. Assume conversely that G/A has just one class of Sylow Δ-subgroups; it will be enough for us to show that if B is a Sylow Δ-subgroup of G and C any Δ-subgroup, then a conjugate of C lies in B. By hypothesis there is a g in G such that $(CA/A)^{gA} \leq BA/A$, that is, $(CA)^g \leq BA$ so that $C^g \leq BA$. By Theorem IV.8.c (since B is finite) there is an h in BA so that $C^{gh} \leq B$. This completes the proof of the first assertion of the theorem; the second assertion follows directly from the first.

VII.2.b. Corollary. *Let A be a solvable normal Π-subgroup of a group G, let the exponent of A be finite, and let the index of A in G be a Π'-number; then for any $\Lambda \subset \Pi'$, G has only one class of Sylow Λ-subgroups if and only if G/A does, and G satisfies the Sylow Λ-theorem if and only if G/A does.*

Proof. If A is abelian, the statement of the corollary follows directly from VII.2.a. We can also conclude from VII.2.a that for each natural number n the corollary is true for $G/A^{(n)}$ when it is true for $G/A^{(n-1)}$. Since A is solvable, $A^{(n)} = 1$ for some n, and the corollary is true for G.

In view of IV.8.d and VII.2.b (note that A is a Π-group in VII.2.b and a Π'-group in IV.8.d), we have the following result.

VII.2.c. Theorem (*Schur-Zassenhaus*). *If A is a solvable normal Π'-subgroup of a finite group G, and if the index of A in G is a Π-number, then G satisfies the Sylow Π-theorem.*

The proof of the next proposition is straightforward and is left to the reader.

VII.2.d. Proposition. *Let H be a normal Π-subgroup of a group G. Then*

(1) *K/H is a Sylow Π-subgroup of G/H if and only if K is a Sylow Π-subgroup of G.*
(2) *All the Sylow Π-subgroups of G are conjugate if and only if the same is true of those of G/H.*
(3) *All the Hall Π-subgroups of G are conjugate if and only if the same is true of those of G/H.*
(4) *G satisfies the Sylow Π-theorem if and only if G/H does.*

VII.2.e. Proposition. *Suppose that a finite group G has a normal subgroup K, that K has only one class of Sylow Π-subgroups for a set of primes Π, and that these are solvable. Then the Sylow Π-subgroups of G are solvable if and only if the same is true of G/K.*

Proof. Let S be a Sylow Π-subgroup of G; then S is an extension of $S \cap K$ by KS/K. Since KS/K is contained in a Sylow Π-subgroup of G/K, it follows that S is solvable if the Sylow Π-subgroup of G/K are solvable. This proves one part of the theorem.

To prove the other part of the theorem we suppose that the Sylow Π-subgroups (and hence in fact all the Π-subgroups) of G are solvable and that T is a subgroup of G containing K so that T/K is a non-solvable Π-subgroup of G/K. If K is a Π'-group, by IV.7.c, T has a Π-subgroup R isomorphic to T/K and hence R is non-solvable. But this is contrary to the hypothesis that the Sylow Π-subgroups of G are solvable. On the other hand, if K is not a Π'-group, then K has a Sylow Π-subgroup $V \neq 1$. Let $N = \mathfrak{N}_T(V)$. Then by IV.2.e (by the hypothesis K has only one class of Sylow Π-subgroups), $T = NK$ and therefore $T/K = NK/K \cong N/N \cap K$. From IV.7.c applied to the group N/V with normal subgroup $(N \cap K)/V$, we see that N has a subgroup W with W/V a Π-group isomorphic to $N/N \cap K$. It follows that W is a non-solvable subgroup of G, contrary to the hypothesis that all Π-subgroups of G are solvable. This proves the theorem.

VII.2.f. Proposition. *Let H be a Hall Π-subgroup of a group G for a set of primes Π, and let K be a normal subgroup of G. If $K \leq R \leq HK$, then $H \cap R$ is a Hall Π-subgroup of R, and HK/K is a Hall Π-subgroup of G/K.*

Proof. Since H is a Hall Π-subgroup of G, $|G:H|$ is a Π'-number. Then since $H \leq HK \leq G$, $|HK:H|$ is a Π'-number, and hence H is a Hall Π-subgroup of HK. Now $R = (H \cap R)K$ since $K \leq R$, and we let $R = \bigcup_{i=1}^{n} (H \cap R)x_i$ be a coset expansion of $H \cap R$ in R with $x_i \in K \leq R$. Thus $x_i x_j^{-1} \notin H \cap R$ for $i \neq j$, and hence $x_i x_j^{-1} \notin H$. It follows that $HK = \bigcup_{i=1}^{n} Hx_i$ is a coset expansion of H in HK. Since H is a Hall Π-subgroup of HK, n is a Π'-number, and hence $H \cap R$ is a Hall Π-subgroup of R.

To prove the second assertion of the theorem, we note that $H \leq HK \leq G$ so that $|G:HK|$ is a Π'-number m. Then if $G = \bigcup_{k=1}^{m} HKy_i$, it follows easily that $G/K = \bigcup_{k=1}^{m} (HK/K)(y_iK)$ and hence HK/K is a Hall Π-subgroup of G/K, as was to be shown.

As a consequence of the second assertion of VII.2.f, we have the following.

VII.2.g. Corollary. *If a group has a Hall Π-subgroup, so does each of its homomorphic images.*

VII.2.h. Theorem. *If K is a normal subgroup of the finite group G, and if, for a set of primes Π, both K and G/K have exactly one class of Hall Π-subgroups each, those of G/K being solvable, then G also has exactly one class of Hall Π-subgroups.*

Proof. The theorem is true when $G = K$ and we proceed by a double induction—first on $|G|$, and then for groups of the same order on $|G/K|$. If G has a non-trivial normal Π-subgroup U contained in K, then, by the induction assumption (K/U has exactly one class of Hall Π-subgroups by (3) of VII.2.d), the theorem is true in G/U and hence, by (3) of VII.2.d again, the theorem is true in G.

We now treat separately the two cases where K is not a Π'-group and K is a Π'-group. First, suppose that K is not a Π'-group. Let V be a Hall Π-subgroup of K ($V \neq 1$, since K is not a Π'-group), and let N be the normalizer of V in G; the conjugate class of V is an intravariant family in K and hence by IV.2.e, $G = KN$. If $G = N$, the theorem follows in view of the remark above about U. Accordingly we need only consider the case that $N < G$. In this case the theorem holds in N by the induction assumption; for the hypotheses hold in N since $N/(N \cap K) \cong G/K = KN/K$ and $N \cap K$ has only the one Hall Π-subgroup V. But $|G/N|$ is a Π'-number, namely, the number of conjugates of V in G which is the same as the number of conjugates of V in K, since K has only one class of Hall Π-subgroups (the index $|K:W|$ of any subgroup W, such that $V \leq W \leq K$, is a Π'-number, since V is a Hall Π-subgroup of K). It follows that the Hall Π-subgroups of N are Hall Π-subgroups of G, and therefore, since the theorem holds in N, G has Hall Π-subgroups. If S is any Hall Π-subgroup of G, then, by VII.2.f, $S \cap K$ is a Hall Π-subgroup of K and hence, by the hypothesis, there is a $k \in K$ so that $(S \cap K)^k = V$. It follows that $(\mathfrak{N}(S \cap K))^k = N$. But $S \cap K \lhd S$ and hence $S \leq \mathfrak{N}(S \cap K)$ so that $S^k \leq N$. Since the theorem is true in N, it follows from this that any two Hall Π-subgroups of G are conjugate, as we wished to show when K is not a Π'-group.

We now consider the case where K is a Π'-group. If Q is the complete inverse image of a Hall Π-group of G/K, then Q/K is a solvable Hall Π-subgroup of G/K by the hypothesis; it follows from (vi) of Section VII.1 that Q contains a normal subgroup R so that R/K is a p-group for some prime p of Π. Since p is the only prime of Π that divides $|R|$ (K is a Π'-group), it follows that R satisfies the Sylow Π-theorem and hence has exactly one class of Hall Π-subgroups Consequently, by the induction assumption (either because $|Q| < |G|$ or, if $|Q| = |G|$, because $|G/R| < |G/K|$), Q has exactly one class of Hall Π-subgroups. Thus in what follows we need only consider the case that $Q < G$, K being a Π'-group. Since the Π-share of Q is equal to the Π-share of G, it follows that any Hall Π-subgroup S of Q is a Hall Π-subgroup of G. The proof will now be completed when we show that if T is any Hall Π-subgroup of G, then T is a conjugate of S. But this follows directly from the hypothesis on G/K. For there is a $g \in G$ such that $(TK/K)^{gK} = SK/K$, or equivalently that $T^g < SK = Q$; thus a conjugate of T is a conjugate of S by the theorem in Q. This completes the proof of the theorem.

The following special case of VII.2.h is of interest.

VII.2.i. Theorem (*Schur-Zassenhaus*). *If, for a set of primes Π, K is a normal Π'-subgroup of a finite group G, and if G/K is a solvable Π-group, then G has exactly one class of Hall Π-subgroups.*

In view of the recent result of Feit and Thompson [5] that a group of odd order is solvable, it follows that either a Π-group or a Π'-group is solvable. Hence we have the following summary of the results of IV.7.c, VII.2.c, and VII.2.i.

VII.2.j. Theorem. *If, for a set of primes Π, K is a normal Hall Π'-subgroup of a finite group G, then G satisfies the Sylow Π-theorem.*

3. Sylow theory for finite solvable groups

We begin with a general theorem from which we can, in particular, derive several interesting consequences about Sylow theory for solvable groups.

VII.3.a. Theorem (*P. Hall*).   *Let Π be a set of primes and K a normal subgroup of a finite group G such that G/K satisfies the Sylow Π-theorem. Suppose also that the Hall Π-subgroups of G/K are solvable and that K has a nilpotent Hall Π-subgroup; then G satisfies the Sylow Π-theorem.*

Proof.   In view of IV.6.b, K satisfies the Sylow Π-theorem, and therefore by VII.2.h it is only necessary to show that every Sylow Π-subgroup of G is (contained in) a Hall Π-subgroup of G. The proof will be by induction on $|G|$, the case $|G| = 1$ being trivial. Let S be a Sylow Π-subgroup and H a Hall Π-subgroup of G.

First we assume that KS is a proper subgroup. Evidently KS/K is a Π-subgroup of G/K and HK/K a Hall Π-subgroup of G/K so that, by the assumption on G/K, there is an element g in G such that $(KS/K)^{gK} \leq KH/K$ and therefore $(KS)^g \leq KH$. Now KH satisfies the hypothesis of the theorem (with the pair $\{KH, K\}$ in place of the pair $\{G, K\}$); so that, if KH is a proper subgroup, it follows (since H is a Hall Π-subgroup of KH and $S^g \leq KH$) that S^g and H are conjugate in KH. Accordingly we can assume that $KH = G$. But then, by VII.2.f, $H \cap KS$ is a Hall Π-subgroup of KS so that, by induction, there is a conjugate of S in $H \cap KS$ and in particular in H. Thus a conjugate of S lies in H and hence S is in fact a Hall Π-subgroup when we assume that KS is proper in G. Accordingly, we assume in the rest of the proof that $KS = G$.

There are now two cases. First, suppose $K \cap S \neq 1$. Since all Π-subgroups of K are nilpotent, $K \cap S$ is a direct product of prime-power groups; all of them are characteristic in $S \cap K$ and at least one of them, P say, is a non-trivial p-group for some p of Π. Let M be the normalizer of P in G. We shall show that M satisfies the hypothesis of the theorem with the pair $\{M, M \cap K\}$ in place of the pair $\{G, K\}$. We do this as follows. Let R be a Sylow p-subgroup of $M \cap K$ containing P; then for each prime r in Π there is (in view of the hypothesis on K), a Sylow r-subgroup S_r of K such that $R \leq S_p$ and $\prod_{r \in \Pi} S_r$ is a Hall Π-subgroup of K. It follows at once that $M \cap K$ contains S_q for each q different from p; the group generated by these S_q and R is a nilpotent Hall Π-subgroup of $M \cap K$. Since P is characteristic in $S \cap K$, it is normal in S, so that $M \geq S$. Thus $G = KM$ (since indeed $G = KS$), so that $G/K \cong M/M \cap K$ and M

satisfies the hypothesis of the theorem with $\{M, M \cap K\}$ in place of $\{G, K\}$. This is true also for M/P with $\{M/P, (M \cap K)/P\}$ in place of (G, K) so that, by induction, M/P satisfies the Sylow Π-theorem. Then by (ii) of Section IV.2, M also satisfies the hypothesis of the theorem; hence, if $M = G$, we have finished. If, on the other hand M is a proper subgroup of G, then, by induction, S is a Hall Π-subgroup of M. But $S \cap M \cap K = S \cap K$, so that $S \cap K$ is a Hall Π-subgroup of $M \cap K$ and hence $P = R$. Then, as S_p satisfies the normalizer condition, $R = S_p$, so that $S \cap K$ is a Hall Π-subgroup of K. Finally $|G:S| = |KS:K| = |K:S \cap K|$ is a Π'-number, so that S is a Hall Π-subgroup of G, as we wished to show.

There only remains to consider the case where $K \cap S = 1$. Since S is solvable, S has an abelian normal p-subgroup B for some prime p of Π. If $B = S$, then B is a Sylow p-subgroup of G by the maximality of S and because the normalizer condition holds in finite p-subgroups. But in this case, a conjugate of S is in H by the Sylow p-theorem; hence, in what follows we need only consider the case that $B < S$ and $KB < KS = G$. By the induction assumption then we can conclude that the Sylow Π-theorem holds in KB. Let N be the normalizer of B in G. We shall next show that N satisfies the hypothesis of the theorem with the pair $\{N, N \cap K\}$ in place of the pair $\{G, K\}$. Since B is normal in S, it follows that $S \leq N$ and hence that $G = KS = KN$; thus $KN/K \cong N/N \cap K$ and therefore $N/N \cap K$ satisfies the hypothesis of the theorem. We must now show that $N \cap K$ has a nilpotent Hall Π-subgroup. To do this we first note that $N \cap K \leq \mathfrak{C}(B)$, since $[N \cap K, B] \leq B \cap K = 1$. It follows that if q is any prime of Π, and Q any Sylow q-subgroup of $N \cap K$, the subgroup generated by B and Q is a Π-group $B \times Q$; hence by the Sylow Π-theorem in KB, $B \times Q$ is contained in a Hall Π-subgroup T_q of KB. Since $T_q \geq B$, $T_q = (T_q \cap K)B$; and by the hypothesis on K, $T_q \cap K$ is nilpotent. Now let P_q be a Sylow p-subgroup of T_q containing B, and suppose in the above that $q \neq p$; then Q is in the centralizer $\mathfrak{C}(P_q)$, and hence the q-share of $|\mathfrak{C}(P_q) \cap T_q|$ equals the q-share of $|N \cap K|$. Now let T be a Hall Π-subgroup of KB. Since the Sylow Π-theorem holds in KB, and the Sylow p-theorem holds in T, it follows that if P is any Sylow p-subgroup of T, then $|\mathfrak{C}_T(P)|$ has q-share equal to the q-share of $|N \cap K|$ for each prime $q \neq p$ of Π. In particular, we see that $|\mathfrak{C}_T(B)|$ has q-share equal to the q-share of $|N \cap K|$ for each prime $q \neq p$ of Π. Since B is central in any Sylow p-subgroup of KB containing B, it follows that the Π-share of $|\mathfrak{C}_T(B)|$ is equal to the Π-share of $N \cap K$ and hence $N \cap K$ has a Hall Π-subgroup (which is nilpotent in view of the hypothesis), as we wished to show.

Since the hypotheses of the theorem hold in N, we conclude that the conclusion does also, either because of the induction assumption if $N < G$; or because, if $N = G$, then the hypotheses and hence conclusion hold in G/B, and consequently in G (since B is a Π-group). Thus S is a Hall Π-subgroup of N and $N \cap K$ is a Π'-group. It follows from this and the Sylow theory applied to KB that B is a Sylow p-subgroup of KB.

By VII.2.f, $H \cap KB$ is a Hall Π-subgroup of KB, and hence a conjugate of $H \cap KB$ contains B. Without loss of generality we may assume that H contains B. Let $V = H \cap N$, so that $B \leq V$ and $V = \mathfrak{N}_H(B)$. Since $H \cap KB \lhd H$, it follows from IV.2.f that $H = (H \cap KB)V$. Then since $G = KH$, $G = KV$; and since $G = [K]S$, $|S|$ divides $|V|$. It follows from the Sylow Π-theorem in N that V is a conjugate of S. Since $V \leq H$, it follows that a conjugate of S is in H, as was to be shown. This completes the proof of the theorem.

VII.3.b. Theorem (*P. Hall*).   *Let Π be a set of primes. If a finite group G has a normal series $1 = G_0, \ G_1, \cdots, G_n = G$ so that, for $i = 1, \cdots, n$, $G_i | G_{i-1}$ has a nilpotent Hall Π-subgroup, then G has a solvable Hall Π-subgroup and satisfies the Sylow Π-theorem.*

Proof.   In view of VII.2.g, we may assume inductively that any proper homomorphic image of G satisfies the conclusion of the theorem. Since G_1 has a nilpotent Hall Π-subgroup, it follows (using VII.2.f with an induction argument) that G_1, and consequently G, has a simple subinvariant subgroup B with a nilpotent Hall Π-subgroup. By (ix) of Section III.6, the normal closure K of B in G is a direct product of isomorphic copies of B, and hence has a nilpotent Hall Π-subgroup. The G and K satisfy the hypotheses of Theorem VII.3.a and the theorem follows.

VII.3.c. Corollary (*Čunihin*).   *Let Π be a set of primes. If the finite group G has a normal series $1 = G_0, \ G_1, \cdots, G_n = G$, so that for*

$i = 1, \cdots, n,$ $|G_i/G_{i-1}|$ *is divisible by at most one prime of Π, then G has a solvable Hall Π-subgroup and satisfies the Sylow Π-theorem.*

VII.3.d. Corollary (*P. Hall*).   *Let Π be a set of primes and G a finite solvable group; then G satisfies the Sylow Π-theorem.*

Using the fact that a countable periodic solvable group is an ascending union of finite groups, one can get the following proposition from VII.3.d.   The proof is left as an exercise for the reader.

VII.3.e. Proposition.   *Let Π be a set of primes and G a countable periodic hyperabelian group.   Then G has a Sylow Π-subgroup S and a Sylow Π'-subgroup T so that $G = ST$.*

It is shown by Kovacs, Neumann and de Vries, [18] that countability is a necessary hypothesis in VII.3.e.   They give examples, mostly of subgroups of the cartesian product of copies of the symmetric groups S_3, to show that the Sylow theorems do not hold in general for infinite groups.

VII.3.f. Theorem (*P. Hall*).   *For $i = 1, 2, \cdots, n$, let p_i be the prime divisors of the order of a finite solvable group G; then G has n subgroups P_i so that P_i is a Sylow p_i-subgroup of G and so that, for $i, j = 1, 2, \cdots, n$, $P_i P_j = P_j P_i$.*

Proof.   For each $k = 1, 2, \cdots, n$, we let Q_k denote a fixed Hall p_k'-subgroup of G.   For each $j = 1, 2, \cdots, n$, let P_j denote the intersection of all the Q_k's except Q_j; and let P_{ij} denote the intersection of all the Q_k's except Q_i and Q_j.   If, for $i \neq j$, p_{ij} denotes the set consisting of the two primes p_i and p_j, then, by IV.2.1, P_{ij} is a Hall p_{ij}-subgroup, and P_i is a Hall p_i-subgroup of G.   It is clear that P_{ij} contains both P_i and P_j; hence, since $|P_{ij}| = |P_i| \, |P_j|$ and $P_i \cap P_j = 1$, it follows that $P_{ij} = P_i P_j = P_j P_i$.   This proves the theorem.

A set of subgroups P_i as in Theorem VII.3.f is a **complete Sylow basis** for G.

VII.3.g. Corollary.   *If a finite group is solvable, it is the product of pairwise commuting nilpotent subgroups.*

Proof.   Let $P_1, \cdots, P_n$ be a complete Sylow basis of G.   Then $P_i P_j = P_j P_i$ by the theorem, P_i is nilpotent since it is a finite p-group, and $G = P_1 P_2 \cdots P_n$.

It will be seen in Chapter IX that the converse of VII.3.g is also true.

4. A theorem of Carter

In the next theorem we see that a finite solvable group has exactly one class of nilpotent subgroups, each of which is its own normalizer. These subgroups are analogous to the Cartan subalgebras of a Lie algebra.   The following theorem is essentially due to Carter; accordingly we call a self-normalizing nilpotent subgroup of a solvable group a **Carter subgroup.**

VII.4.a. Theorem.   *Let G be a finite solvable group.   Then*

(1) *G has exactly one class of Carter subgroups.*
(2) *If K is a Carter subgroup of G and L contains K, then L is self-normalizing.*
(3) *If K is a Carter subgroup of G, then $G = G^\omega K$.*
(4) *If K is a Carter subgroup of G, then $K \cap G^\omega$ is contained in the intersection M of all the normal subgroups of G, each maximal in that it is properly contained in G^ω.*

Proof.   The theorem is trivially true if G is nilpotent (i.e., if $G^\omega = 1$).   We proceed by induction on the order of G, assuming that $G^\omega \neq 1$.   First we prove (2).   If $L = G$, the statement is obvious, so we need only consider the case where $L < G$.   If $x \in \mathfrak{N}(L)$, then K^x is conjugate to K in L by (1) ($L < G$ and therefore the theorem is true in L by the induction assumption); hence there is a $t \in L$ so that $K^t = K^x$, and consequently $tx^{-1} \in \mathfrak{N}(K) = K \leq L$. It follows that $x \in L$ and hence $\mathfrak{N}(L) = L$; thus L is self-normalizing, as was to be shown. This proves (2).

We next prove that (3) is a consequence of (2). Indeed, by (2), $G^\omega K$ is self-normalizing and hence modulo G^ω, K is self-normalizing. On the other hand, modulo G^ω, G is nilpotent and hence (by the normalizer condition in G/G^ω) $G^\omega K = G$. This proves (3).

We now prove that (1) and (4) hold in a group G such that G^ω is a minimal normal subgroup of G. In view of VI.3.o and the fact that G is not nilpotent, there is a prime q dividing $|G|$ so that a Sylow q-subgroup S_q of G is not normal in G or, equivalently, so that if N_q is the normalizer of S_q, then $N_q \neq G$. By IV.2.a, $G^\omega N_q$ is its own normalizer and, since G/G^ω is nilpotent, $G^\omega N_q = G$. Now, if N is any proper subgroup of G so that $G^\omega N = G$, then $G^\omega \cap N = 1$; for $G^\omega \cap N$ is normal in N and is normal in G^ω (G^ω is abelian since it is minimal normal) and hence $G^\omega \cap N = 1$ in view of the minimality of G^ω. It follows then that N_q is a Carter subgroup of G (since N_q is the normalizer of a Sylow q-subgroup and since $G/G^\omega \cong N_q$). Furthermore, if N is any Carter subgroup of G, then, by (2), $G^\omega N$ is self-normalizing and hence is G; then as above ($N < G$ since N is nilpotent) $G^\omega \cap N = 1$, and hence $N \cong N_q$. But this means that N is the normalizer of a Sylow q-subgroup of G, and hence that N and N_q are conjugate in G. Thus (1) and (4) hold in the case that G^ω is a minimal normal subgroup of G.

We complete the proof of (1) in the general case as follows, assuming now that G^ω is not a minimal normal subgroup of G. Let R be a maximal normal subgroup of G so that $R < G^\omega$; and let bars denote subgroups of G modulo R. Then, by the induction assumption, $\overline{G}$ has a Carter subgroup $\overline{S}$, whose complete inverse image S is proper in G in view of (4) and the fact that $R < G^\omega$. It follows from the induction assumption that S contains a Carter subgroup T and that $S = TS^\omega = TR$ since $S^\omega \leq R$. But then T is also self-normalizing in G; for if $x \in \mathfrak{N}(T)$, then $x \in \mathfrak{N}(S)$ since $S = TR$ and R is normal. This means that $\bar{x} \in \mathfrak{N}(\overline{S}) = \overline{S}$ and hence that $x \in S$, whence $x \in T$ since T is self-normalizing in S. Thus T is a Carter subgroup of G.

Suppose now that, for $i = 1, 2$, K_i is a Carter subgroup of G. Then RK_i is self-normalizing in G and hence $\overline{RK_i} = \overline{K_i}$ is both nilpotent and self-normalizing in $\overline{G}$. It follows (from the induction assumption) that there is a $\bar{g} \in \overline{G}$ so that $\overline{K_1}^{\bar{g}} = \overline{K_2}$, or equivalently that $K_1{}^g \leq RK_2$.

But RK_2 is proper in G, for R is proper in G^ω and $\bar{K}_2$ is proper in $\bar{G}$. It follows that $K^g{}_1$ and K_2 are conjugate in RK_2 and hence that K_1 and K_2 are conjugate in G. Thus (1) is proved.

The proof of (4) is immediate. If there were a normal subgroup U of G, maximal in that it were properly contained in G^ω and such that $K \cap G^\omega \not\leq U$, then modulo U, $K \cap G^\omega$ would not be 1. But $K \cap G^\omega \lhd G$ and hence (in view of the maximality of U), modulo U, $K \cap G^\omega$ would be G^ω, so that modulo U, K would contain G^ω and G/U would be nilpotent contrary to the fact that $U < G^\omega$. Thus $K \cap G^\omega$ is contained in every such maximal subgroup U and therefore (4), and consequently the theorem is proved.

The conclusion of (4) in the above theorem can be somewhat strengthened; indeed $K \cap G^\omega \leq (G^\omega)'$ (cf. [24]), but as the proof is laborious it will not be given here.

A closer study, including an interesting generalization of the notion of Carter subgroups, was made recently by Gaschütz in [6].

5. Supersolvable systems

This section is concerned with a class of groups, each having an invariant system with cyclic factors; hence a knowledge of the automorphism groups of cyclic groups is important in the study of these groups. The class of groups under consideration includes all groups with a central system (cf. VI.3.b) and also a special class of hyperabelian groups which properly contains the class of hypercentral groups. We begin with some general notions.

VII.5.a. Definitions. Let G be a group with normal subgroups A and B, $A < B$. A **supersolvable system** of subgroups between A and B is an invariant system between A and B such that the factor at each jump of the system is cyclic. An **ascending supersolvable series** or **hypercyclic series** between A and B is an ascending invariant series between A and B with cyclic factors. A finite hypercyclic series between A and B is a **supersolvable series** between A and B.

VII.5.b. Definitions.   A group is **hypercyclic** if it has a hypercyclic series (between 1 and G); it is **supersolvable** if it has a supersolvable series (between 1 and G).

We list some immediate facts.

  (i) *A supersolvable group is solvable and a hypercyclic group is hyperabelian.*

 (ii) *Abelian groups, nilpotent groups, and hypercentral groups are all hypercyclic.*

(iii) *Subgroups and factor groups of hypercyclic groups are hypercyclic; those of supersolvable groups are supersolvable.*

 (iv) *A semi-direct product of a locally cyclic group by an abelian group is hypercyclic.*

  (v) *An extension of a cyclic group by a hypercyclic group is hypercyclic.*

 (vi) *A finite supersolvable group has a chain of invariant subgroups, each of prime index in the next.*

(vii) *A maximal subgroup of a hypercyclic group has prime index in the group.*

To prove (vii), we let M be a maximal subgroup of a hypercyclic group G and let $G_{\beta+1}$ be the first member of a hypercyclic series of G which is not in M. Then $G = G_{\beta+1}M$ and $G_\beta \le M$.

Furthermore, $G_{\beta+1} \cap M$ is normal in G since G_β is normal in G and modulo G_β, $G_{\beta+1} \cap M$ is normal since it is a subgroup of the cyclic normal subgroup $G_{\beta+1}$. Using bars to express subgroups of the factor group of G by $G_{\beta+1} \cap M$, we see that $\overline{G} = [\overline{G}_{\beta+1}]\overline{M}$ with $\overline{G}_{\beta+1}$ cyclic. Then $\overline{M}$ is maximal in $\overline{G}$, $\overline{G}_{\beta+1}$ has prime order, and consequently $\overline{M}$ has prime index; it follows that M has prime index, as was to be shown.

(viii) *If G has a supersolvable system (respectively, hypercyclic series or supersolvable series) between subgroups A and B and between B and C, then G has a supersolvable system (respectively, hypercyclic series or supersolvable series) between A and C.*

 (ix) *If G has a supersolvable system (respectively hypercyclic series or supersolvable series) and if N is normal in G, then G has a supersolvable system (respectively hypercyclic series or supersolvable series) containing N.*

VII.5.c. Exercise.   *Show that the alternating group A_4 is the group of lowest order that is not supersolvable.*

VII.5.d. Exercise.   *Show that if m and n are relatively prime with $n \neq 2$, then $C_m \operatorname{Wr} C_n$ is not supersolvable, while $C_m \operatorname{Wr} C_2$ is supersolvable.*

Our first basic theorem is as follows.

VII.5.e. Theorem.   *The derived group of a group with a supersolvable system has a central system, the derived group of a hypercyclic group is hypercentral, and the derived group of a supersolvable group is nilpotent.*

Proof.   Let $\{H_\alpha\}$ be the set of subgroups of a supersolvable system of a group G, and for each α let K_α denote $H_\alpha \cap G'$. Then $\{K_\alpha\}$ is an invariant system of G' and is an ascending invariant system of G' when G is hypercyclic. At a jump H_α, $H_{\alpha+1}$, since $H_{\alpha+1}/H_\alpha$ is cyclic, its automorphism group is abelian by the results of Section III.2. It follows that the centralizer of $H_{\alpha+1}/H_\alpha$ in G/H_α contains the derived group of G/H_α; thus $K_{\alpha+1}/K_\alpha$ is central in G/K_α. Consequently, $\{K_\alpha\}$ is a central system of G' and is an ascending central series when G is hypercyclic so that in this case G' is hypercentral. If the group is supersolvable, the ascending central series is finite, and hence the derived group is nilpotent. This proves the theorem.

The next theorem includes the fact that if p is the largest prime divisor of the order of a finite supersolvable group, then G has a normal Sylow p-subgroup. The proof rests on the following basic lemma.

VII.5.f. Lemma.   *Let G be a group with a supersolvable system and let p and q be distinct primes; if a is a p-element of G' and c a q-element of G such that $[a, c] \neq 1$, then q divides $p-1$.*

Proof.   The element $[a, c]$ determines a jump U, V in the supersolvable system; since U is invariant, it follows that modulo U, $[a, c]$

is in the cyclic normal subgroup V. Since any subgroup of a cyclic normal subgroup is itself normal, it follows that, modulo U, both $[a, c]$ and for any prime r, $([a, c]^r)$ are cyclic normal subgroups. Since we may factor out $U([a, c]^r)$ for some prime r, we may assume in the remainder of the proof, without loss of generality, that $[a, c]$ generates a cyclic normal subgroup of G of prime order r.

We first show that $r = p$. Indeed suppose $r \neq p$. Since G' has a central system, then a and $[a, c]$ commute in view of VI.3.j (a has order p, $[a, c]$ has order $r \neq p$); and hence $\mathfrak{S}(a, [a, c])$ is the direct product of its Sylow p-subgroup (a) with its Sylow r-subgroup $([a, c])$. But $\mathfrak{S}(a, [a, c])$ is normal in $\mathfrak{S}(a, c)$, and therefore (a) is normal in $\mathfrak{S}(a, c)$. It follows that $[a, c] \in (a)$ contrary to the facts that $[a, c]$ is an r-element and a is a p-element. Accordingly we conclude that $r = p$ or equivalently that $[a, c]$ has order p.

We next show that $[a, c, c] \neq 1$. Indeed, if $[a, c, c] = 1$, then $[a, c]$ is in the center of $\mathfrak{S}(a, c)$; for $[a, c, a] = 1$ since $\mathfrak{S}(a, c) = (a) \times ([a, c])$. But if $[a, c]$ is in the center of $\mathfrak{S}(a, c)$, then $\mathfrak{S}(a, c)$ is nilpotent of class 2, and hence a and c commute (since a is a p-element and c a q-element) this is contrary to the fact that $[a, c] \neq 1$ and we must therefore conclude that $[a, c, c] \neq 1$. From this last fact it follows (since $([a, c])$ is normal) that c induces a non-trivial automorphism in $([a, c])$ and hence that c has order dividing $p - 1$ by III.2.m. Thus q divides $p - 1$, as the lemma asserts.

VII.5.g. Theorem. *Let G be a periodic group with a supersolvable system, and for each natural number n let Π_n denote the set of primes greater than n. Then G has a unique Sylow Π_n-subgroup for each n.*

Proof. Let n be fixed and let G_n be the complete inverse image of a Sylow Π_n-subgroup of G/G' (so that G_n contains all the Π_n-elements of G). By VII.5.e, G' has a central system and hence, by VI.3.j, G' is a direct product $H \times K$, where H is the Sylow Π_n-subgroup of G' and K is the Sylow Π_n'-subgroup of G'. Let S_n be a Sylow Π_n-subgroup of G_n; then $S_n \geq H$. If $a \in K$ and c is in S_n, then $[a, c] = 1$ by VII.5.f, since $|a| \leq n < |c|$. It follows that K is in the centralizer of S_n and hence that $\mathfrak{N}(S_n) \geq G'$. It follows from this and IV.1.d that $\mathfrak{N}(S_n) = G$. Thus S_n is normal in G. But S_n is also a Sylow Π_n-subgroup of G, since G_n contains all the Π_n-elements of G.

Hence S_n is the unique Sylow Π_n-subgroup of G, as the theorem asserts.

VII.5.h. Corollary. *Let G be a finite supersolvable group, for $i = 1, \cdots, n$ let p_i be the prime divisors of $|G|$ with $p_1 > p_2 > \cdots > p_n$, and for each i let S_i be a Sylow p_i-subgroup of G. Then $S_1, S_1 S_2, \cdots, S_1 S_2 \cdots S_n = G$, are normal subgroups of G; in particular, G has a normal p_n-complement.*

In an arbitrary group G, a set of subgroups $S_1, S_1 S_2, \cdots, S_1 S_2 \cdots S_n$ is said to be a **Sylow tower** for G if each S_i is a Sylow p_i-subgroup for the prime p_i, if $p_i > p_j$ when $i < j$, if $S_1 S_2 \cdots S_i$ is normal in G, and if $G = S_1 S_2 \cdots S_n$.

As an application of VII.5.h, we prove a lemma which will be used to prove Theorem VII.7.d below.

VII.5.i. Lemma. *Let G be a finite group, all of whose proper subgroups are supersolvable, let p be the smallest prime divisor of $|G|$, and let Z be the center of a Sylow p-subgroup P of G. Then either Z is normal in G or Z is central in $\mathfrak{N}(Z)$ and is weakly closed in P.*

Proof. If Z is not normal in G, then $\mathfrak{N}(Z)$ is supersolvable and has a normal p-complement Q by VII.5.h; thus $\mathfrak{N}(Z) = [Q]P$. It follows that $[Z, Q] \leq Z \cap Q = 1$ and therefore, since Z is central in P, that Z is central in $\mathfrak{N}(Z)$. To show that Z is weakly closed in P, we suppose that $Z^g \leq P$, $Z^g \neq Z$. If $Z^g \lhd P$, then $Z \lhd P^{g^{-1}}$ and therefore $P^{g^{-1}} \leq \mathfrak{N}(Z)$. Hence there is an $n \in \mathfrak{N}(Z)$ so that $P^{g^{-1}} = P^n$; and consequently ng is in $\mathfrak{N}(P) \leq \mathfrak{N}(Z)$ so that $g \in \mathfrak{N}(Z)$ contrary to the fact that Z is central in $\mathfrak{N}(Z)$ and $Z^g \neq Z$. We conclude that Z^g is not normal in P and that Z is not normal in $P^{g^{-1}}$. It follows from IV.2.u that G has a p-subgroup H and a p'-element b such that $b \in \mathfrak{N}(H)$, $b \notin \mathfrak{C}(H)$. Now $H(b)$ cannot be G; for in that case H would be a normal Sylow p-subgroup of G and hence Z would be normal in G contrary to our assumption. Since $H(b)$ is proper in G, $H(b)$ is supersolvable. It follows that (b) is a normal p-complement of $H(b)$, and therefore that $H(b) = H \times (b)$ contrary to the fact that $b \notin \mathfrak{C}(h)$. We conclude that if $Z^g < P$, then $Z^g = Z$, and hence that if

Z is not normal in G, then Z is central in $\mathfrak{N}(Z)$ and is weakly closed in P, as the lemma asserts.

6. A criterion for supersolvability

Our next goal is the proof of Theorem VII.6.d below, which leads to a useful criterion for supersolvability analogous in a sense to the criterion for being nilpotent given in VI.6.j. We first give three lemmas.

VII.6.a. Lemma. *If N is a normal subgroup of a group G and if G has a supersolvable system, hypercyclic series, or supersolvable series between N^2 and N, then G has such a system or series between N^k and N^{k-1} for each natural number $k > 1$.*

Proof. The lemma is trivially true for $k = 2$ and we proceed by induction on k. If $\mathscr{F} = \{H_\beta, \beta$ in some index set $B\}$ is the system or series of the hypothesis, let $\mathscr{E} = \{K_\gamma, \gamma$ in some set $C\}$ be the system or series between N^{k-1} and N^{k-2} given by the induction assumption. Then for each pair $\beta, \gamma, \beta \in B, \gamma \in C$, define $M_{\beta\gamma}$ to be

$$\mathfrak{S}(N^k, [H_\beta, K_\gamma], [H_{\beta'}, N^{k-2}] \text{ for all } H_\beta < H_\beta).$$

Then we find that $M_{\beta\gamma} \geq M_{\beta'\gamma'}$ if $H_\beta > H_{\beta'}$ or when $H_\beta = H_{\beta'}$ if $K_\gamma > K_{\gamma'}$, and we leave it to the reader to check that the set of all $M_{\beta\gamma}$ is a complete invariant system of G between N^k and N^{k-1}. Furthermore, if H_β is not a successor, then $M_{\beta\gamma} = M_{\beta\gamma+1}$; whereas if H_β is a successor, then $H_\beta = H_{\beta-1}(x)$, $K_{\gamma+1} = K_\gamma(y)$ with $x \in N$, $y \in N^{k-2}$, and $M_{\beta\gamma+1} = M_{\beta\gamma}([x, y])$. Thus the factors of the set of $M_{\beta\gamma}$ are cyclic at the jumps and hence the set of $M_{\beta\gamma}$ is a supersolvable system between N^k and N^{k-1}; if $\mathscr{F}$ is a hypercyclic series or a supersolvable series, then the same is true of the set of $M_{\beta\gamma}$ and the lemma is proved.

VII.6.b. Lemma. *Let N be an abelian normal subgroup of a group G. If for a prime p, G has a supersolvable system, hypercyclic series, or supersolvable series between pN and N, then G has the same kind of system or series between $p^{k+1}N$ and $p^k N$ for each natural number k.*

Proof. For γ in some set C let $\{H_\gamma\}$ be the system or series given by the hypothesis. Then it is easily verified that $\{p^k H_\gamma\}$ is the system or series required for the lemma to be true.

The proof of the next lemma is straightforward and is left to the reader.

VII.6.c. *Let $H = \Pi_{\alpha \in A} N_\alpha$ be a normal subgroup of a group G such that each N_α is normal in G. For each α let M_α denote $\Pi_{\beta \in A, \beta \neq \alpha} N_\beta$, and suppose that G/M_α has a supersolvable system (respectively hypercyclic series); then G has a supersolvable system (respectively hypercyclic series).*

VII.6.d. Theorem. *Let N be a nilpotent normal subgroup of a group G, and suppose that for each prime p, the Sylow p-subgroup of N/N' has finite exponent. If $G/\Phi(N)$ has a supersolvable system or is hypercyclic, then the same is true of G.*

Proof. Suppose first that N is abelian. Then N is the direct product ΠS_p of its Sylow p-subgroups S_p, and $\Phi(N) = \Pi \Phi(S_p)$. For each prime p let M_p denote $\Pi_{q \neq p} S_q$. Then modulo M_p, G has a supersolvable system (or a hypercyclic series) between pN and N. Hence, by VII.6.b and (viii) of Section 5, G has a supersolvable system (or a hypercyclic series) modulo M_p. Since this is true for each prime p, by VII.6.c, G itself has a supersolvable system (or a hypercyclic series) when N is abelian. In the general case we conclude from the above that G/N' has a supersolvable system (or a hypercyclic series), and then in view of VII.6.a and (viii) of Section 5, we conclude that the same is true of G, as the theorem asserts.

VII.6.e. Corollary. *Suppose that a finite group G has a normal Sylow p-subgroup P for p a prime divisor of $|G|$, and suppose that $G/\Phi(P)$ is supersolvable, then so also is G.*

The above results are reminiscent of the results in Section VI.6.

7. Characterizations of supersolvable groups

VII.7.a. Theorem. *Let G be a group of finite exponent such that for each prime p dividing the exponent of G, there are only finitely many Sylow p-subgroups. If every maximal subgroup of G has prime index in G, then G has a Sylow tower.*

Proof. Let $p_1, p_2, \cdots, p_n$ be the primes dividing the exponent of G with $p_1 > p_2 > \cdots > p_n$. If S_1 is a Sylow p_1-subgroup of G, we shall show that S_1 is normal in G. Indeed, if $\mathfrak{N}(S_1) < G$, then there is a maximal subgroup M of G so that $\mathfrak{N}(S_1) \leq M < G$ with $|G:M|$ a prime number. By IV.1.i, both $|G:\mathfrak{N}(S_1)|$ and $|M:\mathfrak{N}(S_1)|$ are congruent to 1 modulo p_1, and since $|G:\mathfrak{N}(S_1)| = |G:M|\,|M:\mathfrak{N}(S_1)|$, it follows that $|G:M|$ is also congruent to 1 mod p_1. But this is impossible since $|G:M|$ is a prime and hence less than or equal to p_1 (cf. IV.2.m) by the choice of p_1. It follows that S_1 is normal in G. By an induction argument on the exponent of G, G/S_1 has a Sylow tower $S_1 S_2/S_1, \cdots, S_1 S_2 \cdots S_n/S_1$ with S_i Sylow p_i-subgroups of G, and hence $S_1, S_1 S_2, \cdots, S_1 S_2 \cdots S_n$ is a Sylow tower of G.

VII.7.b. Corollary. *A finite group G is solvable if every maximal subgroup has prime index in G.*

VII.7.c. Theorem. *(Huppert.)   A finite group G is supersolvable if every maximal subgroup has prime index in G.*

Proof. The theorem is trivially true if $|G| = 1$; we proceed by induction on $|G|$. Let q be the largest prime dividing $|G|$ and let Q be a Sylow q-subgroup of G. Then Q is normal in G by VII.7.a, and G is solvable by VII.7.b. Therefore, G has a Hall p'-subgroup R so that $G = [Q]R$. We first consider the case where Q is elementary abelian and let M be a maximal subgroup of G containing R (so that $G = QM$). Then $M \cap Q$ is normal in M and hence normal in G since Q is abelian. It follows from IV.8.k that $M \cap Q$ has a complement S in Q which is normal in G. Furthermore $M \cap Q$ has prime index in Q and hence S is cyclic. By the induction assumption (the hypothesis holds for factor groups of G), G/S is supersolvable and hence, by (v) of Section 5, G is supersolvable when Q is elementary abelian. If Q is not elementary abelian, then, by the induction assumption, $G/\Phi(Q)$ is supersolvable and hence, by VII.6.e, G is supersolvable. This proves the theorem.

VII.7.d. Theorem. (*Huppert.*) *If G is a finite group all of whose proper subgroups are supersolvable, then G is solvable.*

Proof. Since the hypothesis holds for proper factor groups and subgroups, it follows that by an induction on the order of G we may assume that A/B is solvable for all subgroups A and B, $B \lhd A$, except when $A = G$, $B = 1$. Thus it is sufficient to show that G has a non-trivial proper normal subgroup N; for when both G/N and N are solvable, so also is G by VII.1.d.

Now let p be the smallest divisor of $|G|$, let P be a Sylow p-subgroup of G, let $Z = \mathfrak{Z}(P)$, and let $N = \mathfrak{N}(Z)$. If $N < G$, then N is super-solvable and has a normal p-complement M by VII.5.h. Thus $N = [M]P$ and hence by (ii) of Section IV.5, $N' \cap P < P$. By VII.5.i, if Z is not normal in G, Z is weakly closed in P so that, by IV.4.d, G has a non-trivial proper normal subgroup. Since the same conclusion holds if $Z \lhd G$ or if $N = G$, the theorem follows from the remarks already made.

We shall call a chain of subgroups with no proper refinements a **maximal subgroup chain** and shall prove a theorem of Iwasawa as an easy consequence of the above two theorems of Huppert.

VII.7.e. Theorem. (*Iwasawa.*) *Let G be a finite group. Then the following three statements are equivalent.*

(1) *G is supersolvable.*
(2) *All maximal subgroup chains of G have the same length.*
(3) *The length of each maximal subgroup chain of G is equal to the number of prime factors of $|G|$.*

Proof. We prove this by induction on $|G|$, the theorem being trivially true for $|G| = 1$. If G is supersolvable, then all maximal subgroups of G have prime index in G by (vii) of Section 5; it follows from the induction assumption that (1) implies (3). That (3) implies

(2) is obvious. Suppose next that (2) holds; then all maximal subgroup chains of each proper subgroup of G have the same length, and hence, by the induction assumption, each proper subgroup of G is supersolvable. It follows from VII.7.d that G is solvable. Therefore, G has a composition series of length equal to the number of prime factors of $|G|$. Consequently it follows from (2) that every maximal subgroup of G has prime index in G; and therefore, finally, it follows from VII.7.c that G is supersolvable. Thus (2) implies (1) and the theorem is proved.

The next lemma will be used in the proof of the theorem that a finitely generated hypercyclic group is supersolvable.

VII.7.f. Lemma. *If B and K are finite subsets of a group G which has a hypercyclic series $\mathscr{F} = \{A_\lambda\}$, and if A_{λ_0} is the least A_λ in $\mathscr{F}$ which contains B, then there is a finite subset H of A_{λ_0}, H containing B so that $K \subseteq \mathfrak{N}(\mathfrak{S}(H))$.*

Proof. Let $B = B_0$ and let A_{λ_1} be the immediate predecessor (since B_0 is finite) of A_{λ_0}. Then for each pair b, k with $b \in B_0$ and $k \in K \cup K^{-1}$, let the integer n_{bk} and the element c_{bk} of A_{λ_1} be determined by the relation $b^k = b^{n_{bk}} c_{bk}$. The set B_1 of c_{bk} is a finite subset of A_{λ_1}, and if $B_1 \neq \{1\}$. we let A_{λ_2} be the immediate predecessor of the first A_λ in $\mathscr{F}$ containing B_1; thus $A_{\lambda_1} > A_{\lambda_2}$. This argument may be repeated so that we obtain finite sets $B_i \subset A_{\lambda_i}$ for $i = 1, 2, \cdots$, with $A_{\lambda_1} > A_{\lambda_2} > \cdots$, a properly decreasing sequence of $\mathscr{F}$. But since $\mathscr{F}$ is ascending well-ordered, it follows that the sequence obtained is finite, and hence there is an integer r so that $B_r = \{1\}$. But then if $H = \bigcup_{i=0}^{r-1} B_j$, $H \subseteq A_{\lambda_0}$, H is finite, $K \subseteq \mathfrak{N}(\mathfrak{S}(H))$, and the lemma is proved.

VII.7.g. Theorem (*Baer*). *A finitely generated hypercyclic group is supersolvable.*

Proof. It will be sufficient to show that G satisfies the maximum condition; to show this we shall prove that each finitely generated subgroup of a hypercyclic group G satisfies the maximum condition.

This will be done by induction on the minimal number n of generators of the finitely generated abelian group G/N, where N is the Hirsch-Plotkin radical of G. (N contains G' since G' is hypercentral by VII.5.e, hence locally nilpotent by VI.7.f). If $n=0$, $G=N$, and the theorem is true, since a finitely generated locally nilpotent group is nilpotent and satisfies the maximum condition in view of VI.6.a. We assume then that there is a subgroup M containing N so that $n-1$ is the minimum number of generators of M/N, and that for some $x \in G$, $G=M(x)$. By the induction hypothesis all finitely generated subgroups of M satisfy the maximum condition, and we wish to prove the same for $M(x)=G$. If C is a finite subset of $M(x)$, then there is a subset B of M so that C is contained in a subgroup generated by the finite subset $B \cup \{x\}$.

In view of (ix) of Section 5 it follows that G has a hypercyclic series which includes N and M, and therefore, by the previous lemma with $\{x\}$ in place of K, there is a finite subset H of M containing B so that $x \in \mathfrak{N}(\mathfrak{S}(H))$. But $\mathfrak{S}(H)$ and (x) satisfy the maximum condition and hence so also does $\mathfrak{S}(H, x)$ and consequently $\mathfrak{S}(C)$, as was to be shown. This proves the theorem.

8. Some special solvable groups

In this section we consider certain groups whose finite abelian subgroups are cyclic. This condition is of interest since it is satisfied by all subgroups of the multiplicative groups of division rings. The condition that finite abelian subgroups be cyclic is equivalent (as is easily verified) to the condition that subgroups of order the square of a prime be cyclic. We restrict ourselves here to the case of solvable periodic groups; the general case for finite groups is considered in [25]. We begin with two useful lemmas.

VII.8.a. Lemma. *Let K be the kernel of an endomorphism θ of a group G. If $G\theta^2 = G\theta$ and $G\theta \cap K=1$, then $G=[K](G\theta)$.*

Proof. Since K is the kernel of θ, K is normal in G; by hypothesis, $K \cap G\theta=1$, and hence in order for G to be the split extension $[K]G\theta$, we need only show that $G = K(G\theta)$.   Let $g \in G$; then $g\theta = (h\theta)\theta$ for some $h \in G$; hence $((h\theta)g^{-1})\theta = 1$ or $(h\theta)g^{-1} \in K$ so that $g \in K(G\theta)$. Thus $G = K(G\theta)$ and the lemma is proved.

VII.8.b. Lemma.   *Let p be a prime, let A be an abelian normal p-subgroup of a group G, and let g be a fixed p'-element of G.   If γ is the map defined on A by the equation $a\gamma = [a, g]$ for $a \in A$, then γ is an endomorphism of A; and if K is the kernel of γ, then $A = K \times A\gamma$.*

Proof.   If $a, b \in A$, then $[ab, g] = [a, g][b, g]$ by (2) of VI.1.k, and hence γ is an endomorphism.   We shall first show that $A\gamma^2 = A\gamma$. Indeed $A\gamma^2$ is normal in $\mathfrak{S}(A, g)$; if $A\gamma^2 < A\gamma$, then modulo $A\gamma^2$, $A\gamma$ is central in $\mathfrak{S}(A, g)$ and hence $\mathfrak{S}(A, g)$ is nilpotent of class two. Since this is contrary to VI.1.r we conclude that $A\gamma^2 = A\gamma$.   We next show that if K is the kernel of γ, then $K \cap A\gamma = 1$.   Suppose that $1 \neq k \in A\gamma$; then there is a $c \in A$ so that $k = [c, g]$.   It follows that k is the center of $\mathfrak{S}(c, g)$, and hence that $\mathfrak{S}(c, g)$ is nilpotent of class two, again contrary to VI.1.r.   We conclude that $K \cap A\gamma = 1$, and therefore the hypotheses of VII.8.a are satisfied.   It follows that $A = K(A\gamma)$; since A is abelian we have $A = K \times (A\gamma)$, as the lemma asserts.

VII.8.c. Theorem.   *Let G be a hyperabelian periodic group containing no subgroup isomorphic to the quaternion group Q_8.   If for every prime p, subgroups of order p^2 are cyclic, then there is a set of primes Π so that G' is a Sylow Π-subgroup of G, and $G = [G']S$ with S a Sylow Π'-subgroup of G; furthermore both G' and S are locally cyclic.*

Proof.   In view of the hypothesis together with VI.3.i and VI.4.e, all hypercentral subgroups of G (and hence, in particular, all finite p-subgroups of G) are locally cyclic.   We show next that the hypotheses hold in each factor group $\bar{G}$ of G with a kernel of prime order q.   Indeed, if $\bar{a}, \bar{b}$ generate a subgroup of order p^2 of $\bar{G}$, then its complete inverse image is of order p^2q and has a cyclic Sylow p-subgroup of order p^2 (if $p \neq q$) or of order p^3 (if $p = q$).   It follows that $\mathfrak{S}(\bar{a}, \bar{b})$ is cyclic as we wished to show.   Similarly we can show that $\bar{G}$ has no subgroup isomorphic to Q_8 and hence the hypotheses hold in each homorphic image of G with kernel of prime order.

Now G is hyperabelian and has a normal elementary abelian p-subgroup for some prime p; by the hypothesis this must be cyclic. It follows from this and the result of the previous paragraph that G is hypercyclic, and then from VII.5.e that G' is hypercentral. From the first sentence of the proof we then know that G' is locally cyclic.

Now let p be a prime and P a Sylow p-subgroup of G; we shall show that either $P \leq G'$ or $P \cap G' = 1$. We first work modulo the Sylow p'-subgroup Q of G', that is, we assume that Q is 1 and that G' is a p-group; thus P is normal in G. Furthermore P is locally cyclic and hence indecomposable. If g is a p'-element of G, then G induces a map γ_g in P as in VII.8.b, and $P = K_g \times P\gamma_g$ with K_g the kernel of γ_g. Since P is indecomposable, either $P = P\gamma_g$ or $P\gamma_g = 1$. If $P\gamma_g = P$ for some g, then $P = [P, g] \leq G'$. On the other hand, if $P\gamma_g = 1$ for all g, then P is central in G so that G is nilpotent and hence locally cyclic; in this case $G' = 1$ and $P \cap G' = 1$. Thus either $P \leq G'$ or $P \cap G' = 1$ when $Q = 1$; it follows easily that, in the general case when $Q \neq 1$, either $P \leq G'$ or $P \cap G' = 1$, as was asserted. Thus G' is a Sylow Π-subgroup for the set Π of primes p for which G' has p-elements not 1. By VII.3.e, G has a Sylow Π'-subgroup S so that $G = [G']S$. It is clear that S is locally cyclic and the proof of the theorem is complete.

Theorems VII.8.c and VII.7.d have the following interesting consequence for finite groups.

VII.8.d. Theorem.   *Let G be a finite group which has no subgroup isomorphic to the quaternion group Q_8. If, for every prime p dividing $|G|$, subgroups of order p^2 are cyclic, then $G = [G']H$ with G a cyclic Sylow Π-subgroup for some set Π of primes, and H a cyclic Sylow Π'-subgroup.*

Proof.   An easy induction shows that all the proper subgroups of G are supersolvable; hence, by VII.7.d, G is solvable and the theorem then follows from VII.8.c.

We now consider the possibilities for a solvable group, whose finite abelian subgroups are cyclic, and which may contain subgroups isomorphic to Q_8.

VII.8.e. Theorem.   *Let G be a solvable periodic group in which, for all primes p, all subgroups of order p^2 are cyclic, and let Π be the set of primes greater than 3. Then G is countable; G has a normal Sylow Π-subgroup M and a hypercyclic series between 1 and M; and $G = [M]N$ with N a Sylow Π'-subgroup.*

Proof.   Countability follows easily by induction on the length of the derived series since the last non-trivial member is locally cyclic and hence countable.   From this fact and VII.3.e, it follows that $G = MN$, where M is a Sylow Π-subgroup and N is a Sylow Π'-subgroup.   Hence it is only necessary to show that M is normal in G and that G has a hypercyclic series between 1 and M.   We prove this by induction on the derived length of G, it being trivially true for G abelian.

Suppose then that for some n, $G^{(n)}$ is a non-trivial abelian subgroup. Then $G^{(n)} = B \times C$ with B a locally cyclic Π-group and C a locally cyclic Π'-group.   By the induction assumption, G has subgroups H and K containing $G^{(n)}$, such that $G = HK$ and so that $H/G^{(n)}$ is a normal Π-subgroup, $K/G^{(n)}$ a Π'-group, and $H \cap K = G^{(n)}$.   Now C is a Sylow Π'-subgroup of H and hence, by VII.3.e, $H = [C]M$ with M a Sylow Π-subgroup of H.   Since C is locally cyclic and since the primes of Π are larger than those of Π', it follows that C is central in H; hence $H = C \times M$ and M is normal in G (since M is characteristic in H).   Since B is locally cyclic there is a hypercyclic series between 1 and B and, by the induction assumption in G/G^n, there is a hypercyclic series between B and M.   Hence there is a hypercyclic series between 1 and M and the proof of the theorem is complete.

We conclude this section with a theorem which gives a complete classification of periodic solvable groups whose finite abelian subgroups are cyclic; it is based on the following two lemmas.   All the proofs will be left to the reader.

VII.8.f. Lemma.   *The only quaternion group that has an automorphism of odd order is Q_8, and the only indecomposable split extensions of a quaternion group by a group of odd order are the groups R_n defined as follows: $R_n = \mathfrak{G}(a, c \mid a^4 = c^{3^n} = [a^2, c] = 1, \ a a^c = a^{c^2})$. The center of R_n is a cyclic group of order $2(3^{n-1})$ and R_n is a split extension of the form $[Q_8]C_{3^n}$ with C_{3^n} inducing an automorphism of order 3 in Q_8.*

VII.8.g. Lemma.   *The only indecomposable extensions of a quaternion group by a group of even order are either quaternion groups or the groups V_n defined as follows: Let H_n be the group $\mathfrak{G}(c, d \mid c^d = c^{-1}, c^{3^n} = d^4 = 1)$, and let T_n be the split extension of Q_8 by H_n with H_n inducing a group of automorphisms in Q_8, isomorphic to S_3; then if z is the element of order 2 in Q_8, let $V_n = T_n/(zd^2)$.*

VII.8.h. Theorem.   *Let G be a periodic solvable group whose finite abelian subgroups are cyclic.   Then G may be described in one of the following four ways.*

(1) *G is hypercyclic and as in VII,8.d.*
(2) *G is hypercyclic and a split extension of a locally cyclic $2'$-group by a quaternion group.*
(3) *G is as in VII.8.e with N isomorphic to a group R_n of VII.8.f.*
(4) *G is as in VII.8.e with N isomorphic to a group V_n of VII.8.g.*

Chapter *VIII*

GROUP REPRESENTATIONS

The object of this chapter is to present some important theorems on finite groups, the proofs of which to date depend on the theory of group representations. The group algebra is introduced and it is shown that it has no non-zero nilpotent ideals when the characteristic of the underlying field does not divide the group order. A proof is then given for the Wedderburn-Artin-Noether theorem that a ring with minimum condition and with no non-zero nilpotent ideals is a direct sum of matrix rings and hence that the same is true for the group algebra. The characters are introduced and the character theory is developed from the orthogonality relations. Then on the basis of the theory developed, a proof is given for the Burnside theorem that a group is solvable if its order is divisible by at most two distinct prime powers. Also given is a proof of Wielandt's extension of the Frobenius theorem that a group is a split extension if it has a subgroup which is its own normalizer and which intersects each of its conjugates in the identity only.

1. The group algebra

We begin by recalling some elementary notions from ring theory. If A and B are subsets of a ring R, then AB will denote the set of all sums of elements of the form ab with a in A and b in B. It should be noted that the use of the expression AB is different from its use in connection with groups. It follows from the associative law that $A(BC)=(AB)C$ for all subsets A, B, C of R.

The **centralizer** C of a subset A of a ring R is the set of all $c \in R$

such that $ca = ac$ for all $a \in A$.   It is easy to check that the centralizer is always a subring.

An additive subgroup J of a ring R is a **right ideal** of R if $JR \subseteq J$, is a **left ideal** of R if $RJ \subseteq J$, and is an **ideal** of R if $RJ \subseteq J$ and $JR \subseteq J$.   The ring R is **simple** if it has no ideals other than R and 0.

A ring N is **nilpotent** if for some natural number k, $N^k = 0$; here N^k is defined inductively to be $N^{k-1}N$ with N^1 defined to be N. Thus N is nilpotent if there is an integer k so that the product of any k elements of N is zero.   If N is a right or left ideal of a ring, then so also is N^k.

An algebra A over a field F is a right vector space over F in which there is defined an associative bilinear multiplication; that is, if the multiplication is denoted by juxtaposition, $(ab)c = a(bc)$, $a(b + c) = ab + ac$, $(a + b)c = ac + bc$, and furthermore $(ab)\alpha = (a\alpha)b = a(b\alpha)$ for any a, b, c in A and any α in F.   An important example is the full n by n matrix ring over a field F, that is, the set of all n by n matrices with coefficients out of F regarded as a right vector space over F in the usual way, with multiplication the ordinary matrix multiplication.

If N is a right ideal of R, then RN is an ideal; since $(RN)^k$ is contained in RN^k, it follows that RN is nilpotent when N is nilpotent. Hence R has a non-zero nilpotent right ideal if and only if it has a non-zero nilpotent ideal (if $RN = 0$, then in fact N is an ideal).   If N is a non-zero nilpotent ideal of R, then for some natural number k, $M = N^k$ is a non-zero ideal of R such that $M^2 = 0$.

We now introduce the notion of the group algebra.   If G is a group with elements $1 = g_1, g_2, \cdots, g_t$, then each right multiplication by a fixed element g_j of G induces a permutation of the group elements, mapping g_i onto $g_i g_j$ for each $i = 1, \cdots, t$.   If V is a t-dimensional vector space over a field F with basis $B = \{e_1, \cdots, e_t\}$ and if ϕ is a one-one map of G onto B such that $g_i\phi = e_i$, then the permutation of the basis vectors sending e_i onto $g_i g_j\phi$ defines in a natural manner a linear transformation of V.   There are t such linear transformations, one for each g_j: they generate a subalgebra of the algebra of all linear transformations in V, which will be denoted by G_F and will be called the **group algebra of G over F**.   The t linear transformations generating G_F will again be denoted by $g_1, \cdots, g_t$ and the multiplicative subgroup of G_F which they generate will be denoted by G again since it is isomorphic to G.   This isomorphism of G into G_F is called the **regular representation** of G (cf. Section 3 below).   It is clear that

G_F is a vector space over F and that the dimension of G_F over F is t; in fact, the set of elements $g_1, g_2, \cdots, g_t$, is a basis for G_F over F; and the action of G on G_F is the same as the action of G on V.

VIII.1.a. Theorem. *Let G be a finite group and F a field, whose characteristic does not divide the group order; then the group algebra G_F has no non-zero nilpotent ideals.*

Proof. Suppose that G_F has a non-zero nilpotent ideal; then by the remark above, G_F has a non-zero nilpotent ideal M such that $M^2 = 0$. Now M is a subspace of the vector space G_F, in which the group G is acting, and for all g in G, $Mg \subseteq M$. Then by IV.8.m, there is a complementary subspace N of G_F so that $Ng \subseteq N$ for all g in G and hence N is a right ideal of G_F.

If 1 is the identity of G and hence of G_F, it follows from the vector space decomposition, $G_F = M \oplus N$, that $1 = m + n$ with m in M, n in N. Then from the equation $1 = 1^2 = (m+n)^2 = m^2 + mn + nm + n^2$, it follows that $1 = mn + n^2 = (m+n)n = n$; for $m^2 = 0$, since $M^2 = 0$, and nm is in the ideal M as well as in the right ideal N, whose intersection with M is 0. Then since $1 = n$, 1 is in N: but N is an ideal so $N = G_F$ and $M = 0$ contrary to assumption. We conclude that G_F has no nilpotent ideals as the theorem asserts.

The proof of the following proposition is direct and is left to the reader.

VIII.1.b. Proposition. *If $g_1, \cdots, g_t$ are elements of a finite group G and if $\alpha_1, \cdots, \alpha_t$ are elements of a field F, then $g_1\alpha_1 + \cdots + g_t\alpha_t$ is in the center of the group algebra G_F if and only if $\alpha_i = \alpha_k$, when g_i and g_k are in the same conjugate class. Thus if b_j is the sum of the elements of the jth conjugate class of G, $j = 1, \cdots, m$, then $\{b_1, \cdots, b_m\}$ is a basis for the center of G_F.*

2. The Wedderburn-Artin-Noether theorem

Before proving the Wedderburn-Artin-Noether theorem we shall present some basic facts about rings and matrix algebras which will be useful in applying the theorem to the case of the group algebra. The proofs are simple computations and are left to the reader.

VIII.2.a. Proposition.   *The center of the full n by n matrix ring A over a division ring D is the set of scalar matrices αI, where α is in the center of D and I is the identity matrix of degree n.   Thus if D is a field, the center of A has dimension one over D.*

VIII.2.b. Proposition.   *If A and D are as in VIII.2.a, then A is a simple ring (that is, A has no proper non-zero ideals).*

VIII.2.c. Proposition.   *Let the ring R be the direct sum $\sum_{\alpha \in M} R_\alpha$ of its ideals R_α; then the center of R is the direct sum of the centers of the R_α. If each R_α is a simple ring (but not a ring of prime order with zero multiplication), then every ideal of R is generated by some subset of the R_α.   Thus if ψ is a homomorphism of R, ψ is an isomorphism of the direct sum of a subset of the R_α onto $R\psi$.*

VIII.2.d. Proposition.   *If F is an algebraically closed field, then F is the only finite dimensional division algebra over itself.*

We now give an important step in the argument of the main theorem of this section.

VIII.2.e. Theorem (*Schur's Lemma*).   *Let V be a non-zero additive abelian group and let R be a subset of $\mathfrak{E}(V)$ so that $vR = V$ for each non-zero $v \in V$ (here vR denotes the additive subgroup of V generated by all the vr with $r \in R$); then the centralizer D of R in $\mathfrak{E}(V)$ is a division ring.*

Proof. If $\eta \in D$, $\eta \neq 0$, then $V\eta \neq 0$ and $V = V\eta R = VR\eta = V\eta$. If H is the kernel of η, then $H = 0$; for if $h \in H$, $h \neq 0$, then $h\eta = 0$ and $hR = V$ leading to the contradiction that $0 = h\eta R = hR\eta = V\eta = V$. Thus η is a one-one map of V onto V and has a well-defined inverse η^{-1}.   But η^{-1} also commutes with each $r \in R$; for $\eta r = r\eta$ implies that $\eta^{-1}\eta r \eta^{-1} = \eta^{-1} r \eta \eta^{-1}$ or $r\eta^{-1} = \eta^{-1} r$.   Hence D is a division ring, as the theorem asserts.

The following corollary will be needed in Chapter IX.

VIII.2.f. Corollary.   *If, in VIII.2.e, R is a finite abelian group, then R is cyclic.*

Proof.   Since R is abelian it is contained in its centralizer D, and hence is contained in the multiplicative group of a field.   But in a field the equation $x^n - 1 = 0$ has at most n solutions and hence the multiplicative group of a field has at most one subgroup of order n. It follows from II.4.q that any finite abelian subgroup of the multiplicative group of a field is cyclic and the corollary follows.

VIII.2.g. Theorem (*Wedderburn-Artin-Noether*).   *Let R be a ring with no non-zero nilpotent ideals and such that every properly decreasing sequence of right ideals is finite.   Then R is the direct sum of a finite number of uniquely determined ideals A_i, each of which is isomorphic to the full n_i by n_i matrix ring of some degree n_i over some division ring D_i.*

Proof.   The hypothesis implies that R contains a minimal non-zero right ideal V.   Let K be the right annihilator of V; that is, K is the set of all k in R such that $Vk = 0$.   Then K is an ideal of R; for $KR \subseteq K$ since $VKR = 0$, and $RK \subseteq K$ since V is a right ideal, so that $V(RK) = (VR)K \subseteq VK = 0$.   Now RV is also an ideal of R, and the subsequent argument will show that RV is a full matrix ring and that R is the direct sum of the two ideals RV and K.

Since $RV \cap K$ is an ideal of R which is nilpotent (for $RVK = 0$), the hypothesis implies that $RV \cap K = 0$.   Consequently, RV, as a ring of right multipliers of the additive group of V, is isomorphic to a subring of the full ring of endomorphisms $\mathfrak{E}(V)$ of the additive group of V and will accordingly be identified with that subring.

In view of the minimality of V, $vR = V$ for each non-zero v in V, for vR is a right ideal which cannot be zero since in that event the right ideal generated by v, namely, the set $\{vR + nv\}$, n ranging over the set of integers, would be nilpotent contrary to hypothesis.   Then since $vR = V$, it follows that $vRV = V^2 = V$ for any non-zero v in V, and hence, by VIII.2.e, the centralizer of RV in $\mathfrak{E}(V)$ is a division ring D.

The position is now that D is a division ring of endomorphisms of V so that V can be regarded as a right vector space over D and we can consider sets of linearly independent elements of V over D. Before we do this, for any x in V denote by $J(x)$ the right annihilator of x in RV; that is, the set of all elements j of RV such that $xj = 0$. It is evident that $J(x)$ is a right ideal of R. The argument of the next two paragraphs will prove that, for any elements $x_1, x_2, \cdots, x_{n+1}$ of V linearly independent over D, $J(x_1) \cap \cdots \cap J(x_n)$ properly contains $J(x_1) \cap \cdots \cap J(x_{n+1})$. Call this proposition P_n.

We begin by proving P_1. Suppose that P_1 is false and let x_1, x_2 be two elements of V linearly independent over D such that $J(x_1)$ does not contain $J(x_1) \cap J(x_2)$ properly; that is, $J(x_1) \leq J(x_2)$. Since both these elements are different from zero, we have (from the third paragraph of the proof) $x_1 RV = x_2 RV = V$, so that a map μ from V to V can be defined from the equation $(x_1 b)\mu = x_2 b$ for all b in RV. That μ is well defined, is clear; for if $x_1 b = x_1 b'$, then $b - b' \in J(x_1)$ so that $b - b' \in J(x_2)$ and $x_2 b = x_2 b'$. Furthermore, μ is in D; because it is clearly an endomorphism of V and, for any a in RV, $(x_1 b)\mu a$ $= (x_2 b)a = x_2 ba = (x_1 ba)\mu$. This means that $(x_1\mu - x_2)b = 0$ for all b in RV. However, $x_1\mu - x_2 \neq 0$ since x_1 and x_2 are linearly independent, so that $(x_1\mu - x_2)RV = V$. This contradiction establishes P_1.

Now we shall prove that P_{n-1} implies P_n for $n > 1$. If

$$x_1, x_2, \cdots, x_{n-1}$$

are elements of V linearly independent over D, then P_{n-1} implies that $x_n(J(x_1) \cap \cdots \cap J(x_{n-1})) \neq 0$. Now $J(x_1) \cap \cdots \cap J(x_{n-1})$ is a right ideal of R contained in RV so that $x_n(J(x_1) \cap \cdots \cap J(x_{n-1}))$ is a right ideal of R contained in V. By minimality it must be V so that to each v in V there is an element b of $J(x_1) \cap \cdots \cap J(x_{n-1})$ such that $v = x_n b$. Assume that P_n is false for the elements

$$x_1, x_2, \cdots, x_{n+1}$$

so that $J(x_1) \cap \cdots \cap J(x_n) = J(x_1) \cap \cdots \cap J(x_{n+1})$. Then a map μ^* can be defined from V into V by the rule $x_n b \mu^* = x_{n+1} b$, for all b in $J(x_1) \cap \cdots \cap J(x_{n-1})$. The proof that μ^* is well defined is similar to that for μ in the preceding paragraph. Obviously μ^* is in $\mathscr{E}(V)$,

and in fact $\mu^* \in D$; for, if a is any element of RV, we have $(x_n b)\mu^* a$
$= (x_{n+1} b)a = x_{n+1} ba = (x_n ba)\mu^*$.   As before, $x_n \mu^* - x_{n+1} \neq 0$ but

$$(x_n \mu^* - x_{n+1})b = 0$$

for all b in $J(x_1) \cap \cdots \cap J(x_{n-1})$.   Thus

$$J(x_1) \cap \cdots \cap J(x_{n-1}) = J(x_1) \cap \cdots \cap J(x_{n-1}) \cap J(x_n - x_{n+1})$$

which contradicts P_{n-1}, since $x_1, x_2, \cdots, x_{n-1}, x_n\mu^* - x_{n+1}$ are n
linearly independent elements.   The assumption that P_n is false is
untenable and, by induction, the proposition is true for all n.

We come now to the point of the argument of the preceding two
paragraphs.   If V had an infinite set of linearly independent elements,
R would have an infinite properly descending sequence of right ideals,
which is impossible.   Hence V is of finite dimension over D, say
dimension n for the sake of definiteness.   Suppose that $z_1, z_2, \cdots, z_n$
are n elements of V linearly independent over D, and that $y_1, y_2, \cdots, y_n$
are any elements of V.   We shall find an element d of RV such that
$y_i = z_i d$ for each i, so that in fact RV is isomorphic to the full ring of
linear transformations of V over D, that is, to the full n by n matrix
ring over D.   Since $z_1, z_2, \cdots, z_n$ are linearly independent, there
exists for each i an element a_i not in $J(z_i)$ but in $J(z_j)$ for all $j \neq i$.
Then $z_i a_i \neq 0$ and, since $z_i a_i RV = V$, there is an element b_i of RV
such that $z_i a_i b_i = y_i$ and $z_j a_i b_i = 0$ if $i \neq j$.   Then the element
$d = a_1 b_1 + a_2 b_2 + \cdots + a_n b_n$; has the required property.

If now r is any element of R, $z_i r \in V$ so that $z_i a = z_i r$ for suitable a
in RV, this relation holding for all i.   Then $a - r$ lies in the right
annihilator K of V so that $R = RV + K$.   But we have seen already
that $RV \cap K = 0$ so that R is the direct sum of RV and K.

If we now let A_1 stand for RV and if V_2 is a minimal right ideal of
R in K, then by repeating the above arguments we see that $R = A_1$
$\oplus A_2 \oplus K_2$ with A_2 a full matrix algebra over some division ring
D_2 and K_2 the intersection of K with the annihilator of V_2.   Because
of the minimum condition for R this process must cease in a finite
number of steps; $R = A_1 \oplus \cdots \oplus A_m$, each A_j a full matrix ring over
a division ring D_j, and an ideal of R as the theorem asserts.   The
uniqueness of the A_j follows from VIII.2.c and VIII.2.b.

From VIII.1.a and VIII.2.g we now deduce the following important
theorem.

VIII.2.h. Theorem.   *Let F be a field whose characteristic does not divide the order of a finite group G; then the group algebra G_F is isomorphic to a direct sum of matrix rings over division rings. If F is algebraically closed, the matrix rings are matrix algebras over F itself and their number is equal to the number of conjugate classes of G.*

Proof.   Since G_F is finite dimensional and the right ideals are subspaces, all descending chains of right ideals are finite in length; furthermore G_F has no non-zero nilpotent right ideals by VIII.1.a, and hence the first statement of the theorem follows from VIII.2.g.

By the construction of the division rings D in the proof of VIII.2.g, it is clear that an isomorphic copy of F is contained in the center of each D_j, and hence, in view of VIII.2.d, each $D_j = F$ when F is algebraically closed.   Finally, in view of VIII.2.a and VIII.2.c, the dimension of the center of G_F is equal to the number of matrix algebras; it is also equal to the number of conjugate classes of G by VIII.1.b.   This proves the theorem.

The following corollary is of interest; it will be needed in Chapter IX.

VIII.2.i. Corollary.   *If G is an abelian group of finite order t and F is an algebraically closed field of characteristic prime to t, then the group algebra G_F consists of diagonal t by t matrices (that is, the entries are zero except on the main diagonal).*

Proof.   Since G is abelian, G has t conjugate classes; hence by VIII.2.h, G_F is the direct sum of t matrix algebras over F.   On the other hand, the dimension of G_F over F is t and hence each matrix algebra is one dimensional.   Thus G_F consists of diagonal matrices as is asserted.

3. The characters

In this section (with the exception of VIII.3.i) G will denote a group of order t, and G_F its group algebra over an algebraically closed field F, whose characteristic does not divide t.   Then G_F may be identified with $A_1 \oplus \cdots \oplus A_m$ where for each $r = 1, 2, \cdots, m$, A_r is a full t_r by t_r matrix algebra over F; thus $t = \sum_{r=1}^{m} t_r^2$.   Suppose now that for each r, a basis is chosen for the space V_r on which the algebra A_r acts; the union over r, $e_1, \cdots, e_s$, of these bases is a basis for the space in which G_F acts.   Evidently $s = t_1 + t_2 + \cdots + t_m$.   With this choice of basis an s by s matrix (θ_{ij}) represents an element of G_F if and only if $\theta_{ij} = 0$ whenever e_i and e_j are not in the same subspace V_r; in fact, the elements of G_F have the form

$$\begin{pmatrix} B_1 & & & & 0 \\ & B_2 & & & \\ & & \cdot & & \\ & & & \cdot & \\ & & & & \cdot \\ 0 & & & & B_m \end{pmatrix}$$

where for each r, B_r is a t_r by t_r matrix.

One now exploits the fact that for any element a of G_F, the sum $\sum_{g \in G} gag^{-1}$ is central in G_F.   In particular, let E_{pq} be the element of G_F whose (j, k)-component is $\alpha_{jk} = \delta_{jp}\delta_{qk}$ (Kronecker deltas); that is, E_{pq} has 1 in the (p, q)-position and zeros elsewhere.   (The reader is reminded that not *every* position (p, q) is possible.)   If we denote the matrix of the group element g by (γ_{ij}) and that of its inverse by $(\gamma_{ij}{}^*)$ (really we should write $(\gamma_{ij}(g))$ and $(\gamma_{ij}{}^*(g))$), then the (i, k)-component of gE_{pq} is $\sum_{j=1}^{s} \gamma_{ij}\alpha_{jk} = \gamma_{ip}\delta_{qk}$ and the (i, n)-component of $gE_{pq}g^{-1}$ is $\sum_{k=1}^{s} \gamma_{ip}\delta_{qk}\gamma_{kn}{}^* = \gamma_{ip}\gamma_{qn}{}^*$.   It follows that the (i, n)-component of $\sum_{g \in G} gE_{pq}g^{-1}$ is $\sum_{g \in G} \gamma_{ip}\gamma_{qn}{}^*$, with the obvious notational assumption.   Since $\sum_{g \in G} gE_{pq}g^{-1}$ is central in G_F, it follows in the first place from VIII.2.a and VIII.2.c that $\sum_{g \in G} \gamma_{ip}\gamma_{qn}{}^* = 0$ unless $i = n$.

Similarly, $\sum_{g \in G} g^{-1}E_{ni}g$ is a center element; its (q, p)-component is $\sum_{g \in G} \gamma_{qn}\gamma_{ip}$ so that $\sum_{g \in G} \gamma_{qn}{}^*\gamma_{ip} = 0$ unless $p = q$.   Combined with the above remark, this gives $\sum_{g \in G} \gamma_{qn}{}^*\gamma_{ip} = 0$ unless $p = q$ and $i = n$. Let us examine $\sum_{g \in G} \gamma_{np}\gamma_{pn}{}^*$.   If e_p and e_n lie in different V_r, the remark in the first paragraph of this section gives $\gamma_{np} = 0$ so that $\sum_{g \in G} \gamma_{np}\gamma_{pn}{}^* = 0$.   If they lie in the same V_r, then as $\sum_{g \in G} \gamma_{np}\gamma_{pn}{}^*$

is the (n, n)-component of $\sum_{g \in G} g E_{pp} g^{-1}$ and the (p, p)-component
of $\sum_{g \in G} g^{-1} E_{nn} g$, it must be independent of p and n; this is because
$\sum_{g \in G} g E_{pp} g^{-1}$ and $\sum_{g \in G} g^{-1} E_{nn} g$ are central in G_F and so "scalar in
V_r." Summing up the conclusions of this section so far, we have the
following very important relations:

VIII.3.a. Lemma.   *If e_p and e_n lie in the same V_r, there is a scalar β_r
independent of p and n so that $\sum_{g \in G} \gamma_{ip} \gamma_{qn}{}^* = \delta_{pq} \delta_{in} \beta_r$.*

VIII.3.b. Lemma. $\sum_{g \in G} \gamma_{ip} \gamma_{qn}{}^* = 0$ *if e_p and e_n are not in the same
V_r.*

Since $g^* = g^{-1}$, the (i, i)-component of $g^* g$, which is 1, is also given
by the expression $\sum_{j=1}^{s} \gamma_{ij}{}^* \gamma_{ji}$. Summing this over all g in G one
gets $\sum_{j=1}^{s} \sum_{g \in G} \gamma_{ij}{}^* \gamma_{ij} = t$; then from VIII.3.a and VIII.3.b we have
the following.

VIII.3.c. Lemma. $t = \beta_r t_r$.

It is now convenient to introduce the notion of character. Suppose
θ is a homomorphism from the group G onto a group of non-singular
matrices over a field F; then θ is called a **representation** of G. We
already considered the regular representation of G in constructing
the group algebra in Section 1. The function χ which associates to
each element g in G the trace of the matrix $g\theta$ is said to be the **character**
of the representation θ of G. Since for any matrices a and b (b non-
singular) the trace of bab^{-1} is the same as the trace of a, it follows
that χ takes the same value for all the elements of a conjugate class of
G. A function with the latter property is called a **class function**
from G to F.

In particular, let θ_r be the map projecting G_F onto A_r, that is, for a
in G_F, $a\theta_r = a_r$, where a_r is the component of a in A_r. Then θ_r
restricted to G is a homorphism of G which is called an **irreducible
representation** of G. The character χ_r of the representation θ_r is of
particular importance; it will be called a **simple** character. If i

indexes the classes of G, it will be convenient to use the notation χ_{ir} for the value of the character χ_r on the elements of the ith class, and to let i^* index the class of the inverses of the elements of the ith class.

From VIII.3.b it follows at once that $\sum_{g \in G} \chi_r(g)\chi_{r'}(g^{-1}) = 0$ if $r \neq r'$; whereas a straightforward application of VIII.3.a, VIII.3.b, and VIII.3.c (with the same notation as previously for the matrices for g and g^{-1}) gives

$$\sum_{g \in G} \chi_r(g)\chi_r(g^{-1}) = \sum_{g \in G} \left\{ \left(\sum_{j=z+1}^{z+t_r} \gamma_{jj} \right) \left(\sum_{j=z+1}^{z+t_r} \gamma_{kk}{}^* \right) \right\}$$

$$= \sum_{g \in G} \sum_{j=z+1}^{z+1_r} \gamma_{jj}\gamma_{jj}{}^*$$

$$= \beta_r t_r$$

$$= t.$$

In this, $z = t_1 + t_2 + \cdots + t_{r-1}$.

If h_i denotes the number of elements in the ith class, then we may summarize much of the content of this section in the following theorem.

VIII.3.d. Theorem.   *The values of the simple characters of G over F satisfy the following equations*

(1) $\sum_{i=1}^{m} h_i \chi_{ir} \chi_{i^*r'} = t\delta_{rr'}$ *for* $1 \leq r, r' \leq m$;

(2) $\sum_{r=1}^{m} h_j \chi_{jr} \chi_{i^*r} = t\delta_{ij}$ *for* $1 \leq i, j \leq m$.

Proof.   The equations of (1) are a restatement of the equations preceding the theorem.

If $(h_i\chi_{ir})'$ is the matrix whose (r, i) coefficient is $h_i\chi_{ir}$, if $(\chi_{i^*r'})$ is the matrix whose (i, r') coefficient is $\chi_{i^*r'}$, and if I is the identity m by m matrix, then equations (1) may be rewritten in matrix form $(h_i\chi_{ir})'(\chi_{i^*r'}) = tI$. But this implies that the two matrices commute; so that $(\chi_{1^*r'})(h_i\chi_{ir})' = tI$. This latter matrix equation may be rewritten as the equations of (2) and the theorem is proved.

Of special importance is the fact that the m simple characters are a basis for the space of class functions from G to F. This can be seen as follows. In the first place, the space of class functions from G to

F is an m-dimensional vector space over F since there are m classes; and the functions may be regarded as m-tuples from F. On the other hand, the matrix $(\chi_{i*r'})$ is non-singular in view of the matrix equation in the proof of VIII.3.d; hence the m columns of the matrix are linearly independent m-tuples of F. It follows that the set of m simple characters χ_r of G is a basis for the space of class functions from G to F; that is, if ϕ is a class function, then $\phi = \sum_{r=1}^{m} \lambda_r \chi_r$ for suitable λ_r in F.

Next the scalar product (ϕ, ψ) of the two class functions ϕ and ψ is defined by means of the equation $(\phi, \psi) = 1/t \sum_{g \in G} \phi(g)\psi(g^{-1})$, where t is the order of G. It is clear that this scalar product is bilinear and symmetric; that is, $(\phi + \psi, \omega) = (\phi, \omega) + (\psi, \omega)$, $(\phi, \psi) = (\psi, \phi)$, and $\lambda(\phi, \psi) = (\lambda\phi, \psi) = (\phi, \lambda\psi)$, $\lambda \in F$. The equations of VIII.3.d may now be written in the form $(\chi_r, \chi_{r'}) = \delta_{rr'}$.

It should be noted that if $\phi = \sum_{r=1}^{m} \lambda_r \chi_r$, then $(\phi, \chi_r) = \lambda_r$ in view of the preceding equation; hence $\phi = \sum_{r=1}^{m} (\phi, \chi_r)\chi_r$ and furthermore $(\phi, \psi) = \sum_{i=1}^{m} (\phi, \chi_i)\chi_i$, $\sum_{j=1}^{m} (\psi, \chi_j)\chi_j) = \sum_{i=1}^{m} (\phi, \chi_i)(\psi, \chi_i)$.

The above results may be formulated as follows.

VIII.3.e. Theorem. *The simple characters χ_r are a basis for the space of class functions from G to F; and $(\chi_r, \chi_{r'}) = \delta_{rr'}$. If ϕ is any class function, then $\phi = \sum_{r=1}^{m} (\phi, \chi_r)\chi_r$, and if ψ is also a class function, then $(\phi, \psi) = \sum_{i=1}^{m} (\phi, \chi_i)(\psi, \chi_i)$.*

The following criterion is useful for applications.

VIII.3.f. Theorem. *Let $\chi_1, \chi_2, \cdots, \chi_m$ be the simple characters of G. Then a class function ϕ from G to F is a character of G over F if and only if ϕ is a sum $\sum_{i=1}^{m} \lambda_i \chi_i$ with the λ_i non-negative integers.*

Proof. Let $\lambda_1, \lambda_2, \cdots, \lambda_m$ be arbitrary non-negative integers. We form the direct sum $R = \sum_{i=1}^{m} \sum_{j=1}^{\lambda_i} A_{ij}$ of λ_1 copies of A_1, λ_2 copies $A_2, \cdots, \lambda_m$ copies of A_m with A_{ij} the image of A_i under an isomorphism ψ_{ij}. Then we define a map θ from G into R as follows;

for $g \in G$ let $g\theta = \sum_{i=1}^{m} \sum_{j=1}^{\lambda_i} (g\theta_i)\psi_{ij}$. It is readily checked that θ is a homomorphism, and hence a representation of G, and that the character of θ is $\sum_{i=1}^{m} \lambda_i \chi_i$. This proves one part of the theorem.

Conversely, if ϕ is a character of G over F, then there is a representation θ of G so that $G\theta$ is a group of non-singular matrices acting in a vector space V over F, with $g\phi$ the trace of $g\theta$. By IV.8.m, V is a direct sum of minimal $G\theta$ invariant subspaces W; that is, each W is minimal with respect to the property that $W(G\theta) \le W$. Let W be such a minimal subspace and let H be the algebra of linear transformations of W generated by the restriction of the elements of $G\theta$ to W, and let ψ_W be a map from G_F onto H defined as follows. For $w \in W$ (with $g_1, g_2, \cdots, g_t$ denoting the elements of G and $\alpha_1, \alpha_2, \cdots, \alpha_t$ being arbitrary in F) let $w((\sum_{i=1}^{t} g_i\alpha_i)\psi_W) = w(\sum_{i=1}^{t} g_i\theta)\alpha_i$. We leave it to the reader to check that ψ_W is a ring homomorphism of G_F onto W; and hence, in view of the third statement of VIII.2.c, ψ_W is an isomorphism of the direct sum of a subset of the A_i. From the minimality of W and the fact that $A_i A_j = 0$ for $i \ne j$, it follows that ψ_W is an isomorphism of some one of the A_i, say A_k for definiteness. Thus, for $w \in W$ and $g \in G$, $w(g\theta) = wg\theta_k$, where $g\theta_k$ is the projection of g in A_k. Hence the trace of $g\theta$ restricted to W equals the trace of $g\theta_k$ acting in W, and therefore the contribution to the character ϕ from W is precisely χ_k. Then if λ_k is the number of minimal subspaces W of the direct decomposition of V such that $W(G\theta) = wA_k$, it follows that $\phi = \sum_{k=1}^{m} \lambda_k \chi_k$. This proves the theorem.

An immediate corollary of VIII.3.e and VIII.3.f is as follows.

VIII.3.g. Corollary. *The scalar product of two characters is a non-negative integer.*

It follows from the above proof that if θ is any representation of a finite group over a suitable field, then θ is the "sum" of irreducible representations θ_i; that is, $\theta = \sum_{j=1}^{m} \lambda_i \theta_i$, in the sense that, if V is the space in which $G\theta$ acts, then V is the direct sum of spaces W so that for each W, $WG\theta = W$ and so that $G\theta$ restricted to W is isomorphic to one of the simple matrix algebras A_i. Thus we have the following theorem.

VIII.3.h. Theorem. *Every representation is the sum of irreducible representations.*

The numbers λ_i are determined by θ; for the character of θ is $\sum_{i=1}^{m} \lambda_i \chi_i$ and the set of χ_i is a basis for the space of class functions so that the λ_i are uniquely determined.   Thus Theorems VIII.3.f and VIII.3.h explain the terminology "simple character" and "irreducible representation."   Usually VIII.3.h with an appropriate but equivalent definition of "irreducible representation" is the starting point for the theory of group representations.

We conclude this section with a description of the character of the regular representation over any field.

VIII.3.i. Theorem. *Let G be a group of order m, and let χ be the character of the regular representation of G over any field F.   Then $\chi(g) = 0$ for $g \neq 1$, $g \in G$, and $\chi(1) = m$.*

Proof.   If θ is the regular representation of G over F, then in view of the construction of G_F in Section 1, for each $g \in G$, $g \neq 1$, $g\theta$ is a permutation matrix, that is, a matrix with exactly one 1 in each row and each column and zeros on the main diagonal.   Since $\chi(g)$ is the trace of the matrix $g\theta$, it follows that $\chi(g) = 0$ for $g \neq 1$.   On the other hand, 1θ is the identity m by m matrix and hence $\chi(1) = m$.   This proves the theorem.

4. A theorem of Frobenius

We begin with a lemma which gives a condition for the existence of normal subgroups of a group.

VIII.4.a. Lemma. *Let χ be the character of a representation θ of a group G of order t over the complex field F, and let K be the set of k in G for which the absolute value $|\chi(k)| = \chi(1)$; then K is a normal subgroup of G.   If H is the subset of h in K such that $\chi(k) = \chi(1)$, then H is the kernel of θ and K/H is abelian.*

Proof.   Since θ is a representation, $G\theta$ is, for some n, a group of n by n matrices over F.   This means that for any g in G, $\chi(g)$ is the sum of the n characteristic roots of $g\theta$, since $\chi(g)$ is the trace of this matrix. Now $(g\theta)^t = I$ (t is the order of G), so that for any characteristic root λ of $g\theta$, $\lambda^t = 1$; for if v is a characteristic vector of $g\theta$ belonging to λ, then $v(g\theta) = \lambda v$ so that $v = v(g\theta)^t = \lambda^t v$.   Hence $\chi(g)$ is a sum of n tth roots of unity.

For any k in K, since $\chi(k)$ is a sum of n roots of unity and $|\chi(k)| = n$, it follows from the geometry of complex numbers that these roots must all be equal, κ for definiteness.   The characteristic equation of $k\theta$ is therefore $(X - \kappa)^n = 0$, so that by the Cayley-Hamilton theorem, $(k\theta - \kappa I)^n = 0$.   But $(k\theta)^t = 1$ so that $k\theta$ also satisfies the equation $X^t - 1 = 0$; since the greatest common divisor of the polynomials $X^t - 1$ and $(X - \kappa)^n$ is $X - \kappa$, it follows that $k\theta - \kappa I = 0$ so that $k\theta = \kappa I$. Thus $k\theta$ is a scalar matrix and so is central in $G\theta$.

Suppose now that k is in H.   Then $\chi(k) = \chi(1) = n$ and all the characteristic roots of $k\theta$ are 1 so that, by the above argument, $k\theta = I$ and k lies in the kernel of θ.   The converse of this is obvious so that H is in fact the kernel of θ.   This means that K is the complete inverse image of a central subgroup of $G\theta$ and hence is normal in G. Since $K/H \cong K\theta$, it follows that K/H is abelian and the proof of the lemma is complete.

The argument of the previous proof may readily be adapted to give the following lemma; the details of proof are left to the reader.

VIII.4.b. Lemma.   *Let χ be the character of a representation θ of a finite group G over the complex field, let $\theta = \sum_{i=1}^{k} \psi_i$, where the ψ_i are irreducible representations of G, and let χ_i be the simple character belonging to ψ_i.   If for some $g \in G$, $\chi(g) = \chi(1)$, then for each $i = 1, \cdots, k$, $\chi_i(g) = \chi_i(1)$.*

It should be noted that if $c = \sum_{g \in G} g$, then the ideal $[c]$ generated by c in G_F is one-dimensional and is one of the matrix algebras—A_1 for definiteness—which are the direct summands of G_F mentioned at the beginning of the previous section.   The representation θ_1, projecting G onto $A_1 = [c]$ is called the 1-*representation;* the character χ_1 of θ_1 has the following properties since $cg = c$ for each $g \in G$.

(1) $\chi_1(g) = 1$.

(2) *If q is in F and $\tilde{q}$ denotes $q\chi_1$, then $(\tilde{q}, \chi_i) = \delta_i q$.*

We now give a proof of Wielandt's extension of a theorem of Frobenius (cf. [31]).

VIII.4.c. Theorem (*Wielandt*).   *Let J be a proper normal subgroup of a subgroup H of a group G, and suppose for each x in G, x not in H, that $H^x \cap H \le J$. If K is the union of all the conjugate classes of G which do not meet $H \setminus J$, then K is a normal subgroup of G, $G = KH$, and $K \cap H = J$.*

Proof.   Let ρ be the regular representation of H/J over the complex field, and let σ be the natural homomorphism of H onto H/J, then $\sigma\rho$ is a representation of H by means of m by m matrices with $m = |H/J|$. If ϕ is the character of $\sigma\rho$, then as in VIII.3.i, $\phi(h) = 0$ for $h \notin J$ and $\phi(j) = m$ for $j \in J$. We also have, in view of VIII.3.f, that $\phi = \sum_{i=1}^{p} \lambda_i \psi_i$ with the λ_i positive integers, and the ψ_i certain simple characters of H.

Our first goal is to construct for each of the above ψ_i a simple character $\tilde{\psi}_i$ of G such that $\tilde{\psi}_i(h) = \psi_i(h)$ for each $h \in H$. To do this we first note that if $h \in H \setminus J$, then the intersection with H of the conjugate class $C_G(h)$ of h in G is precisely the conjugate class $C_H(h)$ of h in H; for if $h = f^x$ with $f \in H$ and $x \in G \setminus H$, then from the hypothesis that $H^x \cap H \le J$ it would follow that h is in J contrary to the choice of h. Now we define the class function $\bar{\omega}_i$ on G by the equations $\bar{\omega}_i(k) = 0$ for $k \in K$, and for $g \notin K$ (by hypothesis there is an $h_g \in H \setminus J$ conjugate to g) we define $\bar{\omega}_i(g)$ to be $\psi_i(h_g) - \psi_i(1)$ which we will write $\psi_i(h_g) - \tilde{n}_i(h_g)$ with $n_i = \psi_i(1)$. Let $\tilde{\psi}_i$ denote $\bar{\omega}_i + \tilde{n}_i$. In view of VIII.4.b, it is clear that for $h \in H$, $\tilde{\psi}_i(h) = \psi_i(h)$.

We now show that each $\tilde{\psi}_i$ is simple; since $\tilde{\psi}_1$ is obviously simple, we assume in what follows that $i \ne 1$. Let T be a transversal of H in G and let $|T| = t$. The hypothesis that $H^x \cap H \le J$ for x not in H implies that H is its own normalizer and that H has t conjugates and that for each $h \in H \setminus J$, $|h^T| = t$. If s denotes $|H|$ and if $\bar{\chi}_j$ is a simple character of G, then

$$(1/st) \sum_{g \in G} \bar{\omega}_i(g) \bar{\chi}_j(g^{-1}) = (1/s) \sum_{h \in H} \bar{\omega}_i(h) \bar{\chi}_j(h^{-1})$$

since $\bar{\omega}_i(k) = 0$.   Thus $(\bar{\omega}_i, \bar{\chi}_j) = (\omega_i, \chi_j)$, where the omission of the bar denotes that the function is restricted to H.   Since ω_i and χ_j are linear combinations with integer coefficients of simple characters of H, it follows from VIII.3.f and VIII.3.g that $(\omega_i, \chi_j) = (\bar{\omega}_i, \bar{\chi}_j)$ is an integer.   In particular, we see that $(\bar{\omega}_i, \bar{\chi}_1) = (\omega_i, \chi_1) = -n_i$.   It can be seen in a similar manner that $(\bar{\omega}_i, \bar{\omega}_i) = (\omega_1, \omega_i) = n_i^2 + 1$ since $\omega_i = \psi_i - n_i\psi_1$.

Since $\bar{\omega}_i$ is a sum of simple characters of G with the coefficient of $\bar{\chi}_1$ equal to $-n_i$, and the other coefficients also integers, and since $(\bar{\omega}_i, \bar{\omega}_i) = n_i^2 + 1$, it follows that $\bar{\omega}_i = \pm\bar{\chi} - \tilde{n}_i$ with $\bar{\chi}$ a simple character of G.   Since $0 = \bar{\omega}_i(1) = \pm\bar{\chi}(1) - \tilde{n}_i$ and since $\bar{\chi}(1) > 0$, it follows that $\bar{\omega}_i = \bar{\chi} - \tilde{n}_i$, and hence that $\bar{\chi} = \bar{\psi}_i$, so that in fact $\bar{\psi}_i$ is a simple character of G.

Now let $\bar{\phi}$ denote $\sum_{i=1}^{p} \lambda_i\psi_i$.   Then $\bar{\phi}(g) = \bar{\phi}(1)$ for $g \in K$ and $\bar{\phi}(g) = 0$ for $g \notin K$, since the same is true for ϕ by what was shown at the beginning of the proof.   Then by VIII.4.a, K is a normal subgroup of G and $K \cap H = J$.   Finally, since $G = \bigcup_{g \in G} KH^g$, it follows from III.1.v that $G = KH$.   This completes the proof of the theorem.

The special case of VIII.4.c where $J = 1$ is due to Frobenius.

VIII.4.d. Corollary (*Frobenius*).   *If H is a subgroup of the finite group G so that for each x in G, x not in H, $H^x \cap H = 1$, then G has a proper normal subgroup K so that $G = [K]H$.*

A group G having a subgroup H so that $H^x \cap H = 1$ for $x \in G$, $x \notin H$, is a **Frobenius group** and the normal subgroup K is the **Frobenius kernel** of G.   We shall see in the next chapter that the Frobenius kernel is always a nilpotent subgroup.

5. A theorem of Burnside

In this section we prove that if Π is a set consisting of at most two primes, then a finite Π-group is solvable.   The proof is based on some elementary properties of algebraic integers as well as on the character theory developed earlier.

We say that an element of a field is an **algebraic integer** if the subring it generates has a finitely generated additive subgroup. Following are some elementary facts about algebraic integers; the proofs follow directly from the definition and are left to the reader.

(i) *The set of algebraic integers is a subring.*

(ii) *An algebraic integer of the complex field is a rational number if and only if it is a rational integer.*

(iii) *The roots of a polynomial with rational integer coefficients and leading coefficient 1 are algebraic integers.*

As a consequence of (i) and (iii) we have the following.

VIII.5.a. Proposition. *The value of a character of a finite group over the complex field is an algebraic integer.*

Proof. As in the proof of VIII.4.a, the value of any character $\chi(g)$ is a sum of roots of unity. In view of (iii), the roots of unity are algebraic integers; and by (i), $\chi(g)$ is an algebraic integer as was asserted.

VIII.5.b. Lemma. *The numbers $h_i \chi_{ir}/t_r$ are algebraic integers for each pair i, r, with $1 \le i, r \le m$.*

Proof. For $j = 1, \cdots, m$, let b_j be the sum of the h_j elements of the jth conjugate class of G in G_F, (F the complex field); then by VIII.1.b, $b_i b_j = \sum_{k=1}^m \alpha_{ijk} b_k$ with each α_{ijk} a rational integer since it is the number of times that an element of the kth conjugate class appears as a product of an element from the ith class by an element of the jth class. For each pair j, r, with $1 \le j, r \le m$, the projection of b_j in A_k is a scalar matrix with diagonal entry β_{jr}. Hence for all i, j, r between 1 and m, $\beta_{ir}\beta_{jr} = \sum_{k=1}^m \alpha_{ijk}\beta_{kr}$. For a fixed i and r the above m equations for $j = 1, \cdots, m$, may be written in vector form

$$\beta_{ir}(\beta_{1r}, \cdots, \beta_{mr}) = (\beta_{1r}, \cdots, \beta_{mr})(\alpha_{ikj})$$

where (α_{ikj}) is the transpose of the matrix (α_{ijk}) with i fixed.

If for definiteness b_1 denotes the sum of the elements in the conjugate class of the identity, 1, of G, then $b_1 = 1$ and hence $\beta_{1r} = 1$ for each r.   It follows that the vector $(\beta_{1r}, \cdots, \beta_{mr})$ is not the zero vector and, therefore, β_{ir} is a characteristic number for the characteristic vector $(\beta_{1r}, \cdots, \beta_{mr})$ of the matrix (α_{ijk}).   Hence β_{ir} is a root of the characteristic equation of (α_{ijk}); and since this equation has integer coefficients and leading coefficient 1, it follows from (iii) that β_{ir} is an algebraic integer.   On the other hand, $t_r \beta_{ir} = h_r \chi_{ir}$, and the lemma is proved.

The following consequence of the above is of independent interest.

VIII.5.c. Theorem.   *The degree of an irreducible representation of a finite group over the complex field divides the group order.*

Proof.   We must show that for $r = 1, \cdots, m$, the integer $t_r = \chi_r(1)$ is a divisor of the group order t.   By (2) of VIII.3.d, $t = \sum_{i=1}^{m} h_i \chi_{ir} \chi_{ir*}$ for each r, and hence $t/t_r = \sum_{i=1}^{m} (h_i \chi_{ir}/t_r) \chi_{i*r}$.   It follows from VIII.5.a that χ_{i*r} is an algebraic integer, and then from VIII.5.b that $\sum_{i=1}^{m} (h_i \chi_{ir}/t_r) \chi_{i*r}$ is an algebraic integer.   Thus t/t_r is an algebraic integer as well as a rational number, and hence is a rational integer by (ii).   This proves the theorem.

VIII.5.d. Lemma.   *If χ is a non-zero sum of n tth roots of unity and if $|\chi/n| < 1$, then χ/n is not an algebraic integer.*

Proof.   Let ζ be a primitive tth root of 1 (i.e., $\zeta^t = 1$ and $\zeta^s \neq 1$ for $1 \leq s < t$); and let $K = Q[\zeta]$ be the subfield of the complex field generated by ζ and the rational field Q.   Let q denote $\phi(t)$, ϕ being the Euler ϕ-function.   Then from the Galois theory we know that K has dimension q over Q, that K has a group B of automorphisms of order q, and that Q is precisely the set of elements of K, each of which is left fixed by all the automorphisms of B.   Now suppose that χ/n were an algebraic integer.   Then it follows readily from the definition of algebraic integer that $(\chi/n)\theta$ is also an algebraic integer for each $\theta \in B$.   Again $\chi\theta$ is a sum of n roots of unity so that $|\chi\theta| \leq n$ and

$|(\chi/n)\theta| = |\chi\theta/n| \leq 1$.   On the other hand, $\prod_{\theta \in B} (\chi/n)\theta$ is left fixed by all $\theta \in B$ and hence is in Q; since $\prod_{\theta \in B} (\chi/n)\theta$ is an algebraic integer, it follows from (ii) that it is a rational integer.   However, its absolute value is less than 1 and so it must be zero.   This contradiction establishes the lemma.

VIII.5.e. Theorem (*Burnside*).   *Let G be a finite group in which some conjugate class has exactly $h_j = p^a$ elements for some prime p with $a > 0$.   Then G has a proper non-trivial normal subgroup.*

Proof.   We shall consider the irreducible representations of G over the complex field F, in the notation already established in this chapter. From (2) of VIII.3.d applied to the conjugate class described in the theorem and the class of the identity, it follows that

$$0 = \sum_{r=1}^{m} \chi_{1r}\chi_{jr} = \sum_{r=1}^{m} t_r \chi_{jr} = 1 + \sum_{r=2}^{m} t_r \chi_{jr}.$$

Thus there is an r different from 1 such that $\chi_{jr} \neq 0$ and t_r is prime to p; because in the contrary case this equation would give $0 \equiv 1 \pmod{p}$.

Now since $h_j = p^a$, h_j and t_r are relatively prime and there exist integers s and u so that $sh_j = 1 - ut_r$.   By VIII.5.b, $h_j \chi_{jr}/t_r$ is an algebraic integer, which means that $sh_j\chi_{jr}/t_r = \chi_{jr}/t_r - u\chi_{jr}$ is an algebraic integer.   But χ_{jr} is a sum of roots of unity, so that it is an algebraic integer and finally χ_{jr}/t_r is an algebraic integer.   As we just saw, χ_{jr} is a sum of t_r roots of unity so that $|\chi_{jr}/t_r| \leq 1$; in fact, in view of VIII.5.d. we have $|\chi_{jr}/t_r| = 1$, and hence $|\chi_{jr}| = t_r$.   We now apply VIII.4.a; the subgroup $K = \{x \mid x \in G, |\chi_r(x)| = \chi_r(1)\}$ of that lemma is normal and nontrivial since for any g in the jth class, $|\chi_r(g)| = |\chi_{jr}| = t_r$.   Further, the normal subgroup $H = \{x \mid x \in G, \chi_r(g) = \chi_r(1)\}$ is not the whole of G, for if it were, χ_r would be a multiple of χ_1, contradicting the fact that the simple characters are a basis for the space of class functions from G to F.   Finally, it is impossible that $H = 1$ and $K = G$, for K/H is abelian by VIII.4.a, but G is not.   Hence either H or K is a proper normal subgroup, and the theorem is proved.

VIII.5.f. Theorem (*Burnside*).   *Every group whose order is divisible by at most two primes is solvable.*

Proof. We proceed by induction on the group order. Groups of order 1 are solvable; so we assume that G is a group of order $p^m q^n$ with m and n both greater than 1 (since p-groups are solvable), and we suppose the theorem true for groups of smaller order. Let a be a non-trivial element in the center of a Sylow p-subgroup of G; then the centralizer of a in G has q-power index. If this index is 1, then a is central and generates a (necessarily proper) normal subgroup of G; if the index is greater than 1, then the previous theorem provides a proper non-trivial normal subgroup of G. In either case, G has a proper non-trivial normal subgroup N. Both N and G/N satisfy the hypothesis of the theorem; since they are smaller than G, they must be solvable and hence G is solvable, as the theorem asserts.

Chapter *IX*

SOME RECENT DEVELOPMENTS

In this final chapter we give two characterizations of solvable groups, one due to Philip Hall and one proved recently by Wielandt and Kegel. These theorems depend in an essential way on Burnside's theorem given in Chapter VIII. We conclude with Thompson's recent theorem that a group with a fixed-point-free automorphism of prime order is nilpotent; in particular, we see that the Frobenius kernel of a Frobenius group is nilpotent.

1. A characterization of finite solvable groups

We begin with the notion of the factorization of a group and some elementary facts about it. A group G is **factorized** by its subgroups A and B if $G = AB$; thus every element g of G is of the form $g = ab$ with $a \in A$, $b \in B$. If the above expression for each $g \in G$ is unique, or equivalently if $A \cap B = 1$, then A and B are complementary (cf. I.6.e). The complement of a Sylow p-subgroup, p a prime, is a **Sylow p-complement** or merely a **p-complement**.

We list some elementary facts about the factorization of groups; the reader should verify them.

(i) *If $G = AB$, then $G = BA$, and for each $h, g \in G$, $G = A^h B^g$.*

(ii) *If $G = AB$ and θ is a homomorphism of G, then $G\theta = A\theta B\theta$; if A and B are complementary, then so are $A\theta$ and $B\theta$.*

(iii) *If $G = AB$ and $A \le H$, then H is factorized by A; that is, $H = A(H \cap B)$.*

(iv) *Let $G = AB$ and let $\bar{A} \lhd A$, $\bar{B} \lhd B$; then $\bar{A}\bar{B} = \bar{B}\bar{A}$ if and only if $\bar{A}^h\bar{B}^g = \bar{B}^g\bar{A}^h$ for all g, $h \in G$, and $\bar{A} \cap \bar{B} = 1$ if and only if $\bar{A}^g \cap \bar{B}^h = 1$.*

To prove (iv), note that $\bar{A}\bar{B} = \bar{B}\bar{A}$ if and only if $\bar{A}\bar{B}^{a^{-1}} = \bar{B}^{a^{-1}}\bar{A}$ with $a \in A$, and that the latter holds if and only if $\bar{A}^g\bar{B} = \bar{B}\bar{A}^g$ with $g = ab$.

(v) *Let G be a finite group and p a prime; a subgroup Q of G is a p-complement if and only if it is a Hall p'-subgroup of G.*

IX.1.a. Theorem (*P. Hall*).   *If for each prime p dividing the order of a finite group, G has a p-complement, then G is solvable.*

Proof. The theorem will be proved by induction on the group order, starting from Burnside's theorem (VIII.5.f) that a group whose order is divisible by at most two primes is solvable. Accordingly we assume that at least three primes divide $|G|$.

First we show that for each prime p dividing $|G|$, the Sylow p-complement M of G is solvable. Indeed let $q \neq p$ be a prime dividing $|G|$, and let K be a Sylow q-complement. By IV.2.1, $M \cap K$ is a Hall q'-subgroup of M and hence by (v) above, $M \cap K$ is a complement of a Sylow q-subgroup of M. It follows that the hypothesis of the theorem holds in M and hence, by the induction assumption, M is solvable. Thus for each prime p, the Sylow p-complements are solvable.

Since M is solvable, M has a normal prime power abelian subgroup $\bar{Q}$ with $\bar{Q}$ a q-subgroup for a prime q not equal to p. Let r be a prime dividing $|G|$, r different from p and q. Then (by the Sylow q-theorem in G) there is a Sylow r-complement V of G containing both $\bar{Q}$ and a Sylow p-subgroup P of G. Since $G = MP$, the normal closure of $\bar{Q}$ in G is contained in V; for if $g \in G$, $g = mt$ with $m \in M$ and $t \in P$, and then $\bar{Q}^g = \bar{Q}^{mt} = \bar{Q}^t \leq V$. Thus G has a proper non-trivial normal subgroup H contained in V. But then H is solvable; for V is solvable, V being a Sylow r-complement of G.

Finally we observe that the hypotheses hold for all homomorphic images of G because of (ii) so that by the induction assumption G/H is solvable; then since H is solvable by VII.1.d, G itself is solvable and the theorem is proved.

The converse of IX.1.a is included in VII.3.d and hence we have the following characterization of finite solvable groups.

IX.1.b. Theorem. *A finite group is solvable if and only if it has a p-complement for each prime p.*

IX.1.c. Exercise. *Show that a finite group is solvable if and only if each Sylow Π-subgroup has a complement for each set of primes Π.*

2. A second characterization of finite solvable groups

Three lemmas are needed before giving the theorem leading to the second characterization of finite solvable groups. The argument of the first lemma is adapted from Wielandt [29].

IX.2.a. Lemma. *Let G be a finite group factorized by subgroups A and B, let Π be a set of primes, and suppose that A and B have Hall Π-subgroups M and N, respectively. If $MN = NM$ or if both M and N are contained in the same Π-subgroup of G; then MN is a Hall Π-subgroup of G.*

Proof. The number of elements in MN is $|M| \cdot |N| \diagup |M \cap N|$ (and hence is a Π-number so that MN is a Π-subgroup when $MN = NM$), and since $G = AB$ the number of elements in G is $|G| = |A| \cdot |B| \diagup |A \cap B|$. If d and t are the largest Π-numbers dividing $|A \cap B|$ and $|G|$ respectively, then from the last equation,

$$t = |M| \cdot |N| \diagup d$$

(since M and N are Hall Π-subgroups of A and B). On the other hand, $|M \cap N| \leq d$ so that $t \leq |MN|$; since $|MN|$ is a Π-number and since both M and N are contained in the same Π-subgroup whose order is a divisor of t, it follows that $|MN| = t$ and hence that MN is a Hall Π-subgroup of G, as the lemma asserts.

IX.2.b. Corollary. *If a finite solvable group G is factorized by nilpotent subgroups A and B, and if for some set of primes Π, M and $N* *are Hall Π-subgroups of A and B, respectively, then MN is a Hall Π-subgroup of G.*

Proof. Since G is solvable, by the Sylow Π-theorem in G, M and a conjugate N^h ($h \in G$) of N are in the same Sylow Π-subgroup P of G, and hence by IX.2.a, $MN^h = P = N^hM$. But then by (iv) of Section 1, applied with $G = AB^h$ ($N^h \lhd B^h$ since B and B^h are nilpotent), $MN = NM$, and hence, by IX.2.a again, MN is a Hall Π-subgroup of G, as the corollary asserts.

IX.2.c. Lemma *(Kegel).* *If the group G satisfies the maximum condition for subgroups and has non-trivial subgroups M and N so that $MN^g = N^gM$ for all g in G and so that $MN \neq G$, then G is not simple.*

Proof. In view of the maximum condition we may assume that M is maximal with respect to the property that $MN^g = N^gM$ for all $g \in G$ and so that $MN \neq G$. Since $MN \neq G$, it follows from (i) of Section 1 that if N^* is any conjugate of N, then $MN^* \neq G$. If now M is normal in G, then the lemma is true since M is proper in G. Accordingly we need only consider the case where $\mathfrak{N}(M) < G$. If $\overline{M} = \mathfrak{S}(M, M^n)$ with n any fixed element of N^*, N^* any conjugate of N, then $\overline{M}N^g = N^g\overline{M}$ for all $g \in G$ (this follows from the fact that $MN^{gn^{-1}} = N^{gn^{-1}}M$ and hence that $M^nN^g = N^gM^n$ for all $g \in G$). Furthermore, $\overline{M}N^* \leq \mathfrak{S}(M, N^*) = MN^* \neq G$ and hence, by the maximality of M, $\overline{M} = M$ so that $n \in \mathfrak{N}(M)$. Since this is true for any element n in any conjugate of N, we conclude that the normal closure of N is contained in the proper subgroup $\mathfrak{N}(M)$ of G, and hence that G is not as simple as the lemma asserts.

IX.2.d. Lemma *(Wielandt).* *Suppose that the group G satisfies the maximum condition for subgroups and is factorized by its subgroups A and B: if $\overline{A} \lhd A$ and $\overline{B} \lhd B$, and if T denotes $\mathfrak{N}(\mathfrak{S}(\overline{A}, \overline{B}))$, then*

$$T = (T \cap A)(T \cap B).$$

Proof. If $t \in T$, then $\mathfrak{S}(\overline{A}, \overline{B})^t = \mathfrak{S}(\overline{A}, \overline{B})$ and $t = ab^{-1}$ with $a \in A$, $b \in B$. But $\mathfrak{S}(\overline{A}, \overline{B})^{ab^{-1}} = \mathfrak{S}(\overline{A}, \overline{B})$ if and only if $\mathfrak{S}(\overline{A}, \overline{B})^a$

$= \mathfrak{S}(\bar{A}, \bar{B})^b$ or equivalently if and only if $\mathfrak{S}(\bar{A}, \bar{B}^a) = \mathfrak{S}(\bar{A}^b, \bar{B})$.   But if the last equation holds, this latter subgroup contains $\bar{A}$ and $\bar{B}$ and hence $\mathfrak{S}(\bar{A}, \bar{B})$.   Hence $\mathfrak{S}(\bar{A}, \bar{B}) \leq \mathfrak{S}(\bar{A}, \bar{B})^a$; in view of the maximum condition, $\mathfrak{S}(\bar{A}, \bar{B}) = \mathfrak{S}(\bar{A}, \bar{B})^a$ and a is in T.   Thus if $ab^{-1} \in T$, then $a \in T \cap A$; it follows that $b \in T \cap B$ and hence that

$$T = (T \cap A)(T \cap B),$$

as the lemma asserts.

IX.2.e. Theorem (*Wielandt-Kegel*).   *If a finite group G is factorized by nilpotent subgroups A and B, then G is solvable.*

Proof.   The hypothesis holds for factor groups of G by (ii) of Section 1, and hence, by an induction argument on the group order (the theorem is trivially true for groups of order 1), it follows that if K is a non-trivial normal subgroup of G, then G/K is solvable.   If K is normal in G, $KA \geq A$ and $KA = A(K \cap B)$ by (iii) of Section 1; then in view of the latter equality, $K = (K \cap A)(K \cap B)$ and hence, if $K < G$, K is solvable by the induction assumption.   Thus, if G is not simple, then G is solvable by VII.1.d.

Now if there is a prime p dividing both $|A|$ and $|B|$, and if P is a Sylow p-subgroup of G, then by the Sylow p-theorem, P contains Sylow p-subgroups M and N, respectively, of A^g and B^h for suitable $g, h \in G$.   By IX.2.a, $MN = P = NM$ and then by (iv) of Section 1 ($M \lhd A^g$, $N \lhd B^h$ since A and B are nilpotent), $M^r N^s = N^s M^r$ for all $r, s \in G$.   It follows from IX.2.c that if $G \neq P$, then G is not simple, and hence by what was shown above, G is solvable; if $G = P$, then G is a p-group and hence solvable in this case too.   Thus the theorem is true unless G is a simple group and $|A|$ and $|B|$ are relatively prime.   In view of VIII.5.e, we need only consider the case where neither $|A|$ nor $|B|$ is a prime power; for if $|B|$, for instance, were a prime power, and $h \neq 1$, a central element of A, then $|G:\mathfrak{C}(h)|$ would be a prime power), and hence G would be solvable.

In what follows we assume that G is simple, that $|A|$ and $|B|$ are relatively prime, and that neither $|A|$ nor $|B|$ is a prime power.   We shall let Π designate the primes dividing $|A|$ and shall finish the proof of the theorem in a series of steps.

(1) *If for* g, $h \in G$, $M \lhd A^g$, $N \lhd B^h$, *then* $\mathfrak{S}(M, N) = G$. This is true for $M = A$, since then the normal closure of N in G (which is G as G is simple) is contained in $\mathfrak{S}(A, N)$ ($G = AB^h$ by (i) of Section 1). Suppose now that $M \lhd A$ and $N \lhd B$, with $\mathfrak{S}(M, N) \neq G$. Then if $T = \mathfrak{N}(\mathfrak{S}(M, N))$, $T = (T \cap A)(T \cap B)$ by IX.2.d, and by the induction assumption ($T < G$ since G is simple), T is solvable. It follows that T has a normal subgroup F of prime power order. If $S = \mathfrak{N}(F)$, S is proper in G since G is simple, and S contains a Sylow p-subgroup P of G as well as M and N (for neither $|A|$ nor $|B|$ is a prime power).

We conclude from the above (since $\mathfrak{S}(M, N, P) \leq S < G$) that if $\mathfrak{S}(M, N) \neq G$, then by a change of notation, $\mathfrak{S}(M, N) \neq G$ with M a Sylow p-subgroup P of A and $N \lhd B$. Now the argument above gives that if T is as before, T is solvable, and by the Sylow theory in T, T has a subgroup PQ, with Q containing a conjugate of a Sylow q-subgroup of N. This subgroup PQ has a normal subgroup D with D either a p-group or a q-group. Now $\mathfrak{N}(D) < G$ since G is simple. Hence D cannot be a p-group, since in that case $\mathfrak{N}(D)$ would contain both A and Q and consequently $\mathfrak{S}(A, Q)$ which is G by the first remark of the proof of (1). On the other hand, if D is a q-group, then $\mathfrak{N}(D)$ contains both P, a Sylow p-subgroup of A, and a Sylow r-subgroup R of a conjugate of B.

We conclude that if $\mathfrak{S}(M, N) \neq G$, then, with a change of notation, again we have $\mathfrak{S}(M, N) \neq G$ with M a Sylow p-subgroup of A and N a Sylow q-subgroup of B. But then, by the argument of the previous paragraph, there is a subgroup PQ, with P a Sylow subgroup of A and Q a Sylow subgroup of B; and PQ has a normal subgroup D with D either a p-group or a q-group. Now $\mathfrak{N}(D) < G$ and contains either A and Q, or P and B; thus in either case, since $G = \mathfrak{S}(A, Q) = \mathfrak{S}(P, B)$, we have the contradiction that $G \leq \mathfrak{N}(D) < G$. Accordingly we must conclude that in all cases if $M \lhd A$ and $N \lhd B$, then $\mathfrak{S}(M, N) = G$. Since $G = A^g B^h$ for all g, $h \in G$ by (i) of Section 1, we have proved (1).

(2) *If* $a \neq 1$ *is a central element of* A, *then* $\mathfrak{C}(a) = A$. Suppose that $\mathfrak{C}(a) > A$; then $\mathfrak{C}(a)$ contains an element $f \neq 1$ of B. But this means that $\mathfrak{C}(f)$ contains (a), a central subgroup of A as well as a non-trivial central subgroup (b) of B. By (1), $\mathfrak{S}((a), (b)) = G$, and hence $G = \mathfrak{C}(f)$ contrary to the simplicity of G. We conclude that $\mathfrak{C}(a) = A$, as was asserted in (2).

(3) *If P is a Sylow p-subgroup of A as well as of A^g, then $A = A^g$.*
In the contrary case $\mathfrak{Z}(P)$ is central in a subgroup $\mathfrak{C}(A, A^g)$ which contains A properly, contrary to (2).

(4) *If P is as in (3) and $\mathfrak{Z}(P) < P^g \leq A^g$, then $P^g = P$.* If $P \neq P^g$, then $A \neq A^g$ and hence, if for a prime r dividing $|A|$, $r \neq p$, R denotes the Sylow r-subgroup of A, then $R \neq R^g$ by (3), and consequently $\mathfrak{C}(\mathfrak{Z}(P)) > A$ contrary to (2).

From (3) and (4) we immediately get the following.

(5) *If P is as in (3) and $\mathfrak{Z}(P) < A^g$, then $A = A^g$.*

(6) *If P is as in (3), $\mathfrak{N}(P) = \mathfrak{N}(A)$.* It is clear that $\mathfrak{N}(A) \leq \mathfrak{N}(P)$ since A is nilpotent; if $\mathfrak{N}(A) < \mathfrak{N}(P)$. Then P would be a Sylow p-subgroup of A as well as of a conjugate $A^g \neq A$ contrary to (3).

(7) *If $M \lhd P$, then $\mathfrak{N}(M) = \mathfrak{N}(A)$.* If R is a Sylow r-subgroup of A for a prime $r \neq p$, then $R < \mathfrak{C}(M)$; by VI.1.g, $M \cap \mathfrak{Z}(P) \neq 1$ and hence, by (2), $\mathfrak{C}(M) \leq A$ so that $\mathfrak{C}(M)$ is nilpotent. Since $\mathfrak{C}(M)$ is nilpotent and $\mathfrak{C}(M) \lhd \mathfrak{N}(M)$, it follows that $R \lhd \mathfrak{N}(M)$ and hence that $\mathfrak{N}(M) \leq \mathfrak{N}(R)$ with $\mathfrak{N}(R) = \mathfrak{N}(A)$ by (6). It is clear that $\mathfrak{N}(A) \leq \mathfrak{N}(M)$ and (7) follows.

(8) *If L is a solvable subgroup of G, containing a Sylow p-subgroup P of A, then $L \leq \mathfrak{N}(A)$.* By the Sylow Π-theorem in L (L is solvable), L has a Hall Π-subgroup F which is in a conjugate of A by the Sylow Π-theorem in G (cf. IV.6.b). Hence F is nilpotent, P is normal in F, and any normal subgroup D of P is normal in F; thus by (7), $F \leq \mathfrak{N}(D) \leq \mathfrak{N}(A)$. Now let s be a Π'-number; by the Sylow theorem for solvable groups, L has a solvable subgroup PS with S a Sylow s-subgroup of L. Furthermore, PS has a prime power normal subgroup D which cannot be an s-group since, in that case, $\mathfrak{N}(D)$ would contain P as well as a Sylow q-subgroup Q of G with q a prime dividing $|B|$, $q \neq s$; but in view of (1) this would mean that $\mathfrak{N}(D) = G$ contrary to the simplicity of G. Accordingly, we conclude that D is a p-group and hence that $D \lhd P$. Thus $S < \mathfrak{N}(D) \leq \mathfrak{N}(A)$. We have shown that for every prime dividing $|L|$, $\mathfrak{N}(A)$ contains a Sylow s-subgroup of L, and hence that $\mathfrak{N}(A) \geq L$, as was asserted in (8).

(9) *If* $\mathfrak{N}(B) \cap A \cap A^g > 1$, *then* $A^g = A$. Suppose to the contrary that there is an $f \neq 1$, $f \in \mathfrak{N}(B) \cap A \cap A^g$, and suppose that, without loss of generality, f has prime order p. We observe first that, since for each non-identity $h \in \mathfrak{Z}(B)$, $\mathfrak{C}(h) = B$ by (2), it follows that $A \cap \mathfrak{N}(B)$ induces a group of automorphisms in $\mathfrak{Z}(B)$ with no fixed points; and hence, by IX.4.f below, $A \cap \mathfrak{N}(B)$ has only one subgroup of order p. With this in mind we let $(f) = T$ and shall show that $\mathfrak{N}(T)$ is factorizable; indeed if $ab^{-1} \in \mathfrak{N}(T)$ with $a \in A$, $b \in B$, then $T^{ab^{-1}} = T$ or $T^a = T^b$. But $T^a \in A$ and $T^b \in \mathfrak{N}(B)$, so that by the uniqueness of the subgroup of order p of $A \cap \mathfrak{N}(B)$, $T^a = T = T^b$, whence $a \in \mathfrak{N}(T)$, $b \in \mathfrak{N}(T)$, and $\mathfrak{N}(T)$ is factorized. Since G is simple, $\mathfrak{N}(T) < G$, and therefore by the induction assumption $\mathfrak{N}(T)$ is solvable. Since $\mathfrak{N}(T)$ contains a Sylow r-subgroup of A with r a prime of $|A|$ other than p, it follows from (8) that $\mathfrak{N}(T) \leq \mathfrak{N}(A)$. Since $\mathfrak{N}(T)$ contains $\mathfrak{Z}(A^g)$, it follows that $\mathfrak{Z}(A^g) \leq \mathfrak{N}(A)$ whence, by (5), $A^g = A$ and (9) is proved.

(10) *If* $A \cap A^g > 1$, *then* $A = A^g$. Suppose that $A \neq A^g$. Then $\mathfrak{C}(A \cap A^g) \geq \mathfrak{C}(\mathfrak{Z}(A), \mathfrak{Z}(A^g))$, which subgroup we will denote by H. By (4) $\mathfrak{Z}(A^g) \not\leq A$ and hence $H \not\leq A$. For each Π-prime p, let $\bar{P}$ denote $P \cap H$ and let $\bar{H}$ denote $A \cap H$. Since $\bar{P} \geq \mathfrak{Z}(P)$, any Sylow p-subgroup of H containing $\bar{P}$ is contained in P by (4). It follows that $\bar{P}$ is a Sylow p-subgroup of H and hence that $\bar{H}$ is a Hall Π-subgroup of H. If for each $p \in \Pi$, $\mathfrak{N}_H(\bar{P}) = \bar{H}$, then by IV.5.h, H would have a normal Π-complement and hence a normal Π'-subgroup W of prime power order q. In view of (1) this is impossible since the normalizer of W would then contain both $\mathfrak{Z}(A)$ as well as a Sylow s-subgroup of G for s a Π-prime not q. We conclude that for $\bar{P}$ belonging to some Π-prime p, $\mathfrak{N}_H(\bar{P}) > \bar{H}$. It follows that there is a Π'-element $b \in \mathfrak{N}_H(\bar{P})$ and hence that $(\mathfrak{Z}(P))^b \leq \bar{P} \leq P$; then by (4), $b \in \mathfrak{N}(\mathfrak{Z}(\bar{P}))$ and hence, by (7), $b \in \mathfrak{N}(A)$. Now b is in a conjugate B_1 of B and also in B_1^a for any $a \in A \cap A^g$ since $b \in H < \mathfrak{C}(A \cap A^g)$. By (9) applied to $G = B_1 A$, $B_1 = B_1^a$ or a is in $\mathfrak{N}(B_1)$. Hence $a \in \mathfrak{N}(B_1) \cap A \cap A^g$ and by (9) applied to $G = AB_1$ we see, since $A \neq A^g$, that $a = 1$. Thus we get the contradiction that $A \cap A^g = 1$ if we assume that $A \neq A^g$, and (10) is proved.

Now we come to the contradiction from which we conclude that G could not have been simple as we assumed much earlier. Suppose without loss of generality that $|A| > |B|$. Since A is not normal in G, there is a $g \in G$ so that $A \neq A^g$. By (10), $A \cap A^g = 1$. It follows that AA^g has $|A|^2$ elements. But this is a contradiction since $|A|^2 > |A| \cdot |A| = |G|$. This completes the proof of the theorem.

We can now give a second characterization of finite solvable groups.

IX.2.f. Theorem (*Wielandt-Kegel*). *A finite group G is solvable if and only if for some natural number m, G is a product of pairwise commuting nilpotent groups; that is, G has nilpotent subgroups N_i for $i = 1, 2, \cdots, m$, so that for $1 \leq i, j \leq m$, $N_i N_j = N_j N_i$ and so that $G = N_1 N_2 \cdots N_m$.*

Proof. In view of VII.3.f we need only prove that G is solvable if it is a product of pairwise commuting nilpotent subgroups. Under this hypothesis it is only necessary in view of IX.1.a to show that G has a p-complement for each prime p dividing $|G|$. If Q_i is the p-complement of N_i, then since $N_i N_j$ is solvable by IX.2.e, it follows from IX.2.b that $Q_i Q_j$ is the p-complement of $N_i N_j$ and that $Q_i Q_j = Q_j Q_i$ for all i, j with $1 \leq i, j \leq m$. By an induction argument, $Q_1 Q_2 \cdots Q_{m-1}$ is a p-complement of $N_1 N_2 \cdots N_{m-1}$ and hence, by IX.2.a, $Q_1 Q_2 \cdots Q_m$ is a p-complement of G. This proves the theorem.

3. Thompson's theorem on normal p-complements

IX.3.a. Theorem (*Thompson*). *Let p be an odd prime dividing the order of a finite group G, let P be a Sylow p-subgroup of G, and let Z be a central subgroup of P; let J be the subgroup generated by all the abelian subgroups of P of maximal p-rank (cf. II.4.l) in P. If $\mathfrak{C}(Z)$ and $\mathfrak{N}(J)$ have normal p-complements, then so also does G.*

Proof. We proceed by induction on $|G|$, assuming the theorem true in all groups of order less than $|G|$. In view of the induction assumption, any proper subgroup of G containing P has a normal p-complement.

We first show that if Q is a normal non-trivial p'-subgroup of G, then G has a normal p-complement. We do this by showing that the hypotheses of the theorem hold in $\bar{G} = G/Q$; that is, we shall show that for appropriate subgroups $\bar{J}$ and $\bar{Z}$, $\mathfrak{N}(\bar{J})$ and $\mathfrak{C}(\bar{Z})$ have normal p-complements. Since P is isomorphic to a Sylow p-subgroup of $\bar{G}$, it follows that if the complete inverse image of one of the groups $\mathfrak{N}(\bar{J})$ or $\mathfrak{C}(\bar{Z})$ is proper in G, then it has a normal p-complement and hence the group itself has a normal p-complement. On the other hand, if the complete inverse image of $\mathfrak{N}(\bar{J})$ is G, then $QJ \lhd G$ so that, by IV.2.f, $G = Q\mathfrak{N}(J)$ and hence G has a normal p-complement since $\mathfrak{N}(J)$ does and since $Q \lhd G$. If the complete inverse image of $\mathfrak{C}(\bar{Z})$ is G, then $QZ \lhd G$ so that, by IV.2.f again, $G = Q\mathfrak{N}(Z)$; if $\mathfrak{N}(Z) < G$, then $\mathfrak{N}(Z)$ has a normal p-complement and therefore G does; whereas if $\mathfrak{N}(Z) = G$, then $Z \lhd G$ so that $Q \leq \mathfrak{C}(Z)$, and $G = \mathfrak{C}(Z)$ has a normal p-complement. Thus either G has a normal p-complement (whence G/Q does) or, by the induction assumption in G/Q, G/Q has a normal p-complement and consequently G does. In what follows we assume that G has no non-trivial normal p'-subgroup.

Now let $\mathscr{F}$ be the set of non-trivial p-subgroups H of G such that $\mathfrak{N}(H)$ has no normal p-complement. If $\mathscr{F}$ is empty, then the theorem follows from IV.5.c. Accordingly we consider the case where $\mathscr{F}$ is not empty, and partially order $\mathscr{F}$ by $\leq$ as follows: For $H, K \in \mathscr{F}$, we say that $H \leq K$ if and only if $|\mathfrak{N}(H)|_p \leq |\mathfrak{N}(K)|_p$ (here $|G|_p$ denotes the p-share of $|G|$), and when equality holds in the last relation, if and only if $|H|_p < |K|_p$ or $H = K$.

In what follows we now let H be a maximal element of $\mathscr{F}$ under $\leq$, and let N denote $\mathfrak{N}(H)$. We assume, without loss of generality (i.e., by the Sylow p-theorem in G) that $H \leq P$. First we note that, since $H \in \mathscr{F}$, M has no normal p-complement and hence $H \neq P$; for J, by its definition, is characteristic in P, and hence if H were P, $\mathfrak{N}(J)$ would contain N, whence by (i) of Section IV.5, N would have a normal p-complement. Let P_0 be a Sylow p-subgroup of N, where again without loss of generality we assume that $P_0 \leq P$.

Let $Z_0 = \mathfrak{Z}(P_0)$ and let J_0 be the subgroup generated by the abelian subgroups of maximal p-rank of P_0. We shall show that the hypotheses of the theorem hold when applied to the group N with subgroups P_0, Z_0, and J_0. Indeed it is clear that $Z \leq N$ and hence that $Z \leq Z_0$ so that $\mathfrak{C}_N(Z_0)$ has a normal p-complement. We now show that $\mathfrak{N}_N(J_0)$ has a normal p-complement. If $P_0 = P$, then $J_0 = J$ and $\mathfrak{N}_N(J_0) \leq \mathfrak{N}(J)$ and the assertion follows from the hypothesis on

$\mathfrak{N}(J)$. If $P_0 < P$, then by the normalizer condition in P and the fact that J_0 is characteristic in P_0, $\mathfrak{N}(J_0)$ contains a p-subgroup P_1 with $P_1 > P_0$, whence $\mathfrak{N}(J_0)$ has a normal p-complement by the maximality of H under $\leq$. Thus the hypotheses of the theorem hold in N and, since N has no normal p-complement, we conclude from the induction assumption that $N = G$. In view of the maximality of H under $\leq$, we conclude that H is the largest normal p-subgroup of G, and also that every p-subgroup of G/H has a normal p-complement so that by the induction assumption G/H also has one. Thus G has a subgroup K with $H \lhd K \lhd G$ and K/H a p'-group while G/K is a p-group.

From the facts that $N = G$, that G has no non-trivial normal p'-subgroup, and that $H \lhd K \lhd G$ with K/H a p'-group and G/K a p-group, we see that $\mathfrak{C}(Z) = P$ and also that P is a maximal subgroup of G. For $\mathfrak{C}(Z) < G$ since $\mathfrak{C}(Z)$ has a normal p-complement, and we let $P \leq \mathfrak{C}(Z) \leq M < G$ with M a maximal subgroup of G. If $P < M$, then M has a normal p-complement $B \neq 1$. But then $[B, H] = 1$ since $H \lhd G$. It follows that $K \cap H\mathfrak{C}(H) > H$, and we let L be a minimal normal subgroup of G contained in $K \cap H\mathfrak{C}(H)$ and properly containing H. Then by IV.7.c, there is a subgroup Y so that $L = [H]Y$, and hence $L = H \times Y$. But then Y is a non-trivial normal p'-subgroup of G contrary to our assumption. We conclude from the above argument that $\mathfrak{C}(H)$ is a p-group, that $\mathfrak{C}(Z) = P$, and that P is maximal in G. Furthermore, we conclude from the facts that $\mathfrak{C}(H) \lhd G$ and that H is the maximal normal p-subgroup of G, that $\mathfrak{C}(H) \leq H$, and in particular that $Z \leq H$.

We shall now show that K/H is an elementary q-group for a prime divisor q of $|G|$ not p. If Q is a Sylow q-subgroup of K, then, by IV.2.f, $G = K\mathfrak{N}(Q)$ and hence $H\mathfrak{N}(Q)$ contains a Sylow p-subgroup of G, which we may assume without loss of generality to be P. If Q_0 is the subgroup generated by the elements of order q of the center of Q, then $HQ_0 \lhd H\mathfrak{N}(Q)$ and hence HQ_0P is a subgroup of G which is G itself in view of the maximality of P (and hence $Q_0 = Q$).

Now $J \nleq H$ since $\mathfrak{N}(J)$ has a normal p-complement, whereas G does not. We choose an abelian subgroup A of P not in H, A of maximal p-rank and of minimal order in P. Since H is the maximal normal p-subgroup of G, the centralizer of Q modulo H is Q and hence there is a q-element which does not centralize A. We let R be a subgroup of minimal order generated by H, A and a q-element b not in $\mathfrak{C}(A)$. Thus $R = HQ_1A$ with Q_1 a q-subgroup containing b.

Now R has no normal p-complement, since $\mathfrak{C}(H)$ is a p-group. On the other hand, $\mathfrak{C}_R(Z) = HA$, and if J_1 is generated by the abelian subgroups of maximal p-rank of HA, then $\mathfrak{N}_R(J_1) = HA$ since $J_1 \geq A$ and $\mathfrak{N}_R(A) = A$ modulo H. It follows from the above with the induction assumption that $R = G$ and hence that $HA = P$ and $Q_1 = Q$. In view of the maximality of P, $[(cH/H), (AH/H)] = QH/H$ for all $c \in Q$ and hence, by VIII.2.f, HA/H is cyclic. Furthermore HA/H has order p in view of the minimality of the order of A.

Now let W be the center of H; then by IV.8.k, $W = \mathfrak{C}_W(Q) \times D$ with D normal in WQ. Furthermore $D \neq 1$ since W contains Z and $\mathfrak{C}(Z) = P$. It follows that if V is generated by the elements of order p of D, then $[v, Q] \neq 1$ for each non-identity $v \in V$.

Let $A_0 = A \cap H$; since HA/H is cyclic, the p-rank of A is greater than that of A_0 by at most 1. Since $\mathfrak{S}(A_0, V)$ is abelian, the p-rank of $\mathfrak{S}(A_0, V)$ is no greater than that of A and hence is greater than that of A_0 by at most 1. It follows (since V has exponent p) that $A_0 \cap V$ has index p in V. This is also true of $A_0{}^b \cap V$ and we conclude that V has p-rank less than 3; for if the p-rank of V were 3 or greater, then $A_0 \cap A_0{}^b \cap V \neq 1$ and hence $A \cap A^b \cap V$ would contain an element $v \neq 1$ which is central in G $(G = \mathfrak{S}(H, A, A^b)$ by the maximality of $HA = P$). But this is contrary to the fact that $[Q, v] \neq 1$. We conclude that the p-rank of V is 1 or 2.

Now $Q \cap \mathfrak{C}(V) = 1$ from the minimality of Q and the fact that $[Q, v] \neq 1$; furthermore $A \cap \mathfrak{C}(V) \leq H$ since $V \vartriangleleft G$ and H is the maximal normal p-subgroup of G. It follows that G/H is isomorphic to a group of automorphisms of V. Since G/H is not cyclic, we conclude from III.2.m that the p-rank of V is not 1. Thus the p-rank of V must be 2 and G/H is isomorphic to a subgroup of $L(K, 2)$ (cf. Section III.8) with K the field of p-elements.

Now the order of $L(K, 2)$ is $p(p-1)^2(p+1)$ and the order of a transvection is p, so that by the Sylow p-theorem every element of order p is a transvection and therefore is in $S(K, 2)$. It follows that G/H (since it is generated by p-elements) is isomorphic to a subgroup of $S(K, 2)$.

In view of its order which is $(p-1)p(p+1)$, $S(K, 2)$ can only have a subgroup isomorphic to $[Q]C_p$ with q an elementary abelian q-group if q is 2 since $(p-1)$ and $(p+1)$ are both even when p is odd and p must be smaller than $|Q|$. On the other hand, the only element of order 2 of $S(K, 2)$ is $-I_2$ which is central. Thus we have a contradiction on the assumption that the family, $\mathscr{F}$ is non-empty and the theorem is proved.

The symmetric group S_4 shows that it is necessary for p to be odd in the previous Theorem.

The following theorem follows easily from IX.3.a.

IX.3.b. Theorem (*Thompson*).   *A finite group G is solvable if it has a maximal subgroup which is nilpotent and of odd order.*

Proof.   If M contains a non-trivial normal subgroup K of G, then by an induction argument G/K is solvable; and since K is nilpotent, G is solvable in view of VII.1.d.   Accordingly we need only consider the case where no non-trivial subgroup of M is normal in G, and consequently $|G:M|$ and $|M|$ are relatively prime.   It follows that for each prime p dividing $|M|$, the hypotheses of IX.3.a hold (since both $\mathfrak{N}(J)$ and $\mathfrak{N}(Z)$ are M).   Hence, by IX.3.a, G has a normal p-complement R_p for each prime p dividing $|M|$.   If R denotes the intersection of these R_p, then R is normal in G; by IV.2.1, $|G:R| = |M|$, and hence $G = [R]M$.   If Q is a Sylow q-subgroup of R, then, by IV.2.f, $G = R\mathfrak{N}(Q)$ so that $|M|$ divides $\mathfrak{N}(Q)$ and hence by the maximality of M, $G = [Q]M$.   Thus G is an extension of a q-group by a nilpotent group and is solvable, as the theorem asserts.

4. Fixed-point-free automorphisms

An automorphism σ of a group G is *fixed-point-free* if for each $g \in G$, $g \neq 1$, $g\sigma \neq g$.   In this section we shall show that a group is nilpotent if it has a fixed-point-free automorphism of prime order, or equivalently that the Frobenius kernel of a group (cf. Section VIII.4) is nilpotent.   We shall also show that a finite nilpotent group of fixed-point-free automorphisms of a group is either cyclic or the direct product of a cyclic group with a quaternion group—a result already quoted in the proof of Theorem IX.2.e.

If σ is an automorphism of a group G we shall denote by $\bar{\sigma}$ the map sending the element g of G to $g^{-1}g\sigma$.   It is often convenient to form the holomorph H of G with σ and to let $H = [G](s)$ with an element S of order equal to that of σ and so that the inner automorphism determined by s restricted to G is σ; then $\bar{\sigma}$ is the map sending g to $g^{-1}g^s = [g, s]$. The proofs of the following are immediate.

(i) *If n is the order of an automorphism σ of a group G and if x denotes $y\bar{\sigma} = y^{-1}y\sigma$, $y \in G$, then $x(x\sigma)(x\sigma^2)\cdots(x\sigma^{n-1}) = 1$.*

(ii) *An automorphism σ of a group is fixed-point free if and only if $\bar{\sigma}$ is one-one.*

(iii) *If σ is an automorphism of a finite group G, then σ is fixed-point-free if and only if $\bar{\sigma}$ is onto G.*

In view of (i) and (iii) we have the following:

(iv) *If a finite group G has a fixed-point-free automorphism σ of order n, then for all $g \in G$, $g(g\sigma)(g\sigma)^2 \cdots (g\sigma^{n-1}) = 1$.*

IX.4.a. Exercise. *Show that a finite group is abelian of odd order if and only if it has a fixed-point-free automorphism of order 2.*

If σ is a fixed-point-free automorphism it need not follow that $\bar{\sigma}$ is onto as the following examples illustrate.

IX.4.b. Examples. Let F be the free group $\mathfrak{G}(a, b)$ and let G denote F'. Let σ be the restriction of the inner automorphism determined by a. Then σ is a fixed-point-free automorphism of G, but $G\bar{\sigma} = [F', a] \leq F^3 < F'$ and hence $\bar{\sigma}$ is not onto.

In the above, σ has infinite order. We can exhibit a fixed-point-free automorphism ϕ of finite order such that $\bar{\phi}$ is not onto by taking the group $C = \mathfrak{G}(a, b \mid a^2 = 1 = b^3)$ and letting ϕ be the restriction of the inner automorphism determined by a to the subgroup H generated by C' and b. By V.4.o, $C \cong P(J, 2)$ so that a may be taken to be the matrix $\begin{pmatrix} 0 & 1 \\ -1 & 0 \end{pmatrix}$ and then it is easy to check that ϕ is fixed-point-free. If $\bar{\phi}$ mapped H onto H, then by (i) $x(x\phi)$ would be 1 for all $x \in H$. On the other hand, $x(x\phi) = xx^a = (xa)^2 = 1$ while the square of $\begin{pmatrix} 2 & 3 \\ 1 & 2 \end{pmatrix}\begin{pmatrix} 0 & 1 \\ -1 & 0 \end{pmatrix} = \begin{pmatrix} -3 & 2 \\ -2 & 1 \end{pmatrix}$ is not $\pm I$. Thus ϕ is fixed-point-free while $\bar{\phi}$ is not onto.

The last example also shows that the statement of IX.4.a is not true if the word-finite is omitted.

(v) *If a fixed-point-free automorphism has prime order, then each of its non-trivial powers is also fixed-point-free.*

(vi) *If a finite group G has a fixed-point-free automorphism of prime power order p^k, then $|G| \equiv 1 \bmod p$.*

We say that a subgroup H of a group G is fixed by an automorphism σ of G if $H\sigma = H$. Since $\mathfrak{N}(H)\sigma = \mathfrak{N}(H\sigma)$ we have the following:

(vii) *If H is a subgroup of G fixed by an automorphism σ of G, then $\mathfrak{N}(H)$ is fixed by σ.*

(viii) *Let σ be a fixed-point-free automorphism of a group G; if H is a subgroup of G fixed by σ and if $\bar{\sigma}$ maps H onto H, then the automorphism induced by σ in $\mathfrak{N}(H)/H$ is fixed-point-free.*

For if $g \in \mathfrak{N}(H)$ and $gH\sigma = gH$, then $g\bar{\sigma} \in H$; and hence by the hypothesis with (ii), $g \in H$.

(ix) *Let R be an intravariant subgroup of a finite group G and let σ be a fixed-point-free automorphism of G; then a unique conjugate of R is left fixed by σ.*

For R is intravariant and hence there is a $g \in G$ so that $R\sigma = R^g$. By (iii) there is an $x \in G$ so that $g = x^{-1}x\sigma$. Then $R^{x^{-1}}\sigma = (R\sigma)^{x^{-1}\sigma} = R^{g(x^{-1}\sigma)} = R^{x^{-1}}$. The proof that R is unique will be left to the reader.

(x) *If σ is an automorphism of a group and $\bar{\sigma}$ is onto G, then $\overline{\sigma^{-1}}$ is also onto.*

If $g \in G$, there is an $h \in G$ so that $g^{-1}\sigma = h\bar{\sigma} = h^{-1}h\sigma$; hence $g = h\overline{\sigma^{-1}}$ as asserted in (x).

Before stating the next property we recall that α_g denotes the inner automorphism determined by g.

(xi) *Let σ be an automorphism of a group G such that $\bar{\sigma}$ is a one-one onto map. Then for $g \in G$, $\alpha_g\sigma = \alpha_h^{-1}\sigma\alpha_h$ for some $h \in G$ and hence σ and $\alpha_g\sigma$ have the same order and $\overline{\alpha_g\sigma}$ is also a one-one onto map.*

For there is an h so that $h\bar{\sigma} = g^{-1}\sigma$; hence $g\sigma = (h^{-1}\sigma)h$ so that $\alpha_g\sigma = \alpha_h^{-1}\sigma\alpha_h$. Then $\overline{\alpha_g\sigma} = \alpha_h^{-1}\bar{\sigma}\alpha_h$.

The first statement of (xi) is equivalent to the fact that s and gs are conjugate in the holomorph $[G](s)$ of G with σ.

We are now able to consider the case of a fixed-point-free automorphism of order 3.

IX.4.c. Theorem. *If σ is a fixed-point-free automorphism of order three of a group G and if $\bar{\sigma}$ is onto G, then $[h, 2g] = 1$ for all g, $h \in G$ and hence G is nilpotent of class 3.*

Proof. For $g \in G$ we see by (iv) that $g(g\sigma)(g\sigma^2) = 1$ and that $(g\sigma^2)(g\sigma)g = 1$; consequently, $g(g\sigma) = (g\sigma)g$ and hence $[g, g\sigma] = 1$. It follows then from (xi) that for all $h \in G, [g, g\alpha_h\sigma] = 1$. Thus $[g, g^h\sigma] = 1$ and similarly $[g, g^h\sigma^2] = 1$ so that $g\sigma$ and $g\sigma^2$ commute with g^h. Since $g^{-1} = (g\sigma)(g\sigma^2)$, it follows that g also commutes with g^h and hence with $[g, h]$. Thus $[h, 2g] = 1$ as was to be shown. The theorem then follows from VI.8.d.

IX.4.d. Exercise   *Show that it is necessary that $\bar{\sigma}$ be onto G in IX.4.c (cf. IX.4.b).*

Fixed-point-free automorphisms of order 4 are considered in [7] and [17].

Before the next lemma it is convenient to give the following definitions. Let Φ be a non-trivial group of automorphisms of a group G. A **fixed-point** of Φ is a non-trivial element $g \in G$ such that $g\phi = g$ for all $\phi \in \Phi$; Φ is **fixed-point-free** if each non-trivial $\phi \in \Phi$ is fixed-point-free.

IX.4.e. Lemma. *Let Γ be a finite group of automorphisms of an abelian group P and suppose that Γ is a split extension $[\Phi](\sigma)$. If for each $\phi \in \Phi$, $(\phi\sigma)$ is fixed point-free of prime order q, and if the exponent of P is prime to $|\Phi|$, then Φ has a fixed point. In particular, if Γ is fixed-point-free, then $\Phi = 1$ and Γ is cyclic of order q.*

Proof. A simple counting argument shows that as ϕ ranges over Φ and j over $\{1, \cdots, q-1\}$, $(\phi\sigma)^j$ ranges over $\Gamma - \Phi$. Now by (iv) we see that for $x \in P$, $1 = \prod_{i=0}^{q-1} x(\phi\sigma)^i$ for each $\phi \in \Phi$ and hence that

$$1 = \prod_{\phi \in \Phi} \prod_{i=0}^{q-1} x(\phi\sigma)^i = x^{|\Phi|} \prod_{i=1}^{q-1} \prod_{\phi \in \Phi} (x\sigma^i)\phi.$$

Finally we note that $\prod_{\phi \in \Phi} (x\sigma^i)\phi$ is either 1 or a fixed point of Φ; since $x^{|\Phi|} \neq 1$, it follows that for some j, $\prod_{\phi \in \Phi} (x\sigma^j)\phi$ is a fixed point of Φ as the first statement of the lemma asserts.

The following theorem is also an immediate consequence of the above lemma together with VI.4.e.

IX.4.f. Theorem. *A finite nilpotent fixed-point-free group of automorphisms of an abelian group is either cyclic or a direct product of a cyclic group with a quaternion group.*

Proof. In view of VI.4.e it is sufficient to show that for each prime p dividing the order of the group of automorphisms Γ, there is only one cyclic subgroup of order p in Γ. If Γ had more than one cyclic subgroup of order p, it would have (because of its nilpotency) a subgroup $(\phi) \times (\sigma)$ with ϕ and σ each of order p. But this would be in contradiction to IX.4.e and the theorem follows.

IX.4.g. Theorem. *If G is a finite solvable group with a fixed-point-free automorphism σ of prime order q, then G is nilpotent.*

Proof. We proceed by induction on the order of G. It will be sufficient to show that G has a non-trivial center Z since, by (viii), the induction assumption shows that G/Z is nilpotent and hence, by VI.1.h, G is nilpotent. Since G is solvable, a minimal normal non-trivial subgroup P of G fixed by σ is an elementary abelian p-group for some prime p. Then if r is a prime, $r \neq p$, and R is the Sylow r-subgroup of G fixed by σ (cf. (ix)), and if $PR < G$, by the induction assumption PR is nilpotent so that $R < \mathfrak{C}(P)$. Thus either $G = PR$ for some r or $|G:\mathfrak{C}(P)|$ is a power of p and, by VI.1.g, G has a non-trivial center.

Accordingly we consider the case where $G = PR$. We let Γ be the group of automorphisms of P determined by the restriction of σ and the conjugations by elements of R. Then $\Gamma = [\Phi](\sigma)$ with Φ corresponding to R. It follows from IX.4.e in view of (xi) that Φ has a fixed point. This means that P has a non-trivial element which centralizes R and therefore G has a non-trivial center as was to be shown.

IX.4.h. Theorem (*Thompson*).   *A finite group with a fixed-point-free automorphism of prime order is nilpotent.*

Proof.   Let G be a finite group having a fixed-point-free automorphism σ of prime order q.   If G is a 2-group, then G is nilpotent; accordingly we need only consider the case where there is an odd prime p dividing $|G|$.   Let P be the Sylow p-subgroup of G such that $P\sigma = P$; then if Z denotes $\mathfrak{Z}(P)$ and if J is the subgroup generated by all the abelian subgroups of P of maximal p-rank, $Z\sigma = Z$ and $J\sigma = J$.   If $\mathfrak{N}(J) = G$, then σ induces a fixed-point-free automorphism in G/J; by an induction argument, G/J is nilpotent, and hence, by VII.1.d, G is solvable and then, by IX.4.g, G is nilpotent.   A similar argument shows that G is nilpotent if $\mathfrak{N}(Z) = G$.   Accordingly, we need only consider the case where both $\mathfrak{N}(J)$, $\mathfrak{N}(Z)$, and hence $\mathfrak{C}(Z)$, are proper in G.   Since $Z\sigma = Z$ and $J\sigma = J$, it follows that $\mathfrak{N}(J)\sigma = \mathfrak{N}(J)$ and that $\mathfrak{C}(Z)\sigma = \mathfrak{C}(Z)$.   By the induction assumption, both $\mathfrak{N}(J)$ and $\mathfrak{C}(Z)$ are nilpotent and hence have normal p-complements.   It follows from IX.3.a that G has a normal p-complement R; since R is the Hall p'-subgroup of G, $R\sigma = R$, R is nilpotent by the induction assumption, and hence G is solvable and therefore nilpotent.   This proves the theorem.

IX.4.i. Corollary.   *The Frobenius kernel of a Frobenius group is nilpotent.*

BIBLIOGRAPHY

A selected bibliography of works to which reference is made and of some recent work on the material presented in the text.

BOOKS

[A]   Artin, E., *Geometric Algebra*, Interscience Publishers, Inc., New York, 1957.

[B]   Burnside, W., *Theory of Groups of Finite Order*, Cambridge Univ. Press, Cambridge, 1911.

[C F]   Crowell, R. H., and Fox, R. H., *Introduction to Knot Theory*, Ginn & Co., Boston, 1963.

[C R]   Curtis, C. W., and Reiner, I., *Representation Theory of Finite Groups and Associative Algebras*, Interscience Publishers, Inc., New York, 1962.

[F]   Fuchs, L., *Abelian Groups*, Pergamon Press, Inc., New York, 1960.

[H]   Hall, M., Jr., *The Theory of Groups*, The Macmillan Co., New York, 1959.

[J]   Jacobson, N., *Lectures in Abstract Algebra*, Vols. I and II, D. Van Nostrand Co., Inc., Princeton, N.J., 1951, 1953.

[K]   Kurosh, A. G., *The Theory of Groups*, Vols. 1 and 2, translated, Chelsea Publishing Co., New York, 1955 and 1956.

[Ka]   Kaplansky, I., *Infinite Abelian Groups*, Univ. of Michigan Press, Ann Arbor, 1954.

[S]   Specht, W., *Gruppentheorie*, Springer, Berlin, 1956.

[Z]   Zassenhaus, H. J., *The Theory of Groups*, Chelsea Publishing Co., New York, 1958.

PAPERS

[1]   Baer, R., Supersolvable groups, *Proc. Amer. Math. Soc.* **6,** 16–32 (1955).

[2]   ———, Engelsche Elemente Noetherscher Gruppen, *Math. Annalen* **133,** 256–270 (1957).

[3]   Baumslag, G., and Solitar, D., Some two-generator one-relator non-Hopfian groups, *Bull. Amer. Math. Soc.* **68,** 199–201 (1962).

[3a]   Carter, R. W., Nilpotent self-normalizing subgroups and system normalizers, *Proc. London Math. Soc.*, Third Series 12, 535–563 (1962).

[4] Dlab, V., and Korinek, V., The Frattini subgroup of a direct product of groups, *Czech. Math. J.* 10 (85), 350–358 (1960).

[5] Feit, W., and Thompson, J., Solvability of groups of odd order, *Pac. J. Math.*, 775–1029 (1963).

[6] Gaschütz, W., Zur Theorie der endlichen auflösbaren Gruppen, *Math. Zeit.* **80,** 300–305 (1963).

[7] Gorenstein, D., and Herstein, I. N., Finite groups admitting a fixed-point-free automorphism of order 4, *Amer. J. Math.* **83,** 71–78 (1961).

[8] Gruenberg, K. W., The Engel elements of a soluble group, *Ill. J. Math.* **3,** 151–167 (1959).

[9] Hall, P., Theorems like Sylow's, *Proc. London Math Soc.*. 6 (3), 286–304 (1956).

[10] ———, Some sufficient conditions for a group to be nilpotent, *Ill. J. Math.* **2,** 787–801 (1958).

[11] ———, The Frattini subgroups of finitely generated groups, *Proc. London Math Soc.*, Third Series **11,** 327–352 (1961).

[12] ———, and Higman, G., The p-length of a p-solvable group, and reduction theorems for Burnside's problem, *Proc. London Math. Soc.* **7** (3), 1–42 (1956).

[13] Heineken, H., Eine Bemerkung über engelsche Elemente, *Archiv der Math.* **11,** 22 (1960).

[14] ———, Engelsche Elemente der Länge drei, *Ill. J. Math.* **5,** 681–707 (1961).

[15] Huppert, B., Normalteiler und maximale Untergruppen endlicher Gruppen, *Math. Zeit.* **60,** 409–434 (1954).

[15a] Kegel, O. H., Produckte nilpotenter Gruppen, *Archiv der Math.* **12,** 90–93 (1961).

[16] Kostrikhin, A. I., The Burnside problem, *Izv. Akad. Nauk SSSR* Ser Mat **23,** 3–34 (Russian) (1959).

[17] Kovacs, L. G., Groups with regular automorphisms of order four, *Math. Zeit.* **75,** 277–294 (1961).

[18] Kovacs, L. G., Neumann, B. H., and de Vries, H., Some Sylow subgroups, *Proc. Roy. Soc.* A, **260,** 304–316 (1961).

[19] Maclane, S., A proof of the subgroup theorem for free products, *Mathematika* **5,** 13–19 (1958).

[20] Neumann, B. H., An essay on free products of groups with amalgamations *Phil. Trans. Roy. Soc.* A, **246,** 503–554 (1954).

[21] ———, and Neumann, Hanna, Embedding theorems for Groups, *J. London Math. Soc.* **34,** 465–479 (1959).

[22] Novikov, P. S., On periodic groups, *Doklady Akad. Nauk SSSR* **127,** 749–752 (Russian) (1959).

[23] Plotkin, B. I., On some criteria of locally nilpotent groups, *Uspeki Mat. Nauk* (N.S.) **9,** 181–186 (1954); *Amer. Math. Soc. Translations*, Series 2, **17,** 1–7 (1961).

[24] Schenkman, E., The splitting of certain solvable groups, *Proc. Amer. Math. Soc.* **6,** 286–290 (1955).

[25] Suzuki, M., On finite groups with cyclic Sylow subgroups for all odd primes, *Amer. J. Math.* **77,** 657–691 (1955).

[26] Thompson, J., Finite groups with fixed-point-free automorphisms of prime order, *Proc. Natl. Acad. Sci.* **45,** 578–581 (1959).

[27] ———, Normal *p*-complements for finite groups, *J. Algebra* **1,** 43–46 (1964).

[28] Wiegold, J., Nilpotent products of groups with amalgamations, *Publ. Math. Debrecen* **6,** 131–168 (1959).

[29] Wielandt, H., Über das Product paarweise vertauschbarer nilpotenter Gruppen, *Math. Zeit.* **55,** 1–7 (1951).

[30] ———, Über Producte von nilpotenten Gruppen, *Ill. J. Math.* **2,** No. 4B, 611–618 (1958).

[31] ———, Über die Existenz von Normalteilern in endlichen Gruppen, *Math. Nachr.* **18,** 274–280 (1958).

INDEX

287